W9-APS-483

SCIENCE*PLUS*

TECHNOLOGY △ AND SOCIETY 9

SciencePlus Technology and Society 9 was developed for use in Alberta schools by the Atlantic Science Curriculum Project in collaboration with the Alberta Ministry of Education and Alberta science teachers.

Principal Authors:

Project Director

Charles P. McFadden
Professor of Education
University of New Brunswick

Author-in-Chief

Earl S. Morrison
Professor of Education
University of New Brunswick

Nan Armour
Armour & Associates
Halifax

Allan R. Hammond
Prince Edward Island
Department of Education

John Haysom
Professor of Education
Saint Mary's University

Alan Moore
Professor of Education
Nova Scotia Teachers College

Elinor M. Nicoll
Curriculum Supervisor
Halifax District School Board

M. Muriel Smyth
Fairview Junior High School
Halifax

Developmental Consultants

Ian Strachan
Robert Warren Junior High School
Calgary Board of Education

Jeff Turner
Sherwood Community School
Calgary Board of Education

Harcourt Brace Jovanovich, Canada

Toronto Orlando San Diego London Sydney

Canadian Cataloguing in Publication Data

Main entry under title:
SciencePlus 9 : technology and society

Prepared by Atlantic Science Curriculum Project.
For use in Alberta.
Includes index.
ISBN 0-7747-1323-2

1. Science – Juvenile literature. I. McFadden,
Charles P. (Charles Posa), 1942–
II. Morrison, Earl S. III. Atlantic Science
Curriculum Project.

Q161.2.Q269 1990   500   C89-093850-4

1 2 3 4 5   BP   94 93 92 91 90
Printed and Bound in Canada by Bryant Press

Cover Design
Katinka Oszter

Cover Photo
Michael Schneps/The Image Bank

Cover Separations
Herzig Somerville

Design
Blair Kerrigan/Glyphics

Art Direction
Don Palkowski

Photo Research
Jane Affleck/Liz Kirk/Elaine Freedman

Typesetting
Q Composition Inc.

Colour Separations
Passage Productions Inc.

Table of Contents

Electromagnetics

Environmental Quality

Acknowledgements

The Atlantic Science Curriculum Project is a Canadian science education research and development group working in collaboration with educators in the United Kingdom, the United States of America and other countries. The Alberta Ministry of Education and Alberta science teachers through their collaboration in the development of this edition of *SciencePlus Technology and Society* have made a contribution to science teaching nationally and internationally as well as to their own province.

This edition was developed specifically to support the Alberta curriculum for grade 9. It is a significant extension and modification of learning resources initially developed by the Atlantic Science Curriculum Project (ASCP) for the Atlantic Provinces of Canada and for Ontario. Hundreds of teachers in the Atlantic Provinces and Ontario and scores of institutions and organizations contributed to the initial development. The new work developed for this edition through collaboration with Alberta teachers will in turn be modified and utilized in further editions for Canada, the United States of America, and other countries. The achievement of a high quality resource for science teaching is only possible through the cooperation and collaboration of talented educators from many jurisdictions, whose assistance is hereby acknowledged.

The ASCP would like to single out the following Alberta science educators for their contributions to this work. In the first place, Bernie Galbraith and the curriculum committee working under his leadership at Alberta Education deserve credit for elaborating the curriculum design which resulted in the development by ASCP of three new units and the modification of several others. Bernie Galbraith's advice through all stages of the development of this new material is gratefully acknowledged.

All new materials were developed under the guidance of Ian Strachan and Jeff Turner, who field tested initial and revised drafts of the material. Working closely with Ian and Jeff were Gordon Howard and Marg Kurtze from Robert Warren Junior High School. The cooperation of the Calgary Public School Board is greatly appreciated. Thanks are also due to Glenn Doerksen from the Alberta Ministry of Education, Bonnie Shapiro from the University of Calgary, Donna Smith from the Edmonton Public School Board and Dan Stoker from the SEEDS Foundation who kindly helped to familiarize ASCP with the specific needs of Alberta schools. The ASCP is also deeply grateful to the many anonymous pilot teachers and reviewers whose feedback was very helpful in the development of this edition.

In addition to the contributions of Alberta teachers, this edition of *SciencePlus Technology and Society* benefited from critical reviews and advice from several Canadian scientists and from educators from England and the United States of America. Among these, mention must be made of Clive Carré (Professor of Education, University of Exeter, UK) who has served ASCP as its consultant on language and visual communication in science.

Acknowledgements would be incomplete without special mention of Kevin Ford, Ken Leland, and Mike Wevrick for managerial and editorial assistance, Susan Marshall for copy editing, and Susan McCafferty for project co-ordination in connection with this Alberta edition of *SciencePlus Technology and Society*. Their patience, diplomacy and professionalism are greatly appreciated by the authors. Last, but not least, it must be mentioned that some very talented spouses of the principal authors made substantial contributions by providing critical feedback at every stage. Their patience through years of lost vacations, weekends, and evenings, and their moral support through innumerable periods of crisis is much appreciated.

If this learning resource helps to meet the needs of students and their teachers in Alberta, these acknowledgements may help to explain how this happened and give credit where it is due while leaving the ultimate responsibility for this work with the group of principal authors.

The authors invite you to contribute to the further development of the material in this book by conveying your suggestions for revision to Ian Strachan or Jeff Turner at the Calgary Public School Board or to the Project Director, Atlantic Science Curriculum Project, University of New Brunswick, Fredericton E3B 6E3.

Preface

In our lifetimes, the role of science in all aspects of life has been expanded enormously. And so has the responsibility of parents and teachers to prepare young people for a new and challenging age. The practice of education is shifting from an emphasis on fact recall to the development of understanding, information-processing abilities, inter-personal skills, and commitment to life-long learning. *SciencePlus Technology and Society,* an original Canadian junior high school science textbook series, is the collective effort of many educators dedicated to helping teachers accomplish the new aims for science and technology education. Its content in each year includes life, physical, and earth science.

SciencePlus uses a directed discovery, or inquiry-based approach that challenges students. For reasons of convenient manageability, only 30% of the activities are "hands-on" ones. The remainder utilize the graphic resources of a textbook, and include simulations, historical inquiries, puzzles, and interpretation of graphs, tables, and photographs, among other things. The program was designed to be feasible in real, rather than ideal, classrooms. A minimum of special equipment and facilities is required. Furthermore, the teacher should not need an extensive scientific background to guide the students through the course.

SciencePlus relates science to other curriculum areas. There are discussion and creative writing activities designed to consolidate discoveries made in the practical explorations. These also stimulate critical thinking and promote communication skills. There are reflective tasks to promote the reading of scientific materials with comprehension.

Science is presented in the context of society. Attention is given to major science-related social issues, particularly the need for environmental protection and resource conservation. Students will learn the relevance of science by seeing how it can be applied usefully in realistic, everyday examples. *SciencePlus* supports the aim that all individuals should be able to play an active role in science and technology, and that all students should find science valuable and enjoyable.

Extensive field-testing prior to publication was invaluable for refining the material to its present form. Field-test teachers commented that their students found the activities interesting, relevant, practical, and productive. We hope that all who use this textbook will enjoy similar success.

To the Student

This text was written especially for you. As you read *SciencePlus 9* you will meet many questions which will help you understand what you are reading. There are many things to try, to build, and to investigate, both in and out of class. There are stories to be read, articles to think about, puzzles to be solved, and games to play.

This textbook deals with science ideas you should know. What knowledge will be important to you twenty years from now? Surprisingly, the amount of knowledge in the world can be expected to quadruple in twenty years. Knowledge that is not needed and used is quickly forgotten, but today's important scientific ideas will be just as important twenty years from now. Ideas you understand well now, you will probably understand even better in the future. A good motto might be: Put ideas in your head – facts are in books! The ideas in this book are a part of everyday life. They will help you to make sense of the world. You will find them interesting, challenging, and fun.

The activities in this textbook ask you to observe, think, and explain things in your own words – skills we need to use every day. They are also skills you will need in the future. In many of these activities, you will be acting as a scientist; in this way, you will discover how interesting, absorbing, and challenging science is.

Science in Action

To give you an idea about the kinds of jobs that use science, *Science in Action* sections are included between units in *SciencePlus 9*. These are for you to read after class or when you are finished with your classwork.

We have tried to represent science in action by conversations with people who use science in their work. With their help, we have suggested many ideas for projects. Even if you do only one or two projects, you will experience the excitement that *Science in Action* – real science – can provide. If you like working on a particular project, it might be the beginning of your future career.

You should be warned, however. Some of the words used may be unfamiliar. You may have to refer to a dictionary. And, most important, the project ideas are not easy and are not explained in detail. It is intended that you consult people who work in fields related to the project ideas. Indeed, such contacts will probably be the most valuable part of your project. Don't be shy! Most people are happy to share their knowledge and experience.

Science on Your Own

Following each *Science in Action* section is another feature called *Science on Your Own*. This includes questions and research projects designed to help you better understand the links between science, technology, and society. They are intended for you to do on your own, but you can, of course, get help from relatives, friends, neighbours, local companies, books, magazines, and newspapers. In some cases, you will need to do experiments to find answers to the questions asked. In other cases, you will need to interview people to learn how technology has affected their lives, or to examine your own environment to see how technology and science have affected how you live.

The authors of *SciencePlus 9* dedicate the many years of hard work that went into the writing of *SciencePlus 9* to you, in the hope that you will discover the importance of science in your life and that you will learn to use science to make the world a better place.

Safety

Safety is an important consideration in many scientific activities. While working in the laboratory, you must always be on guard, and aware of how to prevent accidents.

Throughout this book, one (or more) of the following symbols will appear if extra caution is needed in performing an *Exploration*, or other activity. The specific symbols used indicate what kind of hazard is involved. When you see one, be alert and follow the instructions given by the book, and by your teacher.

WEAR GOGGLES   POISON   FLAMMABLE   EXPLOSIVE   CORROSIVE

DIVERSITY OF LIVING THINGS

The Diversity of Living Things in the World

Living Things of All Shapes and Sizes

There are more than two million kinds of living things in the world. All these living things can have very different structures. They come in all shapes and sizes! In this unit you will look at the diversity of living things. **Diversity** is the term biologists use for differences.

Here are illustrations of four living things, or **organisms**. Observe each one carefully. How do they differ from one another?

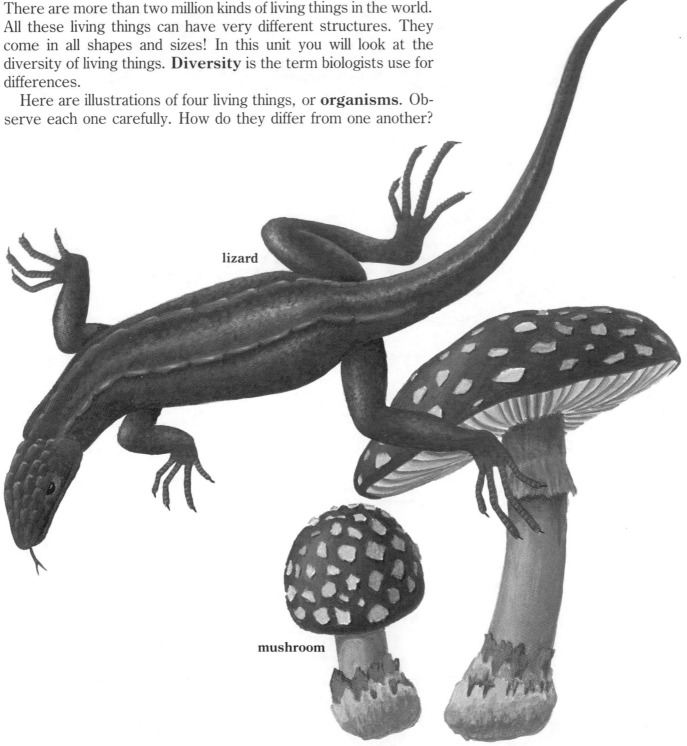

lizard

mushroom

With a classmate, discuss the diversity you see. Here are some questions to help you start.

1. How long is each organism?
2. What features does each organism have: roots, stems, leaves, flowers, eyes, legs, hair, scales, skin, or any others?
3. What one characteristic does each organism have that distinguishes it from the other three?

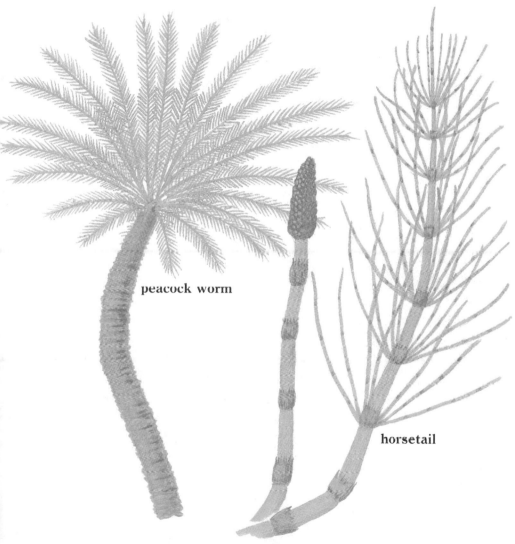

peacock worm

horsetail

   You have just described four living things that illustrate the great diversity of organisms. Living things can differ in size, habitat, appearance, eating habits, and methods of self-protection, among other characteristics. Now you will investigate diversity a little further. Do either Part I or Part II of Exploration 1.

Looking for Diversity Part I

Diversity in a Lawn

While playing ball on the grass or stretching out in your lawn chair to enjoy the sunshine, have you ever stopped to think about what is happening beneath you? There may be a food hunting expedition underway, or a ferocious battle going on right underneath you. You can learn a lot by getting down on your knees and carefully observing a small area of lawn. To do so, you are going to stake out one square metre of ground, preferably the day before the Exploration. Then you are going to study the animal life and the plant life in this square metre of lawn. The tables and questions that follow will help you in this study of diversity. Note that you are asked to start with animal life. Why?

You Will Need

- popsicle sticks (4 per group)
- measuring tape
- heavy string

What To Do

1. Find a convenient grassy area, such as your lawn. Using the measuring tape, measure out one metre of ground and place a popsicle stick at both ends of the tape.
2. Place one end of the tape at a ninety degree angle from one of the popsicle sticks. Measure out one metre and push a popsicle stick into the ground.
3. Repeat Step 2 twice, to complete your square.
4. Tie the string to the popsicle sticks.

5. Carefully approach your staked area to see whether any larger animals, such as butterflies, are present. If you come to the area too quickly or noisily, you may scare away some animals. Now look more closely for any smaller animals that might be hidden among the plants. In your notebook, fill in a table similar to the one shown here. When you have completed the table, analyse this information by considering the following questions. Then share your findings with others.

Quick Sketch of Each Animal (if possible)	Number of Same Kinds (Species) of Animals	Description of Each Animal (including size, appearance, colour, and any other features you observe)	Common Name

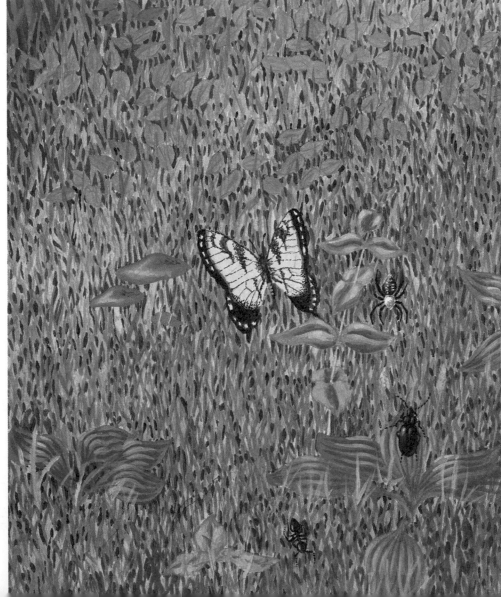

Questions

(a) How many types of animals did you find?

(b) Did you hear animal sounds but not actually see the animal?

(c) Did you find any evidence of animal life, but not the animals themselves?

(d) Which is the smallest animal you found? The biggest?

(e) Which animal did you find in the greatest numbers? The least?

(f) How does animal life affect plant life in your study site?

6. Observe the plant life in your study site, then, in your notebook, fill in a table like the one shown here.

Quick Sketch of Each Plant	Number of Same Kinds (Species) of Plants	Description of Each Plant (including size, appearance, colour, and any other features you observe)	Common Name

(a) How many types of plants did you find?

(b) Which is the smallest plant you found? The biggest?

(c) Which plant did you find in the greatest numbers? The least?

(d) Do all the plants you found have some feature in common? If so, what is it?

(e) How does the plant life affect the animal life in your study site?

Part II

Diversity Around You

What To Do

In your notebook, prepare two tables like those in Part I. Then walk around the neighbourhood of your school and home and fill in your tables. Afterwards, answer the questions which follow.

In Exploration 1, you discovered the diversity which is to be found in the living things around you. Now here are some riddles showing how much more diversity exists. See how many you can solve!

The Puzzling Diversity of Living Things

Part I

Captured in the following riddles is information about the structures, habits, and habitats of some organisms. Read each riddle carefully, then think about what it tells you. Which living thing does each riddle depict? If you do not know what a riddle describes, look at the pictures for some hints. (The pictures are not in order.) If you are really stuck, the answers follow in code. All you have to do is break the code!

Riddle 1

I move slowly when I am young but very quickly when I'm an adult. My diet is flying insects, which I hunt near water. I have to be a strong flier to catch my food. When I stretch my four wings, I look like a helicopter. I have two more legs than a dog and have very large eyes. I am cold-blooded and have an external (outside) skeleton. Sometimes I'm very colourful. Who am I?

Riddle 2

I can walk, run, and swim. I can see well, but my sense of smell is not very sharp. I am warm-blooded. I am very adaptable and can live in many different environments. I really enjoy changing my environment. I care for my young for many years. I stand upright. Who am I?

Riddle 3

I must live in damp or wet places, avoiding the dry heat of summer and the cold of winter. If I am living in a cold climate I become dormant in the winter. If I am a female, I produce young by laying eggs in water. I survive by eating anything which moves and which I can swallow. I can sing very well. I can secrete a sticky white poison that can kill or paralyze dogs or other enemies who may try to eat me. Who am I?

Riddle 4

I live in a lake, marsh, salt bay, or beach. I eat mostly fish and crustaceans. Although I can fly, I can catch fish only by swimming. My great throat pouch is handy for scooping up fish. I can fly by alternating several flaps of my wings with a glide. I always fly with my head hunched behind my shoulders. I nest on the ground in colonies. I have a wing-span of 2.5 m to 3.0 m. My close cousins live only by the ocean, while I venture inland. I am happy to report that these cousins are growing in number even though they suffered from DDT poisoning a few years ago. Who am I?

Riddle 5

I have a very high body temperature. It is usually seven degrees warmer than a human's. My feet are well adapted for grasping things. I have four toes on each foot: two point forward and two point backward. I have stiff, spiny tail feathers that act as a prop when I hunt food. I eat tree-boring insects, ants, acorns, flying insects, berries, and sap. My home, which I make myself, is a hole in a tree. I use my bill to chisel the wood. Who am I?

Riddle 6

I have pointed green stalks above the ground and a rounded brown bulb below. People must pull me out of the soil before I can be useful to them. Cooks use me to improve the taste of food. If people bite me, I can bite back, making their eyes water. Who am I?

(This riddle is based on an Anglo Saxon riddle, over a thousand years old!)

Riddle 7

I live in cold, well-oxygenated water and am a fast, strong swimmer. I am slim, sleek, and colourful. I'm a carnivore and eat mostly insects and smaller members of my own kind. I spawn my eggs during the spring in small, clear streams. I'm cold-blooded. Who am I?

Riddle 8

I undergo wondrous changes during my life. At the beginning, I am a sweet-smelling pink and white blossom. Later I'm a hard green ball that makes your eyes and mouth pucker if you try to eat me. Finally, I become a sweet, juicy, red or yellowish fruit. People say I keep physicians away. Who am I?

Riddle 9

I am a big animal. My mass is about 225 kg, but my tail is only about 15 cm long. I am dark in colour. Generally, I live on forest floors and in thickets. When it begins to get cold and snows, I enter my shelter for the winter. I don't have very good sight but my senses of hearing and smell are keen. Using these senses, I find lots of food: small animals, insects, any flesh, garbage, leaves, grasses, berries, nuts, and fruits. I am a good climber and, if disturbed, may retreat to the upper branches of a tree. Who am I?

Riddle 10

I am warm-blooded, hairy, and feed milk to my young. My teeth tell you what kind of food I eat. I have no upper teeth, but do have a complex stomach. I chew my cud. The males of my kind have huge, branching antlers. I have a heavily maned neck. Humans and mountain lions are my only enemies, but mountain lions usually won't attack me when I'm fully grown. My young are not camouflaged from these enemies until their winter hair grows out. Sometimes you can hear the males of my kind give a high-pitched bugle call. If this call is answered by another male, a battle may follow. Who am I?

Here are the coded answers to the riddles, in order:

1. CQZFNM EKX
2. GTLZM
3. SNZC
4. VGHSD ODKHBZM
5. VNNCODBJDQ
6. NMHNM
7. QZHMANV SQNTS
8. ZOOKD
9. CSPXO ADZQ
10. DKJ

Hint for Decoding: ZMS = ANT

Part II

You Be the Riddler!

Read the riddles over carefully. What characteristics of the organisms in the riddles were used to describe their diversity?

Now try writing your own riddles for some of the living things pictured here. Before you start, do research to find out about the ones you choose. After constructing your riddles, see whether your classmates can solve them.

Why Is There Diversity?

Why are there so many different types of living things? Why isn't there a single "all-purpose" organism? Or at least one all-purpose plant and one all-purpose animal? These are not easy questions. This lesson will help you find some answers.

You already know that many different environments are to be found on our planet. There are deserts and oceans, grasslands and mountains, forests and tundra. In each of these environments there are many different habitats for living things.

Since there is such a variety or diversity of habitats, no single organism can survive in all of them. You can imagine that an organism that lives on the ocean floor would have great difficulty surviving in a desert!

Have you studied the unit on Interactions? It discusses the idea that each organism has a particular role to play in its habitat. Just as no single organism can survive in all habitats, no single organism can play all roles in one habitat.

All this leads to another question. How is each organism suited to play a certain role in a certain habitat? Keep on reading!

Diversity For Survival

Adaptations are the features which organisms have that enable them to survive and produce young. Both animals and plants have many different kinds of structures and behaviours that seem to help them survive in their environments. Here's a list of adaptations to discuss:

(a) Think about the great variety of structures and behaviours (adaptations) which the animals and plants on the right have for obtaining their food:

(b) Can you think of structures or behaviours in animals and plants that could be used for protection? Give some examples.

(c) Consider an animal's locomotion — its movement from place to place. Name some adaptations that various animals have for locomotion. Is each adaptation you thought of related in some way to the organism's habitat?

Disappearing Acts

Some animals in this world have spectacular survival techniques. But you have to be a very good observer to see them. Like escape artists or magicians, some animal species have developed an amazing variety of illusions. To escape the ferocious jaws, beaks, and fangs of hungry predators, they simply "disappear" into their environment! Other animals do the same trick, not to avoid being prey, but in order to catch their own prey.

Some creatures resemble twigs or leaves. Others resemble non-living things like stones. Many creatures blend in perfectly with the colour of their surroundings. The following examples illustrate how the shape and colour of organisms can protect them in their own environments.

The Katydid

Some types of katydids, found in the Amazon region, look like green leaves. If caterpillars nibble at their edges, spots of brown surrounded by yellow rings appear. These markings are just like the spots of decay that would appear on a leaf.

The Chameleon

Some lizards can change their colour to blend in with their immediate surroundings. Old World chameleons, for instance, can change from black to red, yellow, white, or orange, depending upon the colours in their environment.

The Stick Insect

Stick insects look like twigs. Their shape and colour both protect them from being eaten by birds.

The Polar Bear

Polar bears, which are white in colour, blend in with the snow and ice that are usually part of their surroundings.

The Malaysian Mantid

Malaysian mantids look like orchids. Their appearance attracts insects to feed on the "flower nectar". The unsuspecting insects are then devoured by the deceptive mantids.

The Grasshopper

Some young grasshoppers can change their colour to match their environment. For instance, nymphs that eat green leaves become green. Nymphs that eat pink flowers become pink, and those that eat burnt grass turn black!

The Snowshoe Hare

Snowshoe hares are white in winter, to blend in with the snow, and brown in summer, to blend in with trees, grasses, and weeds.

Who Am I?

We each have our special colour and shape;
From our enemies it's a way to escape.

"I'm an extremely changeable fellow;
Any colour will do — black, white, or yellow!"

"As for me, I specialize in white —
So I can match my habitat site."

"I am white too, for part of the year;
But when summer comes, then brown will appear."

"Colours — green and brown — are important for me too
But it's a shape like a leaf that really sees me through."

"Yes, shape is important — I look like a flower.
But that's to bring insects for me to devour."

"I could change colour when I was small.
Then I was a tasty treat for all."

"I have the best trick that you've ever heard
I look like a twig — it'll fool any old bird."

Attention Please!

Some animals are adapted to attract attention. Which animals shown here have an adaptation in order to

(a) attract members of their own kind for mating purposes?

(b) warn possible enemies (predators) of their bitter or smelly secretions or powerful stings?

cardinal

peacock

dragon fish

butterfly

wasp

skunk

Mimicry: False Attention Getting

Some animals, such as the Viceroy butterfly, have false warning colouration to protect themselves from being eaten by predators. The Viceroy butterfly, which is pleasant to the taste, imitates the appearance of the Monarch butterfly, which is distasteful to birds. By using this mimicking technique the Viceroy butterfly escapes being eaten.

viceroy butterfly

monarch butterfly

A bird would avoid these 'eyes'.

There are some very strange examples of mimicry in the animal kingdom. The larvae of the hawkmoth resemble certain poisonous snakes. There are bugs whose backs are formed into sculptures that look like preying ants poised on a leaf.

Another interesting form of mimicry is found in insects that have evolved large eyespots resembling a vertebrate's eyes. These are often on the upper side of the wings, and are usually covered when the insect is at rest. When the insect is disturbed, however, it spreads its wings, exposing the eyespots. Through experiments, one scientist has shown that many birds are frightened by these eyespots.

Something to Research

Find out about the mimicry of the drone fly and the scarlet king snake. What does each mimic? From which animals is each protected by its mimicry?

Plants Also Adapt to Their Habitats

Plants, like animals, are uniquely suited to their habitats. Although plants cannot move about like animals, they do have certain characteristics which allow them to survive and reproduce in particular habitats.

Observe each of the illustrated plants, then select from the list of habitat adaptations the one for which a given plant is adapted. There may be more than one plant for each habitat adaptation.

1. a plant able to hold on to rocks in swift rivers and streams
2. a plant which can store water
3. a plant which can catch insects
4. a plant which can compete with other plants for sunlight
5. a lawnmower-proof plant!
6. a plant which can withstand high winds
7. a plant which grazing animals would not eat
8. a plant capable of living on the surface of a pond

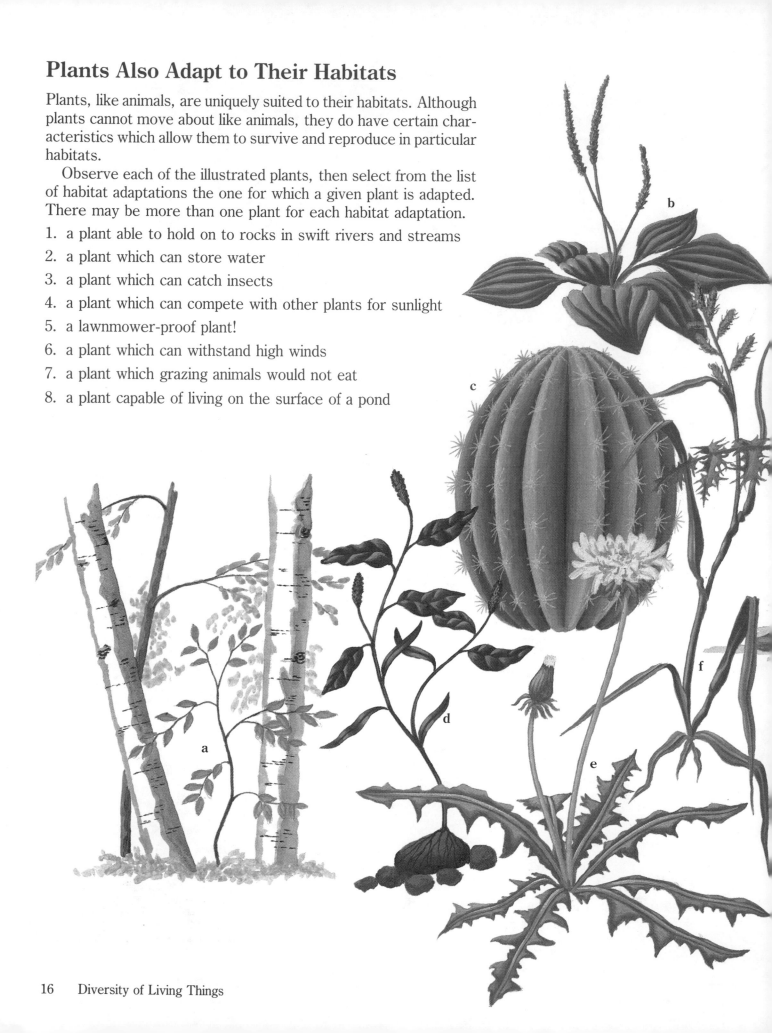

Perhaps you were able to identify some of these plants because you have seen them before. Their common names are as follows:

barnyard grass

barrel cactus

beech tree (young, in maple woods)

broad-leaf plantain

coconut palm

dandelion

duckweed

pitcher plant

pond weed

scotch thistle

sundew

white waterlily

wild rose

Try to match the names to the pictures.

Seed Adaptations

Most plants produce seeds that grow into new plants. But seeds cannot always survive if they simply drop directly beneath the plant that produced them. They may need to move to another area. Many types of seeds, therefore, are adapted to travel, so that their species can survive. This presents a seed dispersal problem.

Look at a pea seed. Do you think it could travel very far on its own? How might you change it so that it has a greater chance to travel and survive? Working with some classmates, design changes in the pea seed that will enable it to do the following:

(a) float on water

(b) be thrown a distance by the parent plant

(c) attract an animal that would carry it to another location

(d) hitchhike on an animal for some distance

(e) be carried by the wind

A Picture Puzzle

Examine each seed closely. Identify the adaptation that is being used to help a given seed travel away from the parent plant. Do these adaptations resemble the suggestions you made for the pea seed?

The Origins of Diversity

Natural Selection

Natural selection is a theory that explains how the features of a species can change over many generations. Charles Darwin developed this theory in the 1800s.

Sometimes a plant or animal develops completely new characteristics which enable it to live successfully in a new habitat. For example, evidence indicates that the dolphin's ancestors once lived on land. Even today, dolphins breathe air through lungs, just as land animals do. But we know them as water animals, because they live in the water and have developed features that make them good swimmers.

Similarly, living things may develop new features permitting them to live more successfully in their own habitat. Not all polar bears, for example, have always been white. But the polar bears that were white were protected because they blended in well with their environment. Hence, they were more successful when they tried to find food and escape predators. The white polar bears survived to reproduce, but the dark polar bears were killed more frequently. Over many years, the white polar bears grew in number, while the dark ones gradually disappeared.

Which polar bear is harder to find?

This dolphin's ancestors once lived on land.

Sometimes the habitat of a species will change in some way. This change may force the species to either move to a new habitat or adapt to the changed habitat. One example of a species that adapted to a new area is the peppered moth, which you are about to examine in detail. Study the research data given below. Do these facts support the theory of natural selection?

The Case of the Peppered Moth

Date:
The 1800s, during the Industrial Revolution

Place:
England, near the industrial city of Birmingham

Researcher:
Professor Kettlewell and his assistants

White moth on a light trunk

Dark moth on a dark trunk

Research Subject:
The peppered moth. Peppered moths have lived in the forests of England for thousands of years. They rest on the trunks of trees during the day and, while resting, are the diet of many birds. Peppered moths vary in colour, from light-coloured to dark-coloured.

Research Problem:
Did air pollution (from the many new industries), which covered tree trunks with black soot, affect the survival of the peppered moth?

Conditions:
Before the Industrial Revolution, the tree trunks were light-coloured. The trunks and branches were also covered with silvery-white lichen.

As the Industrial Revolution progressed, pollution in the air and rain killed the lichen and blackened the tree bark.

Hypothesis:
Kettlewell formed a hypothesis about the peppered moth. (Form your own hypothesis. It should include the effect that you think the Industrial Revolution had on the survival of the peppered moth.)

Procedure:
With his assistants, Kettlewell then experimented to test his hypothesis. He used the following procedure:

1. They located two areas: a wooded area with lichen-covered oak trees, and a wooded area which had been subjected to pollution for many years.
2. They released a known number of light-coloured and dark-coloured peppered moths into each area.
3. After a given time, they recaptured as many moths as they could.

Results:
In the unpolluted area, more light-coloured moths survived. In the polluted area, more dark-coloured moths survived.

Discussing the Results:
1. Do these results support your hypothesis? (They supported Kettlewell's hypothesis.)
2. How can you explain the results?
3. Why didn't Kettlewell release the moths into the polluted area only?
4. Do Kettlewell's findings support the theory of natural selection, or not?

Darwin's Finches

In 1835, Charles Darwin spent five weeks visiting the Galapagos Islands, as the naturalist on H.M.S. *Beagle*. He observed, recorded, collected, and preserved everything he could of the islands' natural history. There were many strange and colourful animals and birds. But what excited him most were drab little birds that made unmusical sounds — finches. These birds all resembled one another closely, except for one set of features — the size and shape of their beaks. Separated for thousands of years on the different islands of the Galapagos, the finches of each island had adapted to their own environment in certain ways. The differences among the finches of the various islands are shown in this table.

Charles Darwin

The Differences Among Some of Darwin's Finches

Name of the Finch	Feeding Habit	Form of Beak
small tree finch	Uses delicate bill to eat aphids and small berries.	
large tree finch	Grinds fruit and insects with parrot-like bill.	
small ground finch	Uses pointed bill to eat tiny seeds and pick ticks from iguanas.	
large ground finch	Conical bill enables it to eat large, hard seeds.	
cactus finch	Longish bill probes for nectar in cactus flowers.	

1. How is the structure of the beak suited to the diet of each group of finches?

2. Do Darwin's finches support the theory of natural selection or not? Give reasons for your answer.

3. It has been speculated that Darwin's finches reached the Galapagos from the mainland of South America as a single flock perhaps a million or more years ago. Speculate about the following questions, and explain your answers.

   (a) What do you think the original finches looked like? Why?

   (b) Is it possible that the original birds were various species that arrived on the islands at different times?

   (c) Assume that one flock of finches gave rise to the fourteen different species now existing on the islands. For this to occur, would it be significant that the Galapagos consist of many small islands rather than one large one?

   (d) How important would it be for the finches to arrive on the islands in the following situations?

      (i) when no other species with exactly the same diet existed

      (ii) when there were no predators

      (iii) when there were no parasites to live on and weaken the finches

4. How has diversity helped Darwin's finches to survive?

H.M.S. *Beagle* arrives in South America. Can you find the Galapagos Islands on a map?

Adapting a Tale!

Would you like to live in a new, vastly different environment? The Moon. Underwater. A planet in outer space. How would you survive? What adaptations (including technological ones) would help you survive? Think about those strange-looking creatures who disembarked from the *Apollo* and lived and travelled on the Moon for several days.

Create a tale about how you and a group of your friends survived in a very different environment. Describe the conditions of the new environment, the difficulties you would encounter, and the adaptations you would need to survive. You might be able to develop technological solutions (adaptations) to these new problems quite quickly. Changes in the structure or function of organisms' bodies (natural adaptations), however, often take several generations to occur — or may never occur at all. What might happen to your species if the necessary technology was not available?

Loss of Diversity

Have you ever thought about what would happen if there were no diversity of living things, or very little diversity? Imagine what would be the results if the following were true:

(a) All bears were black.

(b) All rabbits were white.

(c) All plants were 5 cm tall.

(d) No insects could fly.

(e) The only living things in the oceans were seals.

A Classroom Conversation

Ms. Gagnon: Do you think diversity and survival are connected?

Edna: I think diversity favours survival.

Malcolm: I disagree. Survival has nothing to do with diversity.

With whom do you agree, Edna or Malcolm? Give reasons for your position.

Perhaps playing the Extinction Game will provide some more ideas to help you argue this point.

The Extinction Game

You have seen that animals may become extinct when their habitat changes. The Extinction Game will help you discover the kinds of changes that may affect the survival of certain animals. To play the game, choose a certain animal from the list that follows. Begin with a population of twenty of your animal. To be a winner in the game you need to finish before your animal becomes extinct. Two to eight people can play at one time. Place extinction cards face down in a pile on the table. (After drawing an extinction card, place it on the bottom of the pile.) Roll the die to determine who begins — the highest goes first. Then, in turn, going clockwise, each player throws the die and makes a move. Remove the animal cards from your pile as required by the extinction cards. If your animal becomes extinct, you are out of the game. Extinction is a process that generally happens over a long time. This length of time may be represented by travelling the path a second time with your surviving population.

Animal Cards

Make 20 cards each for the following animals: whooping crane, bowhead whale, wood bison, sea otter, Peary caribou, eastern cougar, white pelican, Eskimo curlew.

Also make one cardboard token for each animal to travel on the gameboard pathway.

Extinction Cards

Make two copies each of the extinction card.

There is an abundance of food in your area. Two young have been added to your species.

A park has been built in the middle of your habitat. One of your species has died as a result of this disturbance.

Humans are in your territory. They have been successful in killing two of your species.

Humans are in your territory. They have partially destroyed your habitat and killed one of your species.

Interbreeding of your species with a similar species has resulted in no young members being born. One older member has died.

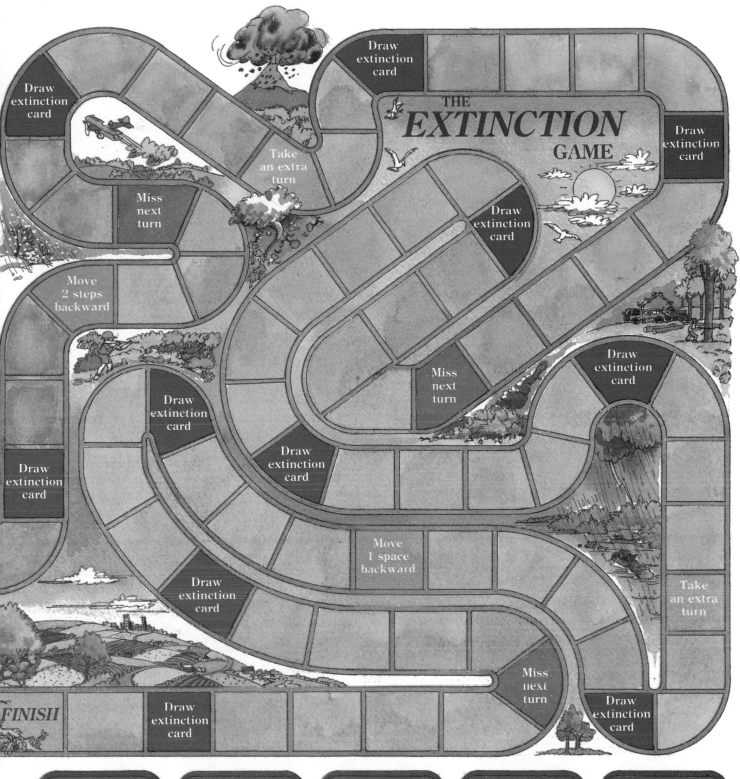

THE EXTINCTION GAME

Draw extinction card

Draw extinction card

Draw extinction card

Take an extra turn

Miss next turn

Move 2 steps backward

Draw extinction card

Draw extinction card

Miss next turn

Draw extinction card

Draw extinction card

Draw extinction card

Draw extinction card

Move 1 space backward

Take an extra turn

Draw extinction card

FINISH

Draw extinction card

Miss next turn

Draw extinction card

Predators are very plentiful in your area. They have killed three of your species.

Humans have cultivated crops in the habitat of your species. Four members of your species have died.

A drought has reduced the food supply in the area of your species. Up to this point, one member has died.

Flooding in the habitat of your species has caused two sudden deaths.

The weather has been exceptionally favourable and your species has reproduced well. Your population has increased by five members.

Pesticides have been sprayed on the food of your species. Two members have died and the rest are in danger.

A tornado has swept through the habitat of your species and killed three members.

Volcanic dust has reduced the solar radiation and caused a food shortage in the habitat of your species. Two members have died.

Harsh winter weather has killed four members of your species.

A disease has killed all the predators of your species. As a result, your species has begun to multiply. It has two new members.

Making Sense of Diversity

Grouping Living Things

As you may well imagine, it is difficult keeping track of over two million kinds of living things! The easiest way of doing this is to group the organisms. You have already had experience with grouping things. For example, in your kitchen, how is the cutlery — knives, forks, and spoons — grouped? Are the good dishes kept in one place and the everyday dishes somewhere else? Are the pots and pans separated from the drinking glasses? Here are some more situations to think about in which items are sorted into groups, or *classified*:

(a) How are the books classified in the school library?

(b) How does the telephone company use grouping to keep track of everyone with a phone?

(c) There are about 25 million people in Canada. How does the postal service group all these people so that mail can be delivered to every individual?

Can you suggest other situations in which items are divided into groups?

Now think about some ways in which you might classify living things.

Try to place all the living things in the illustration into two groups. Then further divide each group into two more subgroups. Invent a name for the living things in each group and subgroup. Your classification system should look like this:

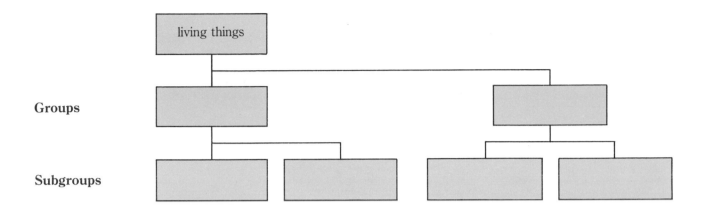

Paulette devised this way to classify the organisms:

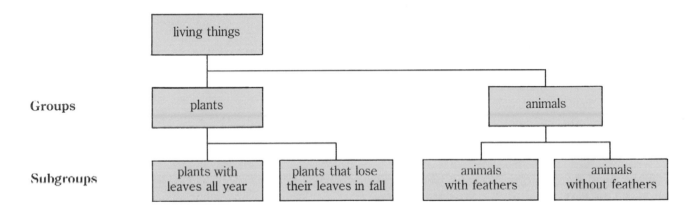

Is your system similar? If not, try to classify the living things in the picture according to Paulette's system.

Now let's look more closely at the differences that help you make a classification.

1. Choose one of the living things in the previous picture. In your notebook, list the distinguishing features that you could use to identify it. Read your list to some of your classmates. Ask them to suggest other organisms that would also be identified by your list.

   How many different organisms did your classmates suggest? Do we always need to talk about *each single living thing* or can we talk about a *group of living things?*

2. You might try doing the same thing again with another organism.

3. Look at the living things in this illustration. Make a group and subgroup diagram that can be used to identify them.

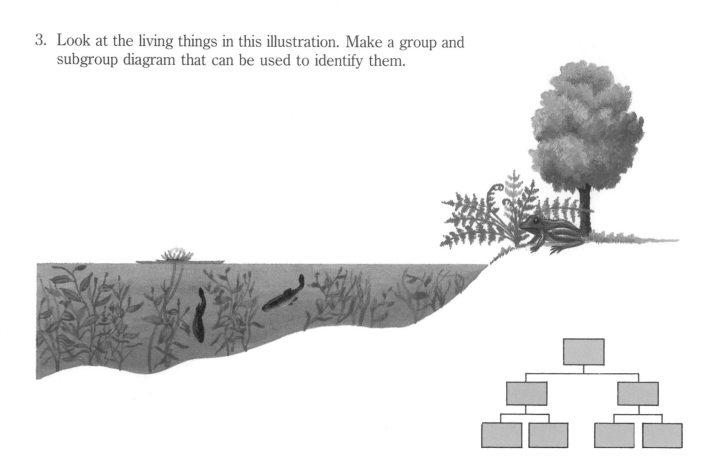

4. Try a slightly different classification scheme for these four plants.

Paulette divided the living things in the picture into plants and animals. Could you use her grouping for the following organisms?

amoeba
(microscopic)

spirogyra
(microscopic)

Biologists, the scientists who study living things, realize the need for a consistent system of classification. For this reason, about one hundred years ago, they divided all living things into two **kingdoms**: the Animal Kingdom and the Plant Kingdom. However, throughout the past century, scientists have been gaining more knowledge about the differences among living things. Biologists have therefore been trying to devise better systems of grouping all organisms. Many biologists now group living things into more than just two kingdoms—as many as three, four, or even five different kingdoms. That means there are living things that are regarded as being neither plants nor animals.

Because it is not necessary to go into great detail now, you will continue to work with the two older, more familiar kingdoms. To help you remember that there are other kingdoms, however, here is how a modern biologist would group the living things shown in the illustrations. Particularly notice the organisms that are neither plant nor animal, but belong in other kingdoms.

moray eel

penguins

snail

snake

mussel

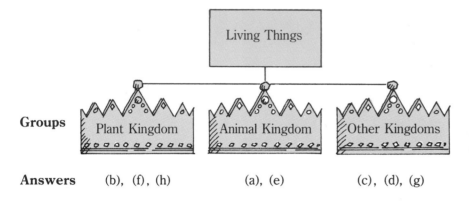

	Living Things	
Groups	Plant Kingdom	Animal Kingdom	Other Kingdoms
Answers	(b), (f), (h)	(a), (e)	(c), (d), (g)

The Animal Kingdom

Because biologists have devised various consistent systems of classification, the two million kinds of living things can be divided into a small number of groups. Imagine you are a biologist. Pictured here are some members of the Animal Kingdom. Try dividing these animals into two groups. (**Hint**: How they support themselves is a consideration.)

Animal Kingdom

giraffe

toad

dog

grasshopper

fish

chick

lobster

salamander

tiger

crocodile

octopus

spider

The more you know about different animals, the easier it is to find useful groupings. To classify, you need to observe the features of animals carefully — not only their outside features, but also their inside features.

What characteristic did you use to classify the animals in the illustration? You, of course, had to depend mostly on what you could observe in the pictures. Biologists often study the real animals, examining them on both the outside and the inside. One feature biologists often use to classify animals relates to the type of support the animals have. Many animals have internal (inside) skeletons with which to support themselves. They can be placed in a group called **vertebrates** — that is, animals with a **vertebral column** or backbone. Other animals depend on a hard external support system. Clams, lobsters, and grasshoppers, for instance, have a hard shell. Earthworms have tough muscles on the outside. Still other animals don't really need a means of support. Their surroundings act like one for them! This is true for many of the animals that live and drift about in the water. All these animals can be placed in a group called **invertebrates** — animals without backbones. Is this the way you divided the animals in the illustration into two groups? If not, do so now for the same animals.

Subgroups of Invertebrates

Here are pictures of some invertebrates. Remember that none of these animals has a backbone for support. Just by looking closely at the pictures, how might you group these animals? What features would you use as a basis for making subgroups of the animals? What names might you devise for the groups you have made?

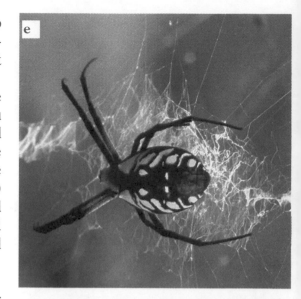

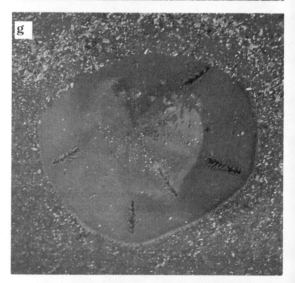

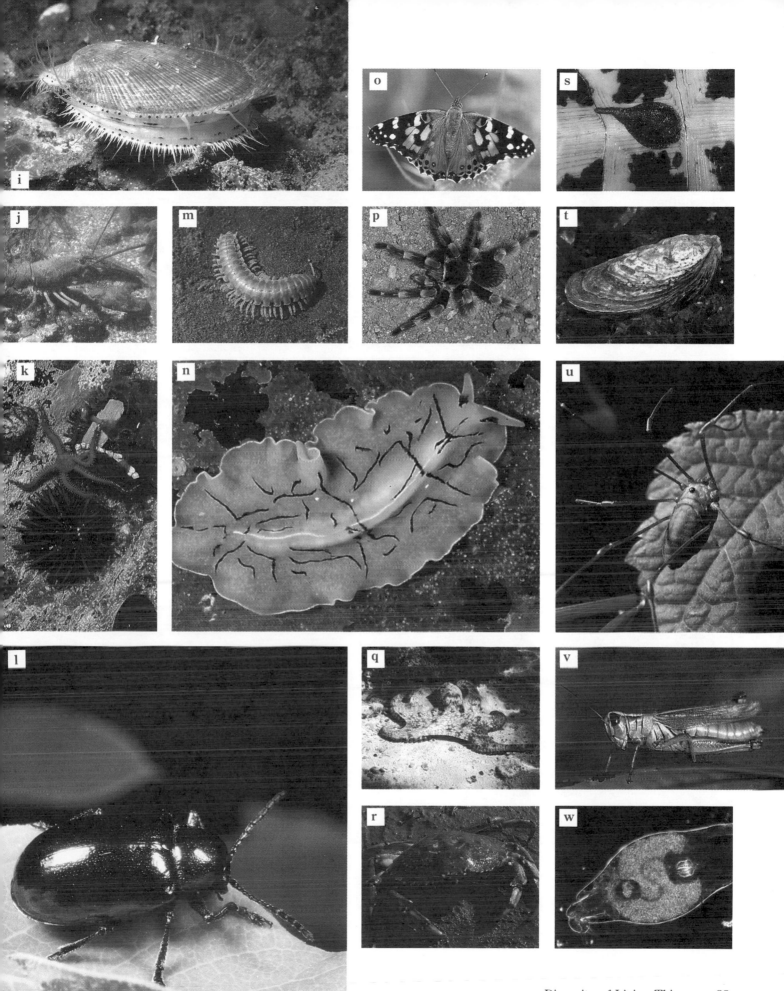

A Biologist's Classification

By studying invertebrates in detail, biologists have developed a classification scheme for them. To help yourself understand their scheme, study these two tables. The tables identify the features that biologists used to classify the invertebrates into different subgroups. After studying the tables and the classification scheme, see whether you can place all the animals pictured on pages 32 and 33 into this scheme. Your task will not be easy; using pictures of animals to observe identifying features is more difficult than using real animals.

The Identifying Features of Invertebrates

Distinguishing Features Biologists Use to Group Animals.	Names of the Subgroups	Examples of Animals in the Subgroups
worm-like, round bodies with many segments	Annelids (means "arranged in rings")	earthworm
very soft bodies, which in most cases are protected by a shell	Molluscs (means "soft-bodied")	clam (example with a shell) octopus (example without a shell)
covered with a spiny skin	Echinoderms (means "spiny-skinned")	starfish
having many jointed appendages (attachments such as legs, feelers, tail, *etc.*)	Arthropods (means "jointed legs")	lobster

The Identifying Features of Arthropods

Distinguishing Features Biologists Use to Make Subgroups of Arthropods.	Names of the Subgroups	Examples of Arthropods in the Subgroups
six legs, three main body parts, wings	Insects	grasshopper
eight legs, two main body parts	Arachnids	spider
more than eight legs, many other kinds of appendages, crusty covering	Crustaceans	lobster
numerous legs	Millipedes/Centipedes	millipede/centipede

A Simplified Classification System for Invertebrates

The blank, _____?_____, indicates that one of the pictured animals belongs here.

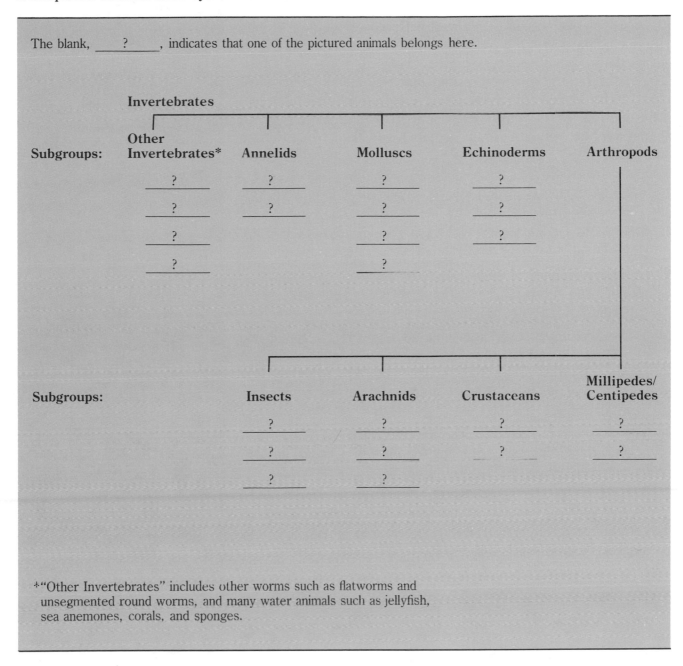

Invertebrates

Subgroups:	Other Invertebrates*	Annelids	Molluscs	Echinoderms	Arthropods
	?	?	?	?	
	?	?	?	?	
	?		?	?	
	?		?		

Subgroups:	Insects	Arachnids	Crustaceans	Millipedes/Centipedes
	?	?	?	?
	?	?	?	?
	?	?		

*"Other Invertebrates" includes other worms such as flatworms and unsegmented round worms, and many water animals such as jellyfish, sea anemones, corals, and sponges.

Now think some more about the subgroups.

1. Into which subgroup did you place each of the invertebrates pictured on pages 32 and 33? Did you have any problems deciding?

2. It is interesting to think about where invertebrates live. How many are found in water? In moist places? On dry land?

3. Does it appear that their structure enables them to live successfully in various places?

Vertebrates

Because you are so well acquainted with the vertebrates around you (including yourself!) you will be able to generate subgroups easily. Here are some vertebrates. They all have backbones. Biologists classify vertebrates into five well-known subgroups. Look at the 15 vertebrates pictured. Can you put them into five subgroups of three animals each? (**Hint**: The covering of each animal will help you find the five groupings.) Give a name to each subgroup.

Now that you have classified the vertebrates into five subgroups and named each one, discuss the following:

1. Identify the normal habitat of the living things in each subgroup. How do their habitats differ?

2. Do the members of each subgroup move in specific ways? Identify the method of locomotion of the members of each subgroup.

3. There are other features besides body covering, habitat, and means of locomotion that members of a subgroup have in common but that may vary from one subgroup to another. Can you suggest some of these features for the subgroups you have identified?

4. The ability of animals to survive in the place where they live is obviously important. Are any features of a subgroup specifically related to the survival of its members?

5. The names of the subgroups of vertebrates commonly used by biologists are found on the next page. Perhaps you suggested a different way to group vertebrates. If so, give your method of grouping and the reasons for your classification.

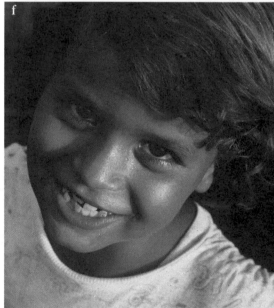

Putting It All Together

Many animals are illustrated on these pages. Your task is to classify them in your notebook, using a classification table like this one. This table is an overall classification scheme for animals. It brings together everything you have learned about classification in the Animal Kingdom.

If your classroom contains any living or preserved specimens which are not represented in the pictures, classify them as well.

Invertebrate Subgroups		Examples
Annelids		
Molluscs		
Echinoderms		
Arthropods	Insect	
	Crustacean	
	Arachnid	
	Millipede/Centipede	
(Other)		

Vertebrate Subgroups	Examples
Fish	
Amphibians	
Reptiles	
Birds	
Mammals	

Sometimes the outward appearance of an animal can fool you. Remember to examine each animal carefully. For example, the turtle does have a hard covering, but it is not a mollusc. Why not?

The Plant Kingdom

You have seen that the great number of animals led scientists to develop a classification scheme for them. Increasing knowledge of the differences among animals helped make this possible. Biologists found it equally useful to do the same for plants. At this stage, it may not be clear to you why these particular groupings have been chosen. Nonetheless, use them to classify plants around you. Practise by using the labelled pictures of plants.

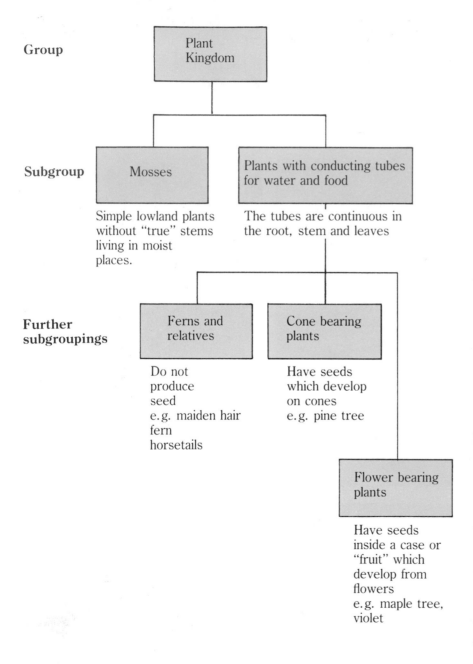

Group

Plant Kingdom

Subgroup

Mosses

Simple lowland plants without "true" stems living in moist places.

Plants with conducting tubes for water and food

The tubes are continuous in the root, stem and leaves

Further subgroupings

Ferns and relatives

Do not produce seed e.g. maiden hair fern horsetails

Cone bearing plants

Have seeds which develop on cones e.g. pine tree

Flower bearing plants

Have seeds inside a case or "fruit" which develop from flowers e.g. maple tree, violet

cedar

rose

oak

fiddlehead fern

moss

Ordering Diversity

The Swedish scientist, Carolus Linnaeus, who lived in the 18th century, can be called the "master of order". He was the first to devise a scientific system of classifying living things according to their similarities. It is essentially his system that we still use today. You can see Linnaeus's classification system at right:

You might be wondering why some of the groupings in Linnaeus's classification system have Latin names. In Linnaeus's time, Latin was the language used by all educated people. In fact, "Carolus Linnaeus" is a latinized form of "Karl von Linné" — his real name!

It was Linnaeus's ambition to name all the living things in the world. He did not quite achieve this goal, but he did name over 770 plants and 4400 animals.

Carolus Linnaeus

A Name You Can Claim

Where do you fit into Linnaeus's system? First, you are clearly a member of All Living Things. Next, you belong to the Animal Kingdom. Because you are a vertebrate (you have a backbone), you belong to Phylum Chordata. Then, because you are warm-blooded, have hair (not feathers), and were born alive (instead of hatching from an egg), you fit into Class Mammalia. There are certain similarities between you and other animals such as gorillas and chimpanzees, so the next grouping you belong to is Order Primates. The next two categories are Family Hominidae and Genus Homo. The final, and most specific, grouping is Species *Homo sapiens*. (You might find it interesting to look in a dictionary to see what your species name means.)

You have more in common with other human beings (*Homo sapiens*) than you do with other primates, such as chimpanzees. But you have more in common with chimpanzees than you do with other mammals, such as cats, for instance. However, there are still more similarities between you and cats than between you and maple trees, which are also living things.

Every single type of living thing, from a fungus to a frog, has its own species name. For example, your pet dog is *Canis familiaris*. Don't get him confused with *Canis lupus* — the wolf!

Now do some more research. What are some creatures that belong to the Animal Kingdom? To Phylum Chordata? To Class Mammalia? To Order Primates? To Family Hominidae? To Genus Homo?

	All Living Things
(Group)	Kingdoms
(Subgroup)	Phyla (singular: Phylum)
(Further Subgroupings)	Classes
	Orders
	Families
	Genera (singular: Genus)
	Species

A Legend: Wisakedjak Names All Creatures

A Cree legend says that the fox was the first animal to be given a name. This happened because one animal outsmarted Wisakedjak, the great spirit of the Western Indians, who said he was very "foxy." Wisakejak named all the animals, fishes, birds and insects and he told each of them where and how to live.

He told the fishes they must live in the water and could swim. He told the ducks that they could live on the water, on land and even fly in the air to escape their enemies. Wisakedjak gave the deer a white tail and said he could run fast and jump far. Squirrels could climb trees and hide in the tallest branches. To the slow porcupines he gave a special suit of quills which all animals learned to respect. Rabbits were trained to sit very still so they could not be seen.

Dr. Ivan H. Crowell

Do you recall any animals' names that are quite descriptive of what the animals are like?

There are many stories about how animals and plants attained their characteristics. This painting illustrates the Ojibwa folktale of how they received their colours.

The Same But Different . . . Diversity Within Species

Do you recall your scientific name? Right, you're a *Homo sapiens*. This is the name of the species to which you belong. Every person you know belongs to this species. All the organisms within a species are alike. Thus, you share certain characteristics with all human beings: the general arrangement of your facial features, the number of your fingers and toes, and the ability to reason, to name just a few. People belonging to the same family tend to resemble each other even more closely. This is known as a family resemblance. It occurs because every person inherits certain characteristics from his or her parents, grandparents, and so on.

Despite family resemblances, however, everyone is unique. You are "one of a kind". Not one of your friends or acquaintances is exactly the same as you, nor are you a duplicate of your parents or grandparents or brothers or sisters (even if you are a twin).

EXPLORATION 3

Tracing Similarities and Differences

You are going to investigate some of your own inherited characteristics, to determine how much you are like your family. You will do the same for some of your classmates.

What To Do

In the classroom, work in groups of four. Examine six inherited characteristics of each member of the group. In a table like this one, record how you would classify each member. Repeat this procedure with family members at home.

Every human is unique. How many examples of the diversity of features in Homo sapiens can you identify?

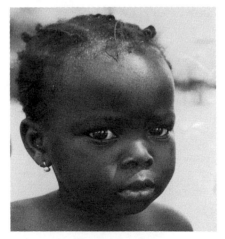

Characteristic	Student				Family	
	You	(2)	(3)	(4)	(1)	(2)
Hand-folding, thumb position (1) Left over right (2) Right over left						
Ear Lobes (3) Attached (4) Free						
Hair Line (5) Widow's Peak (6) No Widow's Peak						
Tongue-rolling (7) Can roll (8) Can't roll						
Digit next to little finger (9) Hair (10) No Hair						
Toe next to big toe (11) Same length or longer (12) Shorter						

Analyse Your Data

1. Study your table, then record how many members in your group have a given characteristic. Then compare results with the other groups in your class.

2. Calculate the percentage of individuals in your group who have each characteristic.

3. Does anyone have all of characteristics 1, 3, 5, 7, 9, and 11? Does anyone have all of characteristics 2, 4, 6, 8, 10, and 12? Are there any two people in the class who have identical characteristics for either of these two groups? Do you realize that there are 64 possible combinations of these six characteristic features of a person?

4. You have looked only at six pairs of characteristics. There are hundreds of other characteristics you might have considered. Do you agree or disagree with these statements?

   "You're *just* like ___(name)___."

   "Why, you are the spitting image of your mother/father!"

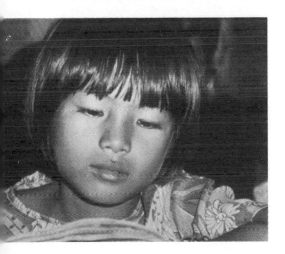

Life Cycles: Living Things Passing Through Diverse Stages

You have seen how much diversity there is in different groups of living things, and within a single group. Many organisms go through a series of stages, from birth to adulthood to the birth of offspring in the next generation. This series of stages in an organism constitutes its life cycle. When you examine the life cycles of living things, you can see that there is also diversity within the different stages of the life of a single living organism. In the life stories of many animals, the young animals live freely (on their own) and look quite different from the adults they will become. How many animals like this can you think of? Let's look at the life stories of three living things.

From Eggs to Frogs

A small, round egg looks very different from an adult frog. Between these two stages in the life cycle of a frog, diverse forms can be observed.

Observing the Changes

You Will Need

- large jar
- pond water
- soft gravel
- pond plant
- tall stick
- terrarium, or
- cardboard box fitted with clear plastic windows
- soil
- small log
- green plant
- dish of water

In the early spring, down by the marsh,
The croaking of frogs is deep and harsh.
When the male sends out his mating song,
The female responds — and before long,
She deposits her eggs in a shallow pond.
Then the male secretes sperm to complete the bond.
The egg divides into millions of cells;
"It's a tadpole," the young lad yells.
But watch for a few weeks and what do you see?
No longer a streamlined shape, swimming so free —
Its gills vanish and its tail disappears
"It's a frog," the young lad cheers.

What To Do

To study the diverse forms in the life cycle of a frog, you must construct two homes. The tadpole nursery is simply a large jar with a layer of gravel on the bottom, into which are placed a pond plant and a tall stick. Add pond water to complete the home.

A small terrarium or a cardboard box fitted with clear plastic windows is the beginning of an ideal froggery. Soil, a small log, a green plant, and a dish of water are all you need to make the frog comfortable and happy.

Don't forget to construct the home so that the frog can obtain plenty of air. Remember to feed it flies, bits of worms, and small insects.

After you have completed the homes, the tenants may move in. At this point, you will begin to keep accurate notes and diagrams so that you can conclude your study with a detailed account of the life cycle of the frog.

Some Suggested Study Procedures

1. Collect some eggs (or spawn, as they are called) from a local pond.

2. Place the eggs into the tadpole nursery. Using a spoon, take a few eggs out of the nursery each day and examine them with a hand lens.

3. Write and draw any changes you observe taking place in the jelly covering.

4. When the eggs have hatched, take out a tadpole and find the outside gills it uses to take in oxygen. Later, try to find the inside gills that will replace the outside gills.

5. Watch the growth of the leg buds and legs. Do the back or the front ones appear first?

6. Observe the tadpoles' tails daily. What happens to the tails?

7. Look for signs of lung development. The tadpoles will begin to use their nostrils to breathe at the surface of the water. When the changing tadpoles climb up the stick and remain out of water, it is time to change residences. Keep one or at the most two frogs, and return the rest to the pond from which they came.

8. Observe the frog(s) carefully for several weeks. Make daily records and drawings which include information about limbs, size, colour, breathing, and locomotion.

9. To summarize your information, make a large diagram in your notebook showing the life cycle of a frog. Include your detailed observations on your diagram or in an accompanying table.

From Eggs to Adult Insects

Insects are more abundant than any other class of animals. They inhabit every part of the Earth except mid-ocean. They have even been found in the atmosphere several kilometres above the Earth. The life cycles of different species vary, but all insects undergo changes as they develop from young forms to adult forms. These changes are easy to identify, because the stages often look quite different.

Here are the life cycles of two insects. Examine the two cycles and the "Label Hints" on page 52 carefully. In your notebook, use the "Label Hints" to label the diagrams.

The Life Cycle of a ___?___

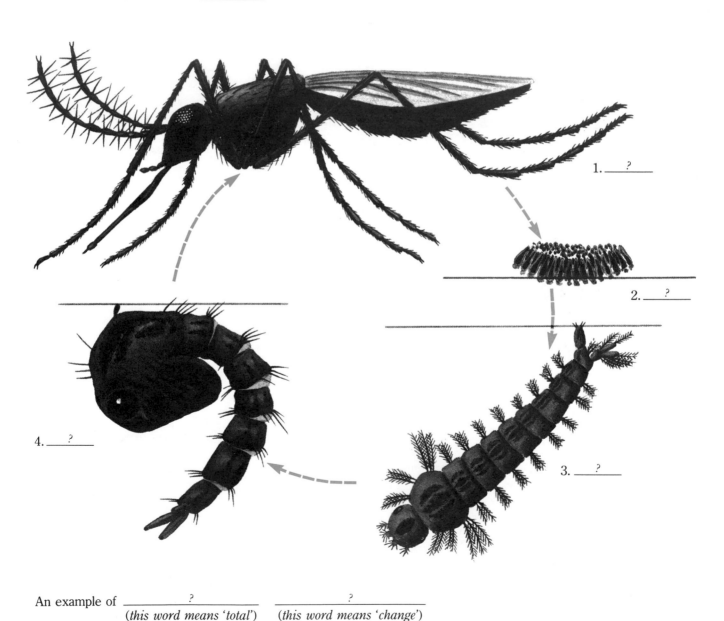

1. ___?___

2. ___?___

3. ___?___

4. ___?___

An example of _____?_____ _____?_____
      (this word means 'total')   (this word means 'change')

The Life Cycle of a ___?___

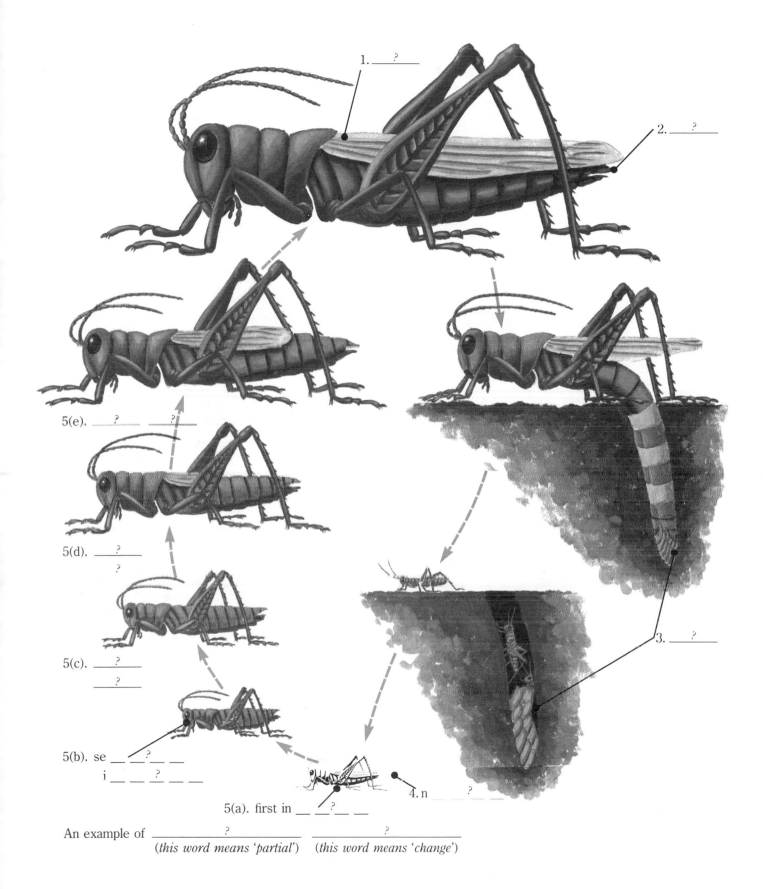

1. ___?___

2. ___?___

3. ___?___

4. n _____?_____

5(e). _____?_____ _____?_____

5(d). ___?___

5(c). ___?___

5(b). se __ __?__ __

i __ __ __?__ __ __

5(a). first in __ __?__ __

An example of _____?_____ _____?_____

(*this word means 'partial'*) (*this word means 'change'*)

Label Hints

Adult The last stage in the life cycle of an insect (and other animals).

Ovipositor The pointed structure at the end of the body of a female grasshopper. The female uses it to lay her eggs.

Cocoon A case for the pupa stage (see below) of many insects.

Egg The beginning stage in the life cycle of an insect (and many other animals).

Larva The stage in some kinds of insects which looks wormlike, moves a great deal, and eats a large amount of food.

Metamorphosis The word that describes the changes which occur from the egg to the adult in insects (and many other animals, such as the frog).

Complete metamorphosis In this kind of metamorphosis, the "in-between" stages are quite different in appearance and structure from the adult.

Incomplete metamorphosis In this kind of metamorphosis, the "in-between" stages have the general appearance of the adult.

Instar The form of an insect between moults.

Moulting The breaking and shedding of the outer skeleton of animals, such as insects, as their soft body grows inside. Grasshoppers have six moults. The wings appear on the fourth moult.

Nymph A grasshopper's young, having an abnormally large head.

Pupa The stage in some insects in which little motion can be seen, but great changes are taking place inside an outer case.

What Is It Really Like?

Your class has been invited to explain life cycles to a group of ten-year-olds. They really like puppets! Write the script for a skit in which one puppet is an elderly mosquito and another is an elderly grasshopper. They're talking about their youth and the changes they went through as they grew up. Towards the end of the skit, another puppet appears — a frog. The frog compares his life cycle with the other two. What would the frog say?

Diversity in Plant Cycles

Do you think that diversity occurs in the stages of the life cycle of a plant? Could there be "young plants" that look and live differently from the adults they will become? Research the life cycle of a fern and you may make some valuable discoveries.

One Form With Many Functions

Help Wanted

Insects are versatile creatures. They have many trades, that is, ways to make a living. There are quite obvious similarities between some insect and human occupations. However, insects have practised their professions for millions of years. Over the years, insects have perfected their tasks so well that individuals now have special jobs to perform for the benefit of their community.

The following want ads are taken from *The Worker's Journal* of Insectville. Study each one closely, then write your own ads for the insects listed here. Do some research to discover what each insect can do. Work in groups of two or three. Each group should prepare one ad for a class edition of *The Worker's Journal*.

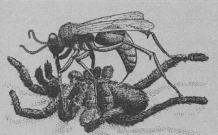

Wanted:
5 female Pepsis wasps

With armoured bodies to hunt tarantulas.

A lethal sting is required to paralyze the tarantula's body. Must have strength to drag the huge tarantulas to evacuated tunnels.

Strong mandibles and legs to dig new tunnels are needed. Each female must be capable of scraping the hair off a section of the tarantula's abdomen, depositing an egg on the cleared spot and filling the burrow with sand and soil before leaving.

Apply Sppw Tunnel 28
(Society for the Preservation of Pepsis Wasps, Inc.)

Needed:
12 Harvester Ants

4 Digger Bees

Wanted:
10 Milking Ants

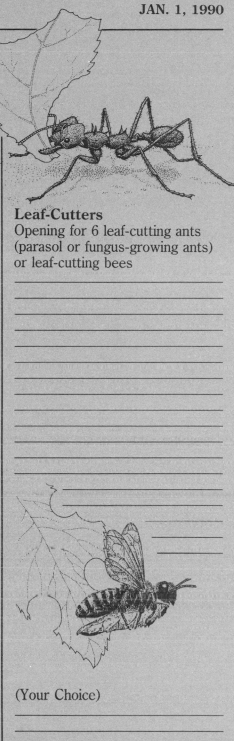

Leaf-Cutters

Opening for 6 leaf-cutting ants (parasol or fungus-growing ants) or leaf-cutting bees

(Your Choice)

Appendages

Here's another riddle for you: How is your thumb like a monkey's tail? Give up? They're both **appendages**, or protruding parts of the body. In fact, your entire hand and arm are appendages. So are an insect's antennae or feelers.

Appendages are adaptations designed to help an animal perform various specialized tasks. Therefore, its appendages help the animal live successfully in its environment.

A Closer Look at Appendages

Part I
Designing an Animal

What To Do

Design an animal with appendages which allow it to accomplish the following:

1. The animal lives in water.
2. Its heavy body receives a large amount of support as the animal walks.
3. It can walk on the bottom of a body of water for kilometres without stopping.
4. It can dart away suddenly from its enemies by swimming.
5. It can create water currents to bring food in the water to its mouth.
6. It tests its food before eating it.
7. It has appendages to hold larger pieces of food.
8. It can break hard bits of food apart.
9. Its diet includes shelled animals.
10. It has appendages to hold its young as it moves about.
11. It has formidable defensive weapons.

In your notebook, draw the creature you designed. Does it look like any animal you have seen before?

Have you ever seen animals like these?

Part II
A Close Look at the Appendages of a Lobster or Crayfish

You Will Need

- newly cooked lobster (or preserved crayfish)
- 2 tweezers
- hand lens
- newspaper

What To Do

Cover your desk with newspaper, then place your specimen on its back on the paper. Beginning at the front end, examine the lobster's (or crayfish's) appendages. You will find that the appendages are usually paired. Tweezers will help you separate the smaller appendages.

Your task is to find each lettered pair of appendages in the diagram. Now suggest how you think each appendage might be used. Is the lobster well designed for the accomplishments listed in Part I? How did your design compare with the lobster?

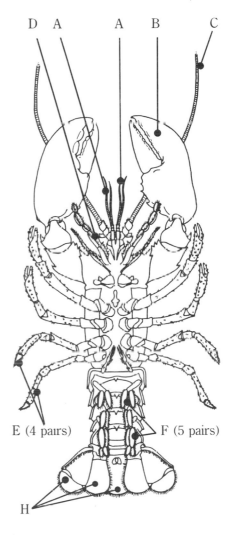

Brain Teasers

1. Search through this unit to locate each word for which the definition is given. (Be alert! A few words which you have not studied are included in this exercise.)

A. soft-bodied animals, most of them having shells   _ _ _ _ _ _ _ ₁₉ _

B. animals with feathers   _ _ _ _ ₁ _

C. the beginning stage in the life cycle of insects and many other animals   _ _ ₁₄ _ _

D. simple land plants   _ _ _ _ ₄ _ _

E. a group of animals or plants that have certain permanent characteristics in common   _ _ _ _ _ ₂ _ _

F. a worm-like stage in some kinds of insects; moves a great deal and eats much food   _ _ _ ₅ _ _

G. animals without backbones   _ _ _ _ _ _ _ _ ₁₆ _ _ _ _

H. the Swedish scientist who devised a scientific way of classifying living things by their similarities   _ _ ₁₀ _ _ _ _

I. the breaking and shedding of an animal's outer skeleton as the soft body inside grows larger   _ _ _ ₂₀ _ _ _ _

J. an animal with soft damp skin   _ _ _ _ ₁₅ _ _ _ _

K. animals with backbones   _ ₃ _ _ _ _ _ _ _ _

L. a grasshopper's young, having extremely large heads   _ _ ₈ _ _ _

M. worms with many segments   _ _ ₁₀ _ _ _ _

N. a stage in some insects during which not much motion can be seen but great changes are taking place inside an outer case   _ _ _ ₁₈ _

O. animals with scales and fins   _ _ ₁₃ _ _

P. the form of an insect between moults   _ _ ₆ _ _ ₅ _

Q. joint-footed or joint-legged animals   _ _ _ _ _ _ ₉ _ _ _

R. features of organisms which enable them to survive
and reproduce

— — — — — — — — —
_____7_____

S. a false attention-getting device

— — — — — —
17

T. a theory that explains how the features of a species
of living things change over many
generations

— — — — — — — — — — — — — —
_____20____11__

U. animals with fur or hair

— — — — — — —
___12___

V. animals with scales but no fins

— — — — — — —
_____7_____

Finally, fill in the blanks to discover a short poem.

— — — — — — — — —
1 2 3 4 5 6 2 7 8

— — — — — — — — —   — —   — — — — , — —
1 2 3 4 5 6 2 7 8   9 10   11 12 10 1   2 10

— — — , — —   — — — ,
12 2 5   2 10   6 4 12

— — — — — — — — —   — —   — — — — — —
1 2 3 4 5 6 2 7 8   9 13   11 2 3 2 10 14

— — — — — —   — —   — — — , — —   — — — — ,
7 15 2 10 14 6   12   13 11 8   12   16 2 5 1

— —   — — — — ,
12   7 5 4 4

— — — — — — — — —   — —   — — — — , — —
1 2 3 4 5 6 2 7 8   9 13   13 9 5 17   9 13

— — — — — , — —   — — Z — ,
6 15 12 18 4   9 13   6 2   4

— — — — , — W — — —   — — K — —
7 15 12 7 6   15 12 7   17 12   4 6

— — — —   — — — — — —   — — — — —
4 12 19 15   11 2 3 2 10 14   7 15 2 10 14

— — — —   — —
6 20 19 15   12

— — — — —   — — — — — — — — .
14 5 4 12 7   6 20 5 18 5 2 6 4

2. Now it's time to use your imagination as well as what you have learned. You have probably heard that a picture is worth a thousand words. Your challenge is to design a picture which shows a meaningful story about the diversity of living things. Here are some captions to get you started — but remember, you may have a much better idea for a caption.

- Sizes of Living Things (diversity of size)
- Living Things Are in Shape (diversity of shape)
- Habitats for Sale (diversity of habitats)
- Kick the Habit (diversity of habits)
- Worker Wanted (diversity of function)
- Who's in the Lead? (diversity in the numbers of different species)
- Chaos in Control (diversity in organisms)
- I'm Classy! (fitting yourself into the classification system)
- A Name you can Claim (naming organisms according to their classification)

  You're Unique (within a species each individual demonstrates differences)

- Jekyll and Hyde — A Case of Different Identities (diversity of form in life cycles)
- Cycling (life cycles)
- A Jack of All Trades (diversity of functions)
- The Missing Organism (camouflage)
- Attention Everyone (mimicry)
- The Adaptable Organism (natural selection)
- Assistance for Survival Needed (endangered species)

After designing your illustration, join in a group with four other classmates. Tell the story you have depicted to the group. Now exchange pictures with another group, and attempt to tell someone else's story.

3. Meet the Diversicules family. These little organisms are all mixed up and need your help to put themselves in order. Remember classifying other living things in the earlier part of the unit. That's what you do with the Diversicules. Be patient! This is not an easy task. Here is a start:

(1, 2, 3, 4, 5, 6, 7, 8, 9, 10, 11, 12, 13, 14, 15)

(1, 3, 5, 7, 11, 12, 15) (2, 4, 6, 8, 9, 10, 13, 14)

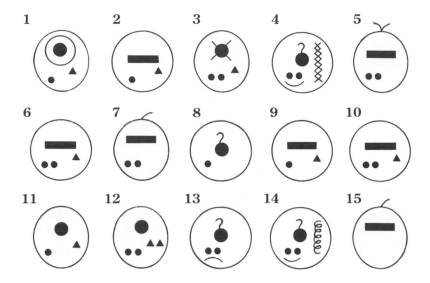

4. Each species of living things is unique. Sharks are no exception. Read the poem "Sharks".

Sharks

Cartilaginous skeletons are a benefit, you see,
They add the flexibility that we
Need to manoeuver through watery depths after innocent prey —
Time does not count . . . we attack night or day.
We sharks are the terrors of the sea,
We are hunters of power and voracity.
We grab, we shred, we tear, we gulp,
Defenceless victims we crush to a pulp.

Form yourselves into small groups. List ten living organisms. Each organism must have at least one characteristic similar to the shark's. Now discuss how each organism differs from the shark.

5. The Animal Kingdom Pie

Can you explain the meaning of this pie chart? Which animals would you place in the missing piece of pie?

6. Diverse Pen Pals!

You have met many living things in this unit, and have observed the many differences among them. Doubtless you were familiar with some of these living things before. But suppose you had a pen pal living in a very different environment, such as Abherra, who lives in hot Ethiopia, or Svetlana, in frozen Oymyakow, Siberia. You want to tell your pen pal about the climate here and the many different kinds of "strange" plants and animals he or she would see during a visit to Canada. Write a letter including this information to your far-away pen pal.

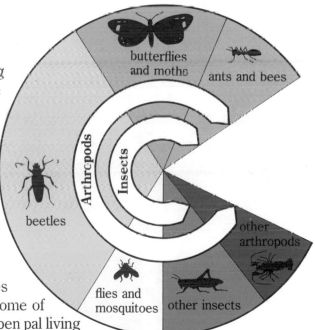

7. The Human Race!

List as many of the characteristics of *Homo sapiens* as you can think of. Let the illustrations guide you.

8. Classify the living things in this illustration according to some consistent system.

A Key That Opens the Door to Living Things

The diversity among organisms, as you have seen, can be simplified by grouping them according to their similarities. All you need is the right key to unlock the identity of a living thing. Study this example of an imaginary key which would help you to identify a small number of organisms.

Can you use the key correctly? Let's use the key, and trace a path through it to discover a Crab.

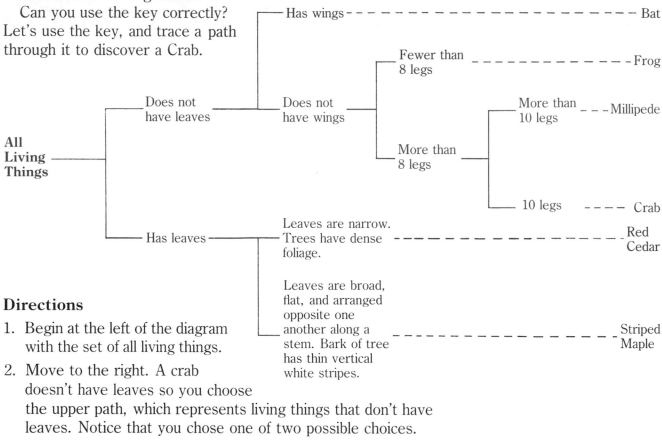

Directions

1. Begin at the left of the diagram with the set of all living things.

2. Move to the right. A crab doesn't have leaves so you choose the upper path, which represents living things that don't have leaves. Notice that you chose one of two possible choices.

3. Again you move to the right. Does a crab have wings? No. Now follow the path that represents "no wings".

4. Move to the right once more. A crab has more than eight legs, so you choose the lower path.

5. This is your last step to the right. A crab does not have more than ten legs; therefore, you choose the path which represents organisms that do not have more than ten legs. You have almost unlocked the door. Follow the dashes and you will read the name "crab".

What would be the path to a striped maple? What are the characteristics of a striped maple? What does the key tell you about millipedes?

The Master Key of Trees

It is your turn to "cut a key" which will unlock the identity to all the trees in your area. You can use the model you used to trace the crab. Remember that in Step 2 you had two choices based on a pair of characteristics. There are other pairs of characteristics which you can use.

First study these characteristics by observing real specimens in your neighbourhood or school surroundings. Most characteristics can also be studied by bringing parts of the trees into the classroom. The characteristics which can be studied vary with the seasons, so don't expect to be able

to fill in all sections of the following chart in a single observation period.

Before designing your key, fill in the table of observations for trees in your area. Then use it to make a key to unlock the identity of the trees.

Here is an example that Jane did.

Name	• Sugar maple
Outstanding Features	• adult tree about 12-18 m high
Fruit	
Flower	• flowers yellowish
Buds	• twigs glossy • many bud scales • buds are brown and sharp • buds are short
Leaves	• leaves moderately lobed (5 lobes)
Bark	• dark and flaky • rough vertical grooves and ridges
Shape	• short trunk • many ascending branches • symmetrical oval head

Unlocking the Doors of Nature

To identify any living organism, all you need is a key that will unlock the door to the organism. To become acquainted with all the insects and birds in your area, design a number of keys at home. Then bring your keys to school and share them with other students. If other people can use your key to find insects or birds with which they are unfamiliar, then you have been successful.

In designing a key to identify insects, it would be helpful for you to study each insect's habitat, colour, size, shape, type of legs and mouth parts, and its adaptation to the environment.

Keys for the identification of birds may be based on size, general body shape, beak or bill shape, tail shape and markings, special markings, and structure of the feet. The illustrations below may assist you with your bird identification key.

1. General Body Shape

Meadow lark — chunky

Grouse — plump

Owl — bulky

Swallow — slender

2. Size

The size can vary greatly. Estimate the size of the bird you are observing.

3. Bill Shape

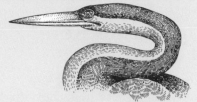

The spear-like bill catches fish and frogs.

The stout, heavy bill cracks seeds.

The slender bill is used to obtain nectar from plants.

The hooked bill tears prey.

The chisel-tipped bill digs insects out of the wood.

The strainer-like bill sieves food from the water.

4. Legs and Feet

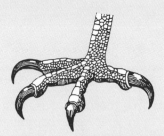

These are the curved, tearing claws of birds of prey.

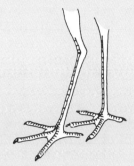

Wading birds have long legs.

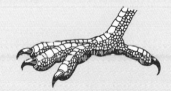

Perching birds have feet like this.

Birds that climb and grasp onto trees have feet like this.

Swimming birds have webbed feet.

5. Special Markings

Does the bird's head have a crest, crown patch, or crown stripes?

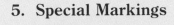

Is the breast striped, spotted, or unmarked?

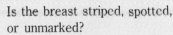

6. Tail Shape and Markings

Is the tail forked, squared, rounded, or another shape?

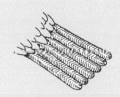

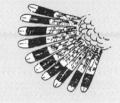

Does the tail have outer white tail feathers, white tail tips, a tail band, or a coloured rump patch?

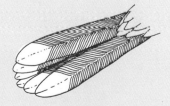

Biology

Lillian Wainwright is a biologist and university teacher who is concerned with how organisms evolve. We met in her laboratory.

Q: What aspects of your work do you find most stimulating?

Lillian: I love being in the laboratory. I love trying to solve problems about living things. As long as the problem is solvable, it is interesting. In recent years I have been interested in what controls certain kinds of activity in the cell.

With respect to teaching, I have always found it stimulating to talk to young people about things that I find most interesting.

Q: Are there any frustrations in your work?

Lillian: Yes, I would say the most frustrating thing is not having enough time for everything I want to do.

Q: Some scientists are very active in speaking out on social issues. Are there any social issues that especially concern you as a scientist?

Lillian: I am particularly concerned about the effects of radiation on living things. I consider the prospects of nuclear war to be a major issue of social importance. I am concerned about the proliferation of nuclear weapons. They are unimaginable weapons. I am not fearful for myself, because I am coming toward the end of my life. But I am concerned for the younger people and the future of the world. After a nuclear holocaust, we might only have cockroaches and ants. There is no such thing as a limited nuclear war. The future for the human world depends on preventing nuclear war.

Q: Are there any research projects in your field that junior high school students could carry out?

Lillian: One area that perhaps is easy to handle and doesn't require much in the way of equipment is the culture of *Drosophila* (fruit flies). Pill boxes can be used as containers. The *Drosophila* will grow on mashed bananas, sprinkled with a little bit of yeast. I suggest as a project the study of the rate of development of the *Drosophila* through the various stages of their life cycle. For example, with mashed banana and yeast in two identical pill boxes, one pill box could be

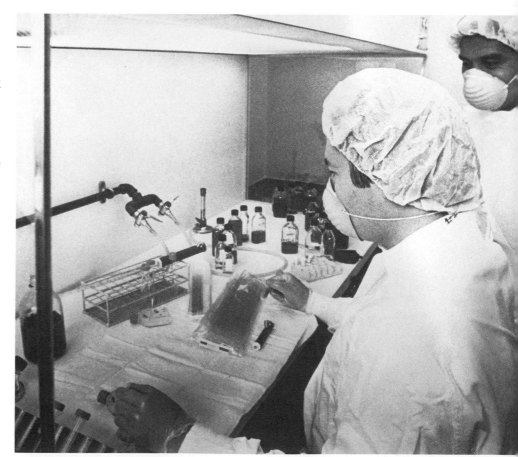

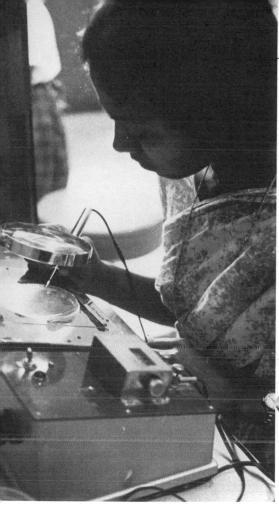

placed in a warm location, the
other in a cold one to determine
the effect of temperature on the
rate of development. As a further
project, the effect of different
kinds of yeast and different kinds
of food could be studied. A little
more sophisticated follow-up would
be to see, at a constant temperature, whether a mutant strain
of the wild type of *Drosophila*
would grow at the same rate as
the normal strain. That gets into
evolution, which I am interested
in.

Q: Where could students obtain
Drosophila?

Lillian: I suggest a university
biology department would be a
source of help.

Agriculture

Are you a serious gardener? Are you interested in becoming one? Or would you like to experience just once the kind of challenge faced by those who produce our food? Then these activities are for you.

There are many kinds of soils, with different *physical characteristics*. At one extreme is clay. Composed of very fine particles, it remains soggy for long periods, bakes hard when it dries out, and doesn't permit the circulation of

Installing a drainage system.

air and water. At the other extreme is sand. Composed of coarse particles, sand does not retain the moisture and nutrients necessary for plant growth.

It is essential to improve the physical characteristics of both these soils. For both, the solution can begin with the same substance: peat moss. Peat moss is the decomposed remains of prehistoric plants. It is found in abundance throughout Canada. Light, coarse, and moisture-absorbing, peat moss can be used

to make either clay or sand more suitable for gardening. However, it adds very few nutrients to the soil.

Plants need nutrients such as minerals for growth. Many soils, including clay and sand, are naturally deficient in these essential nutrients. Other soils' nutrient content becomes depleted after repeated planting of crops. The solution to this problem is adding natural and chemical fertilizers to the soil.

Adding compost to the soil takes care of both problems at once; it improves both the physical characteristics and the nutrient content of the soil. Compost is the result of the decomposition of once-living matter. In forests, for example, leaves, pine needles,

plants, and logs, and dead animals all eventually decompose, returning to the soil the nutrients required by the living plants. Have you ever seen a farmer digging the remains of a previous crop (stalks and leaves) into the ground? This organic material—compost—perhaps the dug-under debris of previous crops, eventually decomposes to provide nutrients for the next crop.

As a project, you can make your own compost. A compost pile consists, first of all, of the organic material to be decomposed, for example, leaves, grass clippings,

organic kitchen garbage, and so on. There is usually an activator to hasten the process, for instance, soil, manure, alfalfa, or bonemeal. Finally, good air circulation is essential.

Decomposing material produces heat. For a contest, agree to a time limit (say two months) and an amount of organic material, and see whose pile heats up the most in that time.

A third factor affecting plant growth is the acidity of soil. You may know from previous studies that acidity is measured on the pH scale, which goes from 0 to 14. 0 is the greatest degree of acidity, 7 is neutral, and 14 is the greatest degree of alkalinity (basicity). Some plants grow best in slightly acidic soil (5.5 to 7.0); examples are beans, blueberries, carrots, peas, radishes, and tomatoes. Others prefer more nearly neutral or slightly alkaline soil (6.0 to 7.5); lettuce, broccoli, spinach, onions, and melons fall into this category. Few vegetables like really alkaline soil, but some flowering plants, especially rock garden plants, thrive on it.

Here is a contest worthy of any gardener: Each contestant is to pick a suitable location for a mini-garden—but it must have poor soil. All contestants should agree on the size of the mini-garden (perhaps one metre by one metre) and on the test crop (radishes are a good choice, because radish seeds can be planted as soon as the ground can be worked and come up quickly). Improve only half of the garden but plant seed in both halves. The goal is to see

who can do the best job of improving the soil. The winner is the person who has the biggest difference in results between the two halves of the garden. To find the winner, the judge(s) might compare the ten best radishes from the improved soil with the ten best radishes from the unimproved soil. Once the soil is prepared for planting, all other conditions must be kept the same.

Each contestant should keep a record of what he or she has done, so the records can be compared afterwards. If possible, a soil testing kit should be obtained, and each contestant should test both the improved and the unimproved soil for nutrients and acidity. In a class discussion, compare the results obtained by the contestants, and try to explain them.

Charles Saunders and Angus MacKay—Pioneer Agriculturalists

The soil was rich and loamy, but the short growing season and frequent droughts challenged pioneer farmers on the Prairies. The essential wheat crops often fell victim to early frosts or periods of drought. The story of how these problems were solved is as fascinating as science fiction. Find out about Angus MacKay (1841-1931), pioneer experimental farmer, and Charles Saunders (1867-1937), plant breeder. Their discoveries are among the most important ever made in Canada: they helped to open up the West and make Canada a leading exporter of wheat.

Sources of Information

- Agriculture Canada
- The Department of Agriculture in your province
- Departments of agriculture at Universities: Nova Scotia Agricultural College, Laval University, MacDonald College at McGill University, University of Guelph, University of Manitoba, University of Saskatchewan, University of Alberta, University of British Columbia

Any good gardening book.

- For information on Charles Saunders and Angus MacKay:
  - *The Canadian Encyclopedia*
  - *Canadians–A Book of Biographies* by Lorne J. Henry, Toronto, 1950
  - *The Canadian Inventions book* by Janis Nostbakken and Jack Humphrey, Toronto, 1976
  - *Canadian Portraits: Pioneers in Agriculture* by Elizabeth Waterston, Toronto, 1957

CHEMICAL
CHANGES

The Chemicals in Our Lives

WASH HANDS AFTER USING CHEMICALS.

GOGGLES MUST BE WORN WHENEVER CHEMICALS ARE USED.

Sulphuric Acid

Do signs like these apply to all chemicals?

Have you met any chemicals in your daily life?

Are all chemicals dangerous?

What do we use chemicals for?

What are chemicals?

Are there any chemicals here?

These are only a few of the questions you will examine in this unit on chemical changes. But before going on, what do you and your classmates think? Some other students were asked what they thought about chemicals; you can read their opinions in the table below. Do you agree or disagree with them? Decide, then record your opinions in your notebook. If you are not sure about a statement, check the column "Uncertain" to indicate that you are "sitting on the fence"!

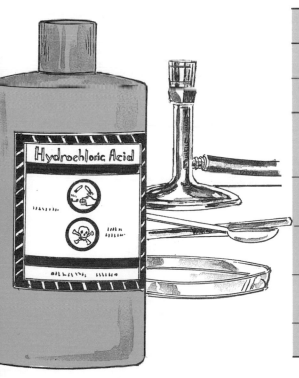

About Chemicals	Agree	Disagree	Uncertain
"All chemicals are bad."			
"We can't live without chemicals."			
"Our house is insulated with urea formaldehyde. Isn't that a chemical?"			
"Living things are made up of chemicals."			
"We need chemicals to keep the spruce budworm under control."			
"I think chemicals are everything around us."			
"Chemicals cause cancer."			

What Are Chemicals?

Part 1

You Will Need

- water
- table salt
- sugar
- blackboard chalk
- baking soda
- nylon threads

What To Do

You would not normally taste chemicals in the laboratory. You will do so in this Exploration only. You probably recognize each of these common substances. They are all **chemicals.** Look at each substance carefully. Feel each one. Taste each one. Are you able to identify these chemicals from your observations? In Part 2 you will further investigate these same chemicals.

CAUTION! Some chemicals are dangerous to feel or taste. The ones mentioned here are not. Do not feel or taste any other laboratory materials.

Part 2

You Will Need

- glass slide
- candle
- eyedropper
- tin lid
- clothespin
- vinegar
- 25 mL of water

What To Do

In the paragraphs which follow, each of the substances you examined is described, and some activities are suggested. From your reading and your own observation, suggest at least one fact you have discovered about each chemical. In your notebook, record your results in a table like this one.

Substance	What I Have Discovered About This Chemical
water	
table salt	
sugar	
blackboard chalk	
baking soda	
nylon	

Water

This must be the most common substance of all. You drink it for survival. You swim in it, sail on it, skate on it. It falls on the Earth as rain, snow, and hail. It is one of Canada's great natural resources.

Place a drop of distilled water on a glass slide and heat it over a candle flame. What remains on the glass slide?

Table Salt

This is one of the oldest known substances. In some areas it was so valuable it was used for money! Throughout the world it is processed in many different ways. In Nova Scotia salt is mined. In Israel salt is obtained through the evaporation of sea water. In some parts of the world, such as northern Zambia, salt is produced from plants.

What do you think: Is the salt you use at home likely to be the same as the salt found in the home of an Israeli student?

Place a few crystals of salt in 25 mL of water and stir. What happens? Can the salt be recovered? How?

Sugar

Did you know that, as an average Canadian, you consume 40 kg of sugar a year? Think of the candies you consume — as well as the sugar found in fruit and even potatoes! Most of our sugar-bowl sugar comes from the juices of sugar cane or sugar beets. It is purified by a chemical process called *refining*.

What do you think: Would the sugar obtained from sugar beets differ in any way from the sugar obtained from sugar cane?

Without tasting, how could you distinguish salt from sugar?

Place a bit of sugar on a tin lid and heat over a candle. Use a clothespin to hold the lid. What happens?

Chalk

"A classroom without chalk is like . . . " Finish this sentence yourself. Chalk contains limestone, which is found in many parts of the Atlantic provinces. Today, chalk is made from chemically-produced calcium carbonate. This is the chemical name for limestone.

Break a piece of chalk into two pieces. Examine the powder on the surface of each piece where you broke it. Is there any difference between one piece of chalk and the other? If you went to a strange land, would you be able to recognize chalk? How?

Add a dropperful of vinegar to a small piece of chalk. What happens?

Baking Soda

What would we do without baking soda? Cakes would be flat, refrigerators would be less sweet-smelling, and more Canadian

stomachs would be upset. Baking soda is a very practical chemical!

Add a drop of vinegar to a small sample of baking soda. Did everyone get the same reaction? What does this tell you about substances?

Nylon

The Second World War brought about many changes. One of them was a shortage of silk from China. Silk stockings became hard to find. But, just in time, a discovery was made. When you mix two substances — adipic acid and hexamethylene diamine — together, they form a new substance with properties or characteristics very much like those of silk. This new substance, nylon, became a plentiful and cheap alternative to silk.

Obtain a few threads of nylon from different sources; they may be different colours. Now, by holding the threads in a wooden clothespin, burn each one. Do they behave differently, or very much the same?

Analysis Please!

By now you have made many observations and inferences about chemicals.

1. Compare your list of discoveries with that of another group of students. Do you agree with their statements?

2. Here are some inferences you may not have made. For each one of these inferences, state an observation from the experiments you just did that would support it:

(a) One bit of a substance is identical to any other bit of the same substance.

(b) Distilled water is a single substance, not a mixture.

(c) If my baking soda bubbles when vinegar is added to it, then everyone else's baking soda will do the same.

(d) A chemical is just one kind of stuff.

Our Discoveries

1. There is nothing else in water except more water.

2. Everyone's table sugar turned black when heated.

3. Table salt is table salt no matter what its source is.

4. Both chalk and baking soda fizzed with vinegar.

5. Nylon always burns the same way, no matter what its colour is.

6. None of the chemicals we used are mixtures.

3. By now, you have discovered how scientists look at chemicals or substances.

First, a chemical is a single substance; while a mixture is made up of two or more substances. Salt water, for instance, is composed of salt and water. Each substance in the mixture can be recognized by its distinctive characteristics.

Second, every part of a chemical or substance is like every other part. This is why you could recognize a piece of chalk whether you found it in your classroom or in the driveway.

Third, a chemical or substance will always behave or look the same under similar conditions. For instance, chalk can always be scratched with a fingernail; water always boils at 100°C at sea level; baking soda and vinegar fizz when mixed together; and nylon threads always burn. Properties or characteristics like these can help you identify a substance.

With a classmate, discuss all the ways you could distinguish the chemicals listed below from one another. How many properties of each did you name? The chemicals are salt, sugar, chalk dust, and baking soda.

4. Here is Rajiv's description of one of the chemicals you examined. Which one is it? Has he named enough properties to positively identify the chemical?

"This chemical is a solid. It's white. If I add vinegar to it, it fizzes and bubbles. It does not dissolve in water."

Something to Think About

Here are some of the chemicals that contribute to the aroma of coffee!

acetaldehyde	formic acid	methylamine
acetic acid	furan	methyl ethyl acetaldehyde
acetone	furfural	
acetyl methyl carbinol	furfuryl acetate	methyl ethyl acetic acid
acetyl propinonyl	furfuryl alcohol	methyl mercaptan
ammonia	furfuryl mercaptan	n-heptacosane
cresols	guaiacol	n-methylpyrrole
diacetyl	hexanoic acid	p-vinylguaiacol
diethyl ketone	hydrogen sulphide	phenol
dimethyl sulphide	hydroquinone	pyrazine
2,3-dioxyacetophenone	isovaleric acids	pyridine and homologues
esters	m-valeric acid	pyrrole
ethyl alcohol	methyl alcohol	resorcinol
eugenol		trimethylamine

There are actually many more chemicals in coffee. Imagine how many there must be in a tree or in you! Just think how many chemicals you must encounter each and every day!

The Chemicals in Your Day

Sasha and Harold are not aware of the different chemicals they encounter each day. Even in the first two hours of their day, they use many chemicals or products containing chemicals.

Here is a description of their morning activities. Make a list of the chemicals or items made up of chemicals which they encounter.

Sasha

Taking a deep breath, Sasha gets up, goes into the bathroom, brushes her teeth with toothpaste containing fluoride, and washes her face with soap. Next come deodorant, eyeshadow, and lipstick. She decides to wear nylons to work today, along with a rayon blouse and wool skirt.

Harold

Harold struggles out of bed, throwing back the sheet. The first thing he does is to take his contact lenses from their cleaning solution, wash them in distilled water, and put them in his eyes. Now he can see! Next, Harold shaves, using mentholated shaving cream, then sprays himself with an aerosol deodorant. He pulls on a polyester sweater and slacks.

They both breakfast on orange-crystal juice, cereal, and toasted bread made from enriched flour. Finally they set off for work, catching a bus.

Just like Sasha and Harold, we all eat, drink, and breathe chemicals. Many chemicals occur naturally in the world — examples are substances such as water and the oxygen in the air. Other chemicals, such as nylon, plastics, and the dyes in lipstick, are made by industrial methods.

Tracking Down Chemicals

What are the chemicals in *your* day? One way to find out is to read the labels on the items you use. They often list the chemicals making up the various items. When you do this, you may be surprised by what else is in your cornflakes besides corn! In your notebook, keep track of the chemicals in your day by recording them in a table. Afterwards, make a collage of labels to display some of these chemicals.

Now write a brief story of your day. Include as many chemicals as you can. Try to add chemicals not mentioned in the account of Sasha and Harold's morning.

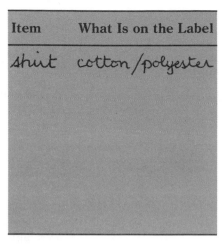

Item	What Is on the Label
shirt	cotton/polyester

Safety First

"There is no need to put on your goggles when you add *sodium chloride* to your french fries, or when your teacher writes on the board with a piece of *calcium carbonate*, and certainly not when you wear your *polyhexanedioic acid diaminohexamide* jacket! Washing your hands is a waste of time after adding *sucrose* to your cereal or after taking some *sodium bicarbonate* for an upset stomach."

Can you replace the chemical names with the common names? For instance, sodium chloride is salt.

However, safety *is* important when you are handling many substances in the home, the classroom, the lab or at work. Each picture on these two pages illustrates one or more safety rules. Can you spot what is being done correctly?

Safety Tips

In groups of two, discuss the safety rules concerning chemicals and other materials that should apply to your classroom. Devise a poster on the theme of safety. Here are some suggestions for the poster:

- Draw cartoons.
- Make diagrams.
- Take photographs.
- Write poems.
- Describe humorous situations.
- List humorous statements.

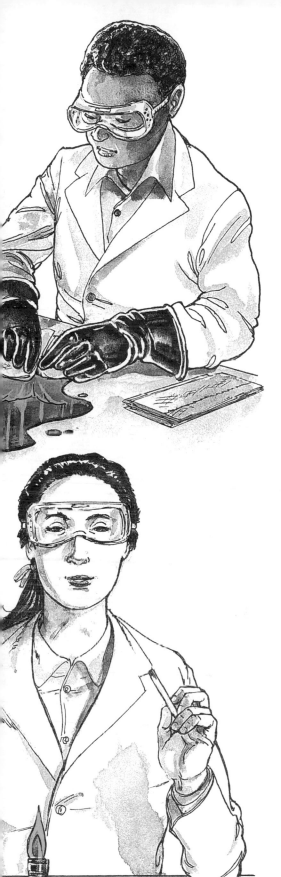

Here is a limerick that was part of one group's poster.

There once was a girl named Di
Who instead of water, drank lye
Her teacher said NEVER
to taste — not EVER
She's now in that Great Lab in the sky.

Warnings!

Detergents are poisonous. Oven cleaners are corrosive, which means they will burn your skin. Drain cleaners contain strong lye, which is also corrosive. Bleaches give off a poisonous, bad-smelling gas — chlorine. Where are these chemicals stored in your home? Could you make any recommendations about storing and using them? What other materials around your home are potentially dangerous?

Below are some of the warning signs used on dangerous household chemicals. Do you know what they mean? What warning signs are on the products in your home?

WEAR GOGGLES   POISON   FLAMMABLE   EXPLOSIVE   CORROSIVE

A Project

Many chemicals have both a common name and a chemical name. The introduction to this section used the chemical names of some chemicals you met earlier in this unit. Can you replace the chemical names with the common names? As you proceed through the unit, you will encounter more common and chemical names for substances. Keep a list of both names for all the substances you meet. You can start with water.

Common Name	Chemical Name	Use
water	hydrogen oxide	Plants and animals need water.
table salt		

Changes Everywhere

All is Change

There is an old saying, "The more things change, the more things stay the same." Does this make sense to you? Does everything change, or are there things which do not change?

In groups of three, examine some changes you may be familiar with. Choose one of the following themes, and list as many changes as you can. With a marker, record your ideas on a piece of bristol board. When you have finished, display your list in the classroom. You will come back to these changes later in the unit.

- kitchen changes
- barbecue changes
- backyard changes
- people changes

Here is a start to "kitchen changes":
1. water boiling
2. plate breaking
3. ....
4. ....

Now that you've finished, have you changed your mind about what you first thought about the saying that began this section?

Classifying Changes

In Exploration 1, you looked at six substances. You also observed a change involving each one. Review what you did in the Exploration, and record a change for each substance in a data table.

In which of all the changes in your table were new chemicals formed? How do you know whether a new chemical has been formed during a change? These are the questions which puzzled Mr. Alexander's class. Let's listen to them as they try to find the answers. Mr. Alexander has just given them the following table, which lists the changes they noticed in Exploration 1. Copy the table into your notebook, and follow along with the class. Don't worry if the answers in your table are different from theirs — yours are probably better! It will be more enjoyable if you work in groups.

My Table of Changes

Chemical	Change
water	
salt	
sugar	
blackboard chalk	
baking soda	
nylon	

Their Table of Changes

	water evaporating	salt dissolving	sugar turning black when heated	baking soda fizzing when vinegar added	breaking chalk	nylon burning when heated
1 Has a new chemical been formed?						
2						
3						
4						
5						
6						
7						

Mr. Alexander:

In row 1, I have written my *question. Has a new chemical been formed as a result of the change? Let's put a "√" under each change when you* believe *a new chemical has been formed. An "X" will mean no new substance or chemical has been formed. José?*

José:

I saw black smoke when we burned the nylon threads. I think a new chemical was formed there.

Sue:

We saw bubbles when the vinegar was added to baking soda. Would that mean we put a "√" under baking soda?

Hal:

The burnt sugar smelled like bad cooking. Something new was certainly formed in that change.

Later, after much discussion about whether a new substance is formed when water evaporates, they agreed to finish the table in this way. Do you agree with their new table?

Their New Table of Changes

	water evaporating	salt dissolving	sugar turning black when heated	baking soda fizzing when vinegar added	breaking chalk	nylon burning when heated
1 Has a new chemical been formed?	X	X	√	√	X	√
2						
3						
4						
5						
6						
7						

Mr. Alexander:

On lines 2 to 7, I would like you to write your own questions. Each question must have a yes or no answer. Each question can be used only once. Hal, what will your next question be?

Hal:

Was there a smell — like bad cooking?

Mr. Alexander:

Fine. Now, working in your groups, decide on your questions and fill each square in the table with a "√" or an "X". We will examine the results in the next class.

Before looking at their questions, copy the table into your notebook and finish it yourself, using your own questions.

Analysis Please!

1. Mr Alexander's class made a long list of questions. Joy copied some of them into her notebook. Here they are. Did you have different questions?

   - Was a new chemical formed?
   - Was there a colour change?
   - Was there any smell?
   - Was the change easily reversible?
   - Was heat given off?
   - Was light given off?
   - Was heat required for the change to happen?
   - Can the original chemical still be used?
   - Were any bubbles formed?

2. The answers to some of your questions may provide valuable clues that a new chemical did form. What are the five most important questions your class can ask?

3. Read this excerpt from Joy's notes, then answer the questions that follow.

   > Today we studied changes. We divided them into two types. In one type, a new chemical was formed. This type of change is called **chemical change**. Burning is an example of a chemical change.
   >
   > If no new chemical is formed, then the change is a **physical change**. Breaking, dissolving, boiling, evaporating, and freezing are all physical changes.
   >
   > Our class concluded that there are some clues which show when a chemical change occurs:
   > - A new colour appears.
   > - Heat or light is given off.
   > - Bubbles form.
   > - The change is not easily reversible.
   >
   > The only problem is that you can't use the same clues for each chemical change! Life certainly is complicated!

   (a) Have you and your classmates identified other ways of detecting chemical changes? What are they?

   (b) Was Joy right? Can't you use the same clues each time to identify a chemical change?

   (c) Are some characteristics present in a chemical change that can also be present in a physical change? For example, heat often *causes* a chemical change. Can it also cause a physical change? If it can, give an example.

(d) In a chemical change, a chemical often disappears or a new one appears. Can you think of a physical change where a chemical seems to disappear, or where a new substance seems to appear?

(e) Butter melts, but can become solid again. Water evaporates, but also condenses. These are both physical changes. Are all physical changes easily reversible?

(f) At the start of this Lesson, you listed a number of changes on a large piece of paper for display. Now, underline all the changes you think are chemical changes.

Physical and Chemical Vocabulary

Kelly, who was also in Mr. Alexander's class, had a very good idea. He decided to make two vocabulary lists, one for each of the two types of changes, physical and chemical. Here are Kelly's lists. Copy them into your notebook, and give an example of a change associated with each word. But think hard — be sure you have the right type of change.

Can you add any words and examples to the two lists?

Physical Vocabulary

Word	Example
grinding	
breaking	
eroding	
evaporating	
melting	
condensing	
drying	
freezing	
....	
....	

Chemical Vocabulary

Word	Example
burning	
rotting	
rusting	
....	
....	

What physical and chemical changes are occurring in this photograph?

Now look up the word "state" in the dictionary. It certainly has many meanings! Here is the word "state" as it is used in science:

"Water exists in three states: in the solid state, as ice; in the liquid state, as water; and in the gaseous state, as water vapour or steam."

What words in the Physical Vocabulary list do you associate with a change in state?

Signs of Chemical Change

More Evidence of Chemical Changes

Let's examine more changes and look again for ways of recognizing whether a chemical change has occurred. You will also observe some new evidence of chemical changes here. But be careful — there are physical changes hidden among the rest. Construct a data table like the one below to record your findings. For each change, decide whether it is physical or chemical, and state your reasons why.

You Will Need

- matches
- tin lid
- iron nail
- eye dropper
- egg shell
- clothespin
- candle
- drinking straw
- test tube
- measuring cylinder
- sample of potato (or cereal or starch)
- limestone
- water
- 2 g of copper sulphate
- vinegar
- 25 mL of milk
- limewater
- cobalt chloride (a few crystals)
- lemon juice
- iodine solution
- baking powder
- dilute hydrochloric acid
- toothpicks

The Change	Physical	Chemical	Reasons or Evidence
A match burns.		✔	1. Heat and light are given off. 2. Colour change occurs. 3. Difficult to reverse change.

What To Do

1. Burn a match. (Be careful!) Hold it over a tin lid in case you have to drop it.

2. Add 1 g of copper sulphate to 10 mL of water and stir. Now do Step 3.

3. Place an iron nail in the copper sulphate solution you made in Step 2.

4. Add 3 eyedroppers of vinegar to 25 mL of milk.

5. Add a dropper-full of vinegar to a piece of egg shell.

6. Heat a bit of candle wax on a tin lid. (Use a clothespin to hold the lid.)

7. Using a drinking straw, blow slowly into a test tube one-quarter full of limewater. (Blow slowly, or you will splash limewater over yourself and others.)

8. Place a few crystals of cobalt chloride on a tin lid and heat. Now do Step 9.

9. Add a few drops of water to the substance remaining in Step 8. Stir with a toothpick. If you don't notice a change, add a few more drops of water.

10. With a match or a straw from a broom, write a word on a piece of paper using lemon juice. Heat the paper gently over a candle flame. Do not burn it.

11. Add a drop or two of iodine solution to a bit of starch. (A slice of potato, some cereal, corn, or a piece of bread may be used instead.)

12. Add a few drops of water to baking powder.

13. Add a few drops of dilute hydrochloric acid to a piece of chalk.

A New Word

Did you notice new evidence that a chemical change occurred? In steps 4 and 7 you observed a *precipitate* — a solid formed as the result of a chemical change.

Chemical Tests

Chemical changes can be used to help identify substances. Here is a table of some common tests for chemical changes. Copy it into your notebook and complete it by recording the observation expected for each test. You have already seen all these chemical changes in this unit.

Test For	Procedure	Result
copper in any substance	Place an iron nail in a solution of the substance.	
carbon dioxide	Pass the gas through limewater.	
water	Add the liquid to blue cobalt chloride.	
starch	Add iodine solution.	
limestone (calcium carbonate)	Add dilute hydrochloric acid. Then test for carbon dioxide.	

Bubble Watch!

Formation of bubbles is often evidence of a chemical change — but not always. Try these changes, and decide which of the bubbles you see result from a chemical change.

You Will Need

- beaker
- water
- seltzer tablet
- bottle of pop
- vinegar
- baking soda
- 10 mL of molasses
- packet of yeast

What To Do

1. Heat water in a beaker until it boils. Is this a chemical change? What are the bubbles made of? How could you prove your answer?
2. Examine a recently opened bottle of pop. Are you observing a chemical change?

3. Drop one-quarter of a seltzer tablet into water. Is this a chemical reaction? What are the bubbles made of? Can you prove it?

Champion Detective of Chemical Change

By now, you should be a champion "chemical change detective". Using a table similar to the one here, make a list of all the clues by which you would recognize a chemical change. Can evidence for a chemical change be observed in every chemical change, or only in some?

What to Look For in Chemical Changes

Evidence of a Chemical Change	Sometimes Observed	Always Observed
1.		
2.		
3.		
4.		
5.		
6.		

4. Let a cold glass of water reach room temperature. Do the bubbles indicate a chemical change?

5. To 50 mL of water, add 10 mL of molasses. The exact amounts you use are not critical. Make a yeast mixture by stirring half a packet of yeast into 25 mL of warm water. Add this to your molasses solution. Place in a warm spot and record all changes over the next few days. Does a chemical change occur?

6. Add a few drops of vinegar to baking soda. Are these bubbles made of the same substance as the one you encountered in Step 2?

Classify These Changes!

Now your knowledge of the two types of changes will be put to the test! Classify the changes listed below as either physical or chemical, then give a reason for your decision. The first one has been done for you.

Change	Type	Reason
A newspaper yellowed after a few weeks.	chemical	Colour change indicates a chemical change.
The steel wool turned the black pot a shiny silver.		
Lightning flashed across the sky.		
Acid caused limestone to fizz.		
The back steps are rotting out.		
The piece of lemon turned the tea cloudy.		
Spilt gasoline dried, but left a bad odour in the room.		
The gravy in the refrigerator jelled.		
A blue-green lobster turned red as it cooked.		
A cavity appeared in a tooth.		
Flash cameras flashed after the wedding.		

Can You Be Fooled by the Clues?

In earlier Lessons, you examined vocabulary lists associated with physical and chemical changes. You also discovered several clues by which physical and chemical changes can be recognized. Here are the clues which show that a chemical change has occurred:

- There is a colour change.
- A gas is given off.
- A solid is formed.

- Heat and/or light are given off.
- A new substance with new identifying properties is formed.

But be careful! Can the clues fool you, as they fooled the students who made the statements below? You be the teacher, and explain (in writing) why each of the following conclusions is wrong.

"When I open a bottle of pop, it fizzes. This shows that a chemical change has occurred."

"Salt is white. When it dissolves in water it becomes colourless and invisible. This colour change is evidence that a chemical change has occurred."

"Heat and light are given off by a light bulb. A chemical change is therefore taking place in the light bulb."

"Ice is often a different colour than liquid water. This is an example of a chemical change."

"The sawdust formed when wood is cut looks quite different from the tree it came from. A chemical change has occurred during the cutting."

Interview a Neighbour

What kinds of people do chemicals and their changes affect? Almost everyone! Cooks, nurses, parents, druggists, chemists, farmers, swimming pool managers, pet fish owners, fishermen, garage owners, joggers, sewage workers, and environmentalists are just the beginning.

Interview someone from your neighbourhood. What chemicals do they use? What changes are involved in their line of work? But first, consider the following:

- Whom shall I interview?
- What shall I ask?
- How shall I record my information?
- What form will my report to my class take?

Suppertime — Can You Spot the Changes?

There are at least ten physical and seven chemical changes concealed in this story. Can you find them and list them in a table?

Liv and Christopher decided to make supper for their parents and grandmother. While Liv cut up the vegetables and cheese for the salad and boiled an egg for slicing, Christopher placed ice cubes into some pop which he had just poured from a freshly opened bottle.

They had also decided to make and cook some hamburger patties and to broil some frozen french fried potatoes. Earlier in the day, Liv had mixed some Jello powder in hot water and allowed it to cool in the refrigerator until it set.

When the meat appeared to be completely cooked, so that it was no longer red, and the french fries were golden brown, they called their parents and grandmother. After the meal, it was time for dessert and coffee. Liv and Christopher boiled some water and poured it into mugs. Instant coffee powder and sugar were stirred in. Almost everything was ready. But where was the milk? They searched for it until they remembered that Christopher had left it outside earlier in the day. It smelled sour and had already started to curdle. So they had to serve the coffee black!

Later, the scraps were placed in the garbage. Their father washed the dishes in steaming hot water and Christopher dried them. Liv finished an oil painting, while their mother read a book. The entire family agreed that they had enjoyed their supper thoroughly, though Granny did have some trouble with her stomach. However, a seltzer tablet soon helped soothe the problem. All in all, it was a successful venture for Liv and Christopher.

Can you write a story containing hidden physical and chemical changes? Try it, then ask a friend to find the changes.

On The Shoulders of Giants

Sir Isaac Newton is recognized as one of the greatest scientists in history. His three laws of motion and theory of gravitation are the cornerstones of modern physics. Newton was always ready to acknowledge his debt to the chain of scientific progress started by others. He once wrote, "If I have seen farther than other men, it is because I have stood on the shoulders of giants." What did he mean?

You have been observing examples of everyday changes. Some of these were chemical changes and others were physical changes. Are you now able to distinguish one from the other? The study of chemical changes is part of a branch of science called chemistry. Chemistry attempts to answer such questions as:

- How does chemical change take place?
- What is the structure of chemical materials; what are the building blocks of chemicals?
- How can new materials be made?
- What are the properties of chemical materials?
- How will different materials react with each other?

Over time, many people have contributed to the understanding of chemistry. Below is a list of some major discoveries. There are many others! The people involved in these discoveries were the giants on whose shoulders successive generations of scientists stood. Each discovery increased our understanding of chemical reactions. As a project, research one of the discoveries. Your encyclopedia will be a useful resource. Have a presentation day where scientists from the past are introduced. An interesting way of doing this is to have each presenter act out the part of the scientist that was chosen for the project.

450 B.C.: Greek philosopher Leucippus of Miletus introduces the concept of an atom. His pupil Democritus expanded on this idea.

1662: Robert Boyle (Anglo Irish) announces what becomes known as Boyle's Law: the pressure and volume of a gas are inversely related.

1670: Robert Boyle discovers the element hydrogen.

1755: Joseph Black (Scottish) discovers carbon dioxide.

1772: Joseph Priestly (English-American) notes that burning hydrogen produces water.

(top to bottom) Robert Boyle, Joseph Priestly, John Dalton, Friedrich Wöhler

1772: Daniel Rutherford (Scottish) and several other chemists discover nitrogen.

1774: Joseph Priestly announces his discovery of oxygen.

1778: Antoine-Laurent Lavoisier (French) discovers that air is a mixture of nitrogen and oxygen.

1781: Lavoisier states that mass is conserved during chemical changes.

1784: Henry Cavendish (English) announces that water is made up of oxygen and hydrogen.

1803: John Dalton (English) reintroduces the idea that matter is made up of atoms.

1828: Friedrich Wöhler (German) produces in the laboratory the first substance, urea, that had previously been produced only by living things, proving that the chemicals that make up living things are basically the same as other matter.

1859: Gustave Kirchhoff and Robert Bunsen (German) show that elements can be identified by the light they emit when heated to a high temperature.

1868: Pierre-Jules-César Janssen (French) and Sir Joseph Lockyer (English) discover helium by observing the sun's spectrum.

1869: Dimitri Mendeleev (Russian) publishes his version of the periodic table of the elements.

1905: Mikhail Tswett (Russian) develops the technique of chromatography – an early method of chemical analysis.

1908: Fritz Haber and Karl Bosch (German) develop a cheap process for making ammonia from nitrogen in the air.

Extensions

Since 1901, achievements in chemistry, physics, medicine, literature and peace have been recognized through the Nobel Prizes. Find out about Alfred Nobel, who established these prizes. How did he make his fortune? (It was based on a chemical change.) Fritz Haber was an early recipient of the Nobel Prize for chemistry (1918). John Polanyi, a Canadian, was the 1986 recipient. Do research on someone who has won a Nobel Prize for chemistry. What was their contribution? Your encyclopedia will have a complete list of Nobel Prize winners.

(top to bottom) Robert Bunsen, Joseph Lockyer, Dimitri Mendeleev, Alfred Nobel

Properties of Matter

Mysterious Drops

Annette's class had a problem. That is, Annette's teacher gave them a problem to solve.

A cold, empty glass was taken from a refrigerator. In a few minutes, small drops began to form on the outside of the glass.

"Water drops!" said one of Annette's classmates.

"Prove it," said the teacher.

How could Annette and her classmates prove that the drops were water? What would you do?

After some discussion, the class came up with a number of suggestions. Working with another student, consider each one and decide whether it is a good plan of action.

Plan 1:
Since it looks, feels, and smells like water, it must be water.

Plan 2:
Collect enough of the drops and find their mass. If 1 mL of the sample has a mass of 1 g, then it must be water.

Plan 3:
Collect the drops and drink them. If they taste like water, then they are water.

Plan 4:
Collect enough drops and find the boiling point of the sample. If it boils at 100°C, then it's water.

Plan 5:
Heat some cobalt chloride crystals until they turn blue. Add some drops of the sample to the blue cobalt chloride. If it turns pink, then the drops are water.

Plan 6:
Try other chemical tests. Try to burn a sample; to make it react with iron or aluminum; to get a chemical reaction with substances such as paper. If the drops do not burn or react with these substances then they are probably water.

Which plan or plans do you prefer? Why? Are there some you should avoid? Can you prove that the drops on the glass are water?

In determining whether the drops are water, you are making use of the *properties* of water. There are two kinds of properties. What would you say "property" means? What other words could be used instead of "property" which would have the same meaning?

Physical Properties of Water

Not only describe what water looks, feels, tastes, behaves like, but also describe what physical changes water can undergo.

Chemical Properties of Water

Not only describe what chemical changes water can undergo, but also describe what chemical changes or reactions will *not* occur.

Aluminum: Its Properties and Uses

How many uses of aluminum are you aware of? The uses of aluminum are determined by its properties.

As you read the following description of this metal, list as many of its properties as you can. Even after reading about it, you may be able to think of other properties not mentioned here.

Afterwards, decide which of the properties are important for the purpose of each aluminum object shown here.

Although aluminum is the most common metallic element found in the Earth's crust, it was not isolated until 1827, by a German named Wöhler. Its name is derived from the Latin word *alumen*, alum, which was a headache remedy.

Aluminum is very versatile. Because its density is small compared to that of most metals, aluminum is used to form lightweight *alloys*. Alloys are a mixture of two or more metals. Aluminum or its alloys are used in canoes, boats, cars, bicycles, and space vehicles.

Aluminum is *ductile* — that is, it can be drawn into a wire. As well, it is *malleable*. This means it can easily be shaped into many useful products, from aluminum siding to aluminum cans. Because it does not corrode and is not poisonous, it can be used to wrap food.

Aluminum is used to make cooking utensils because it is a good conductor of heat. It is bonded to polyester fibre and used to make sleeping bags, because, as a reflector of heat, aluminum reflects body heat inward and keeps a person warm. Aluminum certainly is a "hot property". Can you suggest what new uses it might have in the future?

Guess That Substance!

Each person in your class will write three properties of a substance on one side of an index card or piece of paper and the name of the substance on the other side. A classmate or your teacher will read the properties. The winner is the person who guesses the most substances.

Here is Ralph's index card:

- it's a metal
- it's ductile
- it rusts

Answer: iron or steel

A Chemical Property of Aluminum

The chemical copper chloride is beautiful in appearance. You will use it to examine *one* of the chemical properties of aluminum. As you proceed, record all the chemical changes you observe. CAUTION! Make sure you do not handle the copper chloride. Wash your hands after the experiment.

You Will Need

- 5 g of copper chloride crystals
- 1 square of aluminum heavy foil, 10 cm × 10 cm
- 100 mL of water in a beaker
- 1 stirring rod
- 1 dish

What To Do

1. Add the copper chloride to the beaker of water. Make all the observations you can, then stir to dissolve the copper chloride.

2. *Lightly* crumple the aluminum foil and place it in the beaker. You can push it under the surface of the liquid with your stirring rod.

3. Make as many observations as you can, then try the questions.

Questions

1. What evidence do you have that a chemical change is taking place?

2. Name a physical change that took place.

3. What new properties of aluminum have you discovered? Are they physical or chemical properties?

4. What are some physical properties of copper chloride?

5. Name one chemical property of copper chloride.

6. Examine the red material formed. What do you think it might be?

You can summarize what you did in this Exploration as follows:

Here's what you started with:

- silvery grey aluminum
- greenish-blue copper chloride dissolved in water

Here's what you observed:

- disappearance of aluminum
- disappearance of blue colour
- appearance of reddish powder (Could it be copper?)
- after evaporation of water, a white powder (Could it contain the aluminum that disappeared?)

Summarizing Chemical Changes

In every chemical change, new substances are formed. These new substances are called **products** of the chemical change. When you added vinegar to baking soda, carbon dioxide gas was released. Carbon dioxide is a product of this chemical change. From observing the change, you would not realise that water and sodium acetate were also formed. These are products of this chemical change as well.

The starting substances are called the **reactants** of the chemical change. Baking soda and vinegar are the reactants.

A word equation shows both the reactants and the products of a chemical change:

Reactants ————➤ Products

Can you write a word equation for the reaction between baking soda and vinegar? For the reaction between copper chloride and aluminum?

Review the chemical changes you have observed so far in this unit. Try to identify some of the reactants and some of the products. (Don't worry if there are reactants and products you cannot identify. Often, doing so requires special chemical tests.) Record the ones you can identify in a table like the one below. Keep adding reactants and products to your table as you proceed through this unit.

Chemical Changes

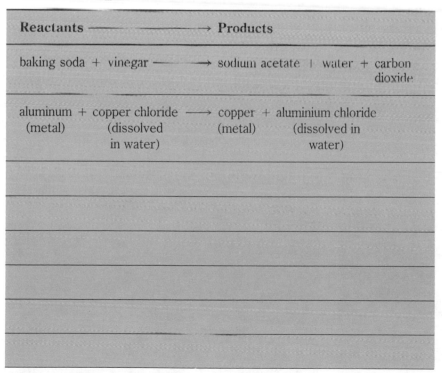

Reactants ——————————→ Products	
baking soda + vinegar ———→ sodium acetate + water + carbon dioxide	
aluminum + copper chloride ⟶ copper + aluminium chloride (metal) (dissolved (metal) (dissolved in in water) water)	

More Reactants and Products

You have seen that chemical changes are part of daily life. Some interesting ones are described below. For each chemical change, try to identify the reactants and products, then write the word equation.

The Ultimate Chemist

Whoever is the cook in your family is the ultimate chemist — mixing chemicals together to form delicious things to eat. A chemical that plays an important part in many recipes is sodium bicarbonate. It is found by itself in baking soda, or mixed with an acid, cream of tartar, in baking powder. During the cooking process, the sodium bicarbonate in baking powder reacts with the cream of tartar to produce carbon dioxide. This reaction causes the cake to rise. Water and sodium tartrate are also formed, but you cannot tell they are there.

Try This at Home

Make your own baking power by adding a few millilitres of cream of tartar to about 5 mL of baking soda. Then add some water. Watch what happens!

Table Salt from Acids and Bases

Concentrated hydrochloric acid can cause severe burns to the skin. Sodium hydroxide, a base found in many drain cleaners, is extremely corrosive and can also burn the skin. However, these two chemicals can react to form an essential part of our diet — sodium chloride, or table salt. Water is also formed in this chemical reaction. How strange it is that two potentially dangerous chemicals can form another chemical which is essential for life!

If you are interested in learning more about acids and bases, try Exploration 5.

Although one of these is formed from the other in a chemical change, you would not put both on your food. Why?

The Gases That Make Up Water

Water, as you know, is a liquid. Heating water to its boiling point can change liquid water into steam, a gas. But it is still the same chemical — water. However, water can be broken apart to form new substances by having an electric current passed through it. Hydrogen gas and oxygen gas are formed. Perhaps some day huge quantities of water may be decomposed by this process, which is called *electrolysis*. The hydrogen produced could be used as a fuel to heat homes and run cars. Hydrogen may be the fuel of the future!

Limestone Caves

If you are a spelunker, your hobby is exploring caves. Spelunking requires a lot of skill and knowledge. Many of the largest and deepest caves in the world are limestone caves.

Water containing dissolved carbon dioxide is one of the reactants in the chemical change that forms limestone caves. This mixture reacts with calcium carbonate (the chemical name for limestone) to form calcium bicarbonate. This chemical is soluble in water. Over time, more and more of the limestone disappears as a result of this chemical change, and caves are formed.

Just for a Change . . .

Do research on a chemical change. In your research, try to determine the reactants and products of that change. Include in your write-up other interesting information you may find. Share your research with your classmates to see whether they can write a word equation for your chemical change.

Here are some possibilities:

- At Kitimat, British Columbia, aluminum is obtained from its ore. How is this done?

- What is the chemical change involved in obtaining iron from iron ore? If there is a steel mill nearby, you might ask the manager for help with this question.

- Plaster of Paris is made from gypsum. What chemical change is involved?

- What can you learn about the reactants and products in making cement?

- Your flashlight dry cell uses a chemical change to produce electricity. What are some reactants and products in this change?

- Talk to a photographer to learn about the chemical changes involved in taking and developing photographs.

According to legend, James Watt experimented with his mother's kettle before inventing the steam engine. Steam engines cause a physical change in water to produce energy. What kind of change in water does electrolysis cause?

How has this cave been formed?

The Nature of Chemicals

Elements and Compounds

Can lead be changed into gold? The earliest chemists — the alchemists — thought it could be. In the course of their work, they discovered many chemical changes, but never the one that they really wanted — a way to convert other metals into gold.

We now know that theirs was an impossible task. All chemicals or substances can be classified as **elements** or as **compounds**. Gold and lead are both elements. So are iron and aluminum. These are just a few of the over one hundred basic materials out of which more complex substances are formed. Elements can combine with other elements in chemical changes to form compounds. Compounds can be decomposed by chemical changes into the elements that make up the compounds. However, one element cannot be changed into another element by means of chemical changes.

Here are three tasks you can try. Each one makes use of your understanding of elements and compounds. The list of elements on page 108 may help you.

An ancient alchemist in his laboratory

Task 1

In your notebook, fill in the blank with the word *element* or *compound*.

All compounds of the ___?___ copper are blue or green. Copper chloride is a green ___?___ . It contains two ___?___ , copper and chlorine. Have you seen the green roofs of Canada's Parliament Buildings? This green colouring is the ___?___ copper carbonate. Two ___?___ found in the air, carbon dioxide and water, react with the ___?___ copper to form this green coating.

During chemical changes, elements react with other elements to form ___?___ . As well, ___?___ can decompose into ___?___ , or compounds can react with compounds to form still other ___?___ . You have already seen examples of all of these types of chemical changes.

Canada's Parliament Buildings

Task 2

The following chemical changes all involve elements. Identify the elements, and state whether each is a reactant or a product of the chemical change.

(a) A flashlight battery uses a chemical change between zinc and ammonium chloride to produce electricity.

(b) Gunpowder, an early Chinese discovery, is made up of sulphur, carbon, and potassium nitrate. Ignition causes a flash or an explosion.

(c) Passing an electric current through water containing some sulphuric acid produces hydrogen gas and oxygen gas.

(d) Skiers sometimes use chemical hand warmers. Each package contains iron filings, carbon, water, and sodium chloride. When these substances are exposed to oxygen in the air, a chemical change occurs, producing heat.

Task 3

Here are some chemical changes you can try to produce. In each case, both elements and compounds are involved. List the elements, as you did in Task 2.

(a) Take a deep breath. The oxygen you are breathing is taking part in a chemical change inside your body to form carbon dioxide.

(b) Wet a piece of steel wool. The rust that forms in a couple of days is a compound made up of iron and oxygen, called iron oxide.

(c) Place a piece of zinc or magnesium ribbon in dilute hydrochloric acid. The bubbles formed are hydrogen gas.

Post Script: The Modern Alchemists

Today's scientists are the modern alchemists. Far more is now known about the nature of chemicals and of chemical changes. Scientists have even made gold — but not by means of a chemical change.

Ninety-one elements exist naturally on Earth. Scientists have created a few more to bring the number to over 100. But it is the 91 naturally-occurring elements that make up *everything* in this world. That's incredible!

An early Chinese war machine with cannons

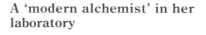

A 'modern alchemist' in her laboratory

Get to Know the Elements

Here is a list of the 91 elements that occur naturally on Earth, and their symbols. The symbols are used as a shorthand method of representing the elements. Uses for some of the elements, or their compounds, are also given here. Use your school library to find some of the uses of the elements with question marks beside them. Do you know about the uses of any of the other elements?

The elements

Element	Symbol	Element	Symbol	Element	Symbol
Actinium	Ac	Helium	He	Protactinium	Pa
Aluminum	Al	Holmium	Ho	Radium	Ra
Antimony	Sb	Hydrogen	H	Radon	Rn
Argon	Ar	Indium	In	Rhenium	Re
Arsenic	As	Iodine	I	Rhodium	Rh
Astatine	At	Iridium	Ir	Rubidium	Rb
Barium	Ba	Iron	Fe	Ruthenium	Ru
Beryllium	Be	Krypton	Kr	Samarium	Sm
Bismuth	Bi	Lanthanum	La	Scandium	Sc
Boron	B	Lead	Pb	Selenium	Se
Bromine	Br	Lithium	Li	Silicon	Si
Cadmium	Cd	Lutetium	Lu	Silver	Ag
Calcium	Ca	Magnesium	Mg	Sodium	Na
Carbon	C	Manganese	Mn	Strontium	Sr
Cerium	Ce	Mercury	Hg	Sulphur	S
Cesium	Cs	Molybdenum	Mo	Tantalum	Ta
Chlorine	Cl	Neodymium	Nd	Tellurium	Te
Chromium	Cr	Neon	Ne	Terbium	Tb
Cobalt	Co	Nickel	Ni	Thallium	Tl
Copper	Cu	Niobium	Nb	Thorium	Th
Dysprosium	Dy	Nitrogen	N	Thulium	Tm
Einsteinium	Es	Osmium	Os	Tin	Sn
Erbium	Er	Oxygen	O	Titanium	Ti
Europium	Eu	Palladium	Pd	Tungsten	W
Fluorine	F	Phosphorus	P	Uranium	U
Francium	Fr	Platinum	Pt	Vanadium	V
Gadolinium	Gd	Polonium	Po	Xenon	Xe
Gallium	Ga	Potassium	K	Ytterbium	Yb
Germanium	Ge	Praseodymium	Pr	Yttrium	Y
Gold	Au	Promethium	Pm	Zinc	Zn
Hafnium	Hf			Zirconium	Zr

Al ?

Cl ?

Au ?

Fe ?

C ?

Mg ?

P Matches

He ?

Pb Car Batteries

Sn ?

Ra X-rays

Na Street-lights

Zn ?

Now select an element from the list and investigate it. What is the origin of its English name? Is its symbol very different from its English name? If so, why? What are its physical and chemical properties? What is its most interesting property? What are some of its uses?

Record your information on index cards, and form a class display about the elements by gluing the cards to a sheet of bristol board.

Here is what Weldon and Betty found out about the elements silver and mercury.

SILVER – SYMBOL Ag

- name comes from Anglo-Saxon word seolfor
- symbol comes from Latin Argentum
- known since ancient times
- best conductor of electricity of all the elements.
- does not corrode.
- does not react with acids
- is not attracted to a magnet.

Mercury – Symbol Hg

- symbol comes from Greek – hydragyros, meaning "water-silver"
- known in ancient times – used by alchemists in their experiments
- is a metal, but is liquid at room temperature.
- used in thermometers, barometers, and hydrometers.
- will dissolve gold and silver to form amalgams.
- will not react with cobalt, nickel or platinum

Acids and Bases

If you were asked to name an acid, what would you answer? Would you be surprised to learn the following facts?

- Vinegar is an acid.

- Milk contains an acid.

- Apples contain an acid, and so does lemon juice.

- Your stomach contains an acid called hydrochloric acid.

As you can see, there are many acids which are already familiar to you. Acids form a class of substances with similar properties. All **acids** have a sour taste. They react with metals, as well as with another class of compounds called bases.

In your home, you can find bases in drain cleaners, in household ammonia for cleaning floors, and in the bottle of milk of magnesia that you may have in your medicine cabinet. **Bases** feel slippery and have a bitter taste. They react with acids.

Acids and bases can be detected through chemical changes. There are some natural dyes which have one colour in acids and another colour in bases. These dyes are called **indicators**. The table below gives the expected colour of three different indicators in acids and in bases.

Three Acid/Base Indicators	Colour	
	In Acids	In Bases
litmus	red	blue
bromthymol blue	yellow	blue
phenolphthalein	clear	pink

In Part 1 of Exploration 5 you will use these three indicators to answer three questions:

(a) What materials are acids or bases?

(b) Can carbon dioxide dissolve in water to form an acid?

(c) What happens when you mix an acid and a base?

In Part 2 you will make your own acid/base indicator out of a red cabbage!

Investigating Acids and Bases

Part 1: A Classroom Activity

You Will Need

- litmus paper
- bromthymol blue
- phenolphthalein
- a variety of substances to test
- beaker of water
- plastic straw
- household ammonia
- dilute hydrochloric acid
- dilute sodium hydroxide
- evaporating dish or other glass container

What To Do

1. What materials are acidic? Which are basic? Use the *litmus* test to find out. Cut each piece of litmus paper into four parts and use them to test different materials. Try lemon juice, apple juice, a tomato, coffee, milk, water, baking soda, milk of magnesia, Tums, aspirin, household ammonia, soap, and anything else that you may have around. Any solid material must be mixed with a few millilitres of water before being tested.

2. Could carbon dioxide be a contributor to the acid rain problem? Obtain a beaker of water and add a few drops of *bromthymol blue*. If your solution is a slight yellow colour, add a drop or two of household ammonia until a blue colour results. Using a plastic straw, blow gently into the solution for a minute or two. What happens? Has your breath affected the acidity of the water? What component of the air you exhale could cause this effect? How might this be related to the acid rain problem?

3. Now make some table salt. To do so, you need a dilute solution of both hydrochloric acid and sodium hydroxide.

Place 5 mL, or 25 drops, of hydrochloric acid in an evaporating dish or another glass container. Add one drop of *phenolphthalein* indicator.

Next, add sodium hydroxide drop by drop, until the solution turns a very faint pink colour. If you think the pink is too intense, add a drop of hydrochloric acid.

Place the dish in a quiet spot to allow the liquid to evaporate. Observe what remains. Examine the crystals under a microscope. This is an example of a **neutralization reaction**. The acid *neutralizes* the base to form a *salt*. Water is formed as well.

---

acid + base → salt + water

hydrochloric acid + sodium hydroxide solution → sodium chloride solution + water

---

Part 2:
Make Your Own Acid/Base Indicator at Home

You have already used three prepared acid/base indicators. Now you will make your own indicator, using a red cabbage.

You Will Need

• red cabbage leaves
• vinegar
• household ammonia
• hot water
• eyedropper
• glass

What To Do

1. Cut a red cabbage leaf into small pieces.
2. Fill a glass one-quarter full with the cabbage pieces.
3. Add enough hot water to fill the glass half-way.
4. Allow the cabbage to soak for 20 min.
5. Save the coloured liquid and throw out the cabbage pieces. The purple cabbage juice is your indicator.

Questions

1. What colour does the cabbage juice indicator turn in acids? Fill a test tube one-quarter full of cabbage juice. Add a dropperful of vinegar.

2. What colour does the cabbage juice indicator become in bases? Again fill a test tube one-quarter full of cabbage juice. This time, add a dropperful of household ammonia. What happens? Continue to add ammonia, a drop at a time. Can you get another colour change?

3. Can you neutralize the basic solution? Try by adding more vinegar! What happened?

Violets are . . . red?

Violets are another natural indicator. Put a bluish-purple violet into a glass and pour some vinegar on it. Wait ten minutes. The violet will turn red!

Part 3: Research

In Part 1, Step 2, you learned an important fact about acid rain. Now find out some more. What causes acid rain? Why is it harmful to the environment? Do research on this important problem. You could also make a classroom display of headlines, articles, and letters to the editor on the issue.

CURE FOR ACID RAIN YEARS AWAY!!

CANADA URGES U.S.A. TO STEP UP FUNDS FOR ACID RAIN

MORE STUDY

The Nature of Burning — A Chemical Change

The role of elements and compounds in chemical changes was not always known. Even a very familiar change like burning mystified observers for thousands of years. Let's listen in on three scientists as they discover what they think burning is all about.

Flashback! Greece, 460 B.C.

Empedocles is eating a simple meal of bread and cheese by the light of an oil lamp. He studies the flame and wonders, "What causes burning?"

Empedocles's Theory and Conclusion

All matter is composed of four elements — earth, air, fire, and water. If a piece of matter contains the element fire, then it will burn.

Wood contains fire — wood burns!
Oil contains fire — oil burns!
Rock does not contain fire — rock does not burn!

Good theory! It works! Or does it?
   What can you do to support his theory — or prove it wrong?
   According to Empedocles's theory, salt is made up of earth and water. What might have been the reasoning behind this conclusion?

Invent a good caption for this cartoon.

Flashback! Germany, 1710

George Stahl is also having dinner, by candlelight. He and his wife are discussing the question that is on everyone's mind: "What causes burning?"

Stahl's Theory and Conclusion

Phlogiston! That's right. All objects that burn contain phlogiston. And when the phlogiston is all gone or when the air becomes saturated with the released phlogiston, then burning stops.

Wood contains phlogiston — wood burns!
Coal contains phlogiston — coal burns!
Rock does not contain phlogiston — rock does not burn!

Good theory! Explains observations! Or does it? Can you suggest any ideas that would support or disprove this theory of burning?

Invent a good caption for this cartoon.

Testing Stahl

You Will Need

- candle
- metal lid
- small weigh-scale
- bottle with a wide opening

What To Do

1. Observe a burning candle. Does anything seem to enter or leave the candle as it burns?

2. Attach the candle to a metal lid. Find the mass of the candle and the lid. Light the candle and after 10 min blow it out. Find its mass again. Using Stahl's theory, explain why its mass is different.

3. Light the candle and place a bottle over it. What happens? How would Stahl explain this?

Flashback! France, 1775

Antoine Lavoisier is eating a dinner of onion soup and frog's legs. A candle is burning. Lavoisier is celebrating. He has devised a new theory of burning.

OXYGEN FROM AIR! COMBINES WITH BURNING MATERIAL & PHLOGISTON THEORY REPLACED!

Le Monde

The best theory!
Explains all observations!

Testing Lavoisier

You Will Need

- steel wool
- weigh-scale balance
- clothespin
- matches
- small can, such as one used for canned salmon

What To Do

1. Place about 1 g of loosely-packed steel wool into a small can. Very carefully find the mass of the steel wool and the can.

2. Now touch a burning match to the steel wool. The steel wool burns! Repeat this three or four times.

3. Find the mass of the steel wool and can again. Was there a mass change? Could Stahl explain this observation with his theory? How would Lavoisier explain it?

4. According to Lavoisier, why would a candle go out after a jar is placed over it? Why does a candle have less mass after burning?

5. Complete this word equation in your notebook:

   iron + _?_ → iron
   (steel wool)   oxide

Somewhere in Canada, 19--

A Grade 9 class is *not* eating dinner by lamplight or candlelight. However, groups of three students are observing a burning candle, and performing three simple experiments. Try the experiments yourself in the next Exploration, to find out what observations the students are making.

Student Conclusions

You Will Need

- candle
- 2 jars
- 25 mL of limewater

What To Do

1. Hold a jar very close to a candle flame. What is being deposited on the jar? Where is the substance coming from?

2. Place another jar over the candle. What is being deposited *inside* the jar? Where is this substance coming from? How could you prove what it is?

3. After the candle has gone out, add 25 mL of limewater to the jar and cover it quickly. Shake. What happens? What does this prove?

4. What evidence did you see that a burning candle produces water when it burns? Carbon dioxide?

5. Complete this word equation in your notebook. Candle + oxygen → ___?___ + ___?___ .

A Challenge

"Dear Lavoisier . . . " Write a letter to Lavoisier congratulating him on his new theory. Tell him how your own candle experiments support his theory of burning.

Candle Facts

- The word "candle" originally comes from a latin word meaning "to shine".

- Candles have been made from fish oil, whale oil, beeswax, tallow, tree bark, cinnamon, bayberry, and paraffin.

- The Native people of the Pacific Northwest used the oily "candle fish" in an interesting way. After drying it, they would place it in the fork of a tree and light it — creating a strange-looking candle!

- North Americans use more than ninety million kilograms of paraffin each year to make candles.

- When a lighted candle is made to give a shadow, the darkest part of the shadow is the brightest part of the flame.

Corrosion: "Slow, Slow Burning"

A candle may burn for several hours. During burning, or **combustion**, carbon and hydrogen, the two elements making up a candle, combine with oxygen to form carbon dioxide and water. Noticeable heat and light are also produced.

In Exploration 7, you saw that steel wool can burn. Iron (steel wool) combines with oxygen to produce iron oxide. This explains why steel wool gained mass in this chemical change.

When iron is exposed to air, it reacts slowly with the oxygen in the air. Again, iron oxide is formed. This much slower chemical change is called corrosion, or rusting. This chemical change can be used to investigate a variety of questions:

1. What percentage of the air is oxygen?

2. Does the air you exhale still contain oxygen? If so, how much?

3. What treatments can speed up or slow down the rusting process?

4. Do different brands of steel wool rust at the same rate?

In the Exploration which follows, you will investigate the first two questions. You may find it interesting to plan experiments for answering the other two questions.

A Study in Corrosion

Question 1

What percentage of the air is oxygen?

You Will Need

- 100 mL graduated cylinder
- thin rubber tubing
- vinegar
- steel wool
- ice-cream container or bowl

What To Do

1. Weigh out 2 g of steel wool.
2. Soak it for a minute in vinegar.
3. Shake the steel wool to remove most of the vinegar, and push it to the bottom of the 100 mL graduated cylinder. Don't pack it too tightly.
4. Place the thin rubber tubing into the graduate, and invert the apparatus into a container of water.
5. Finally, adjust the height of the graduate so that the water level inside and outside is at the 100 mL mark. Clamp the graduate in position, and remove the rubber tubing. The set-up should look like the one shown in the photograph on this page.
6. Record the height of the water level every 3 min for 20 min, or until the water level in the graduate no longer moves.

100 mL graduated cylinder

clamp

equal water level

thin rubber tubing (Remove when water levels are equal.)

Analysing the Results

1. Make a graph of the rate at which the oxygen is removed from the air. Place "volume of oxygen removed" on the vertical axis, and "time in minutes" on the horizontal axis.

2. Calculate the percentage of oxygen in the air, using this formula:

% oxygen in air =

$$\frac{\text{volume that the water rose (in mL)}}{\text{starting volume of air (100 mL)}} \times 100$$

Question 2

Does the air you breathe out contain oxygen? If so, how much?

You Will Need

- 100 mL graduated cylinder
- thin rubber tubing
- vinegar
- steel wool
- ice-cream container or bowl

What To Do

1. To answer Question 2, all you need to do is modify your procedure from Question 1 a little. Push the steel wool to the bottom of the graduate as before, but this time fill the graduate to the very top with vinegar. Invert the apparatus into a large container of water. Now put in the thin rubber tubing. Your set-up will look like this:

2. Take a breath, and blow into the rubber tubing. Breathed air will enter the graduate. Try to lower the water level to the 100 mL mark. Before removing your mouth, pinch the rubber tube. If air enters the graduate, start again.

3. When the water level is at the 100 mL mark, remove the rubber tubing and continue as before.

Analysing the Results

Calculate the percentage of oxygen in exhaled air, using the same formula as in Question 1.

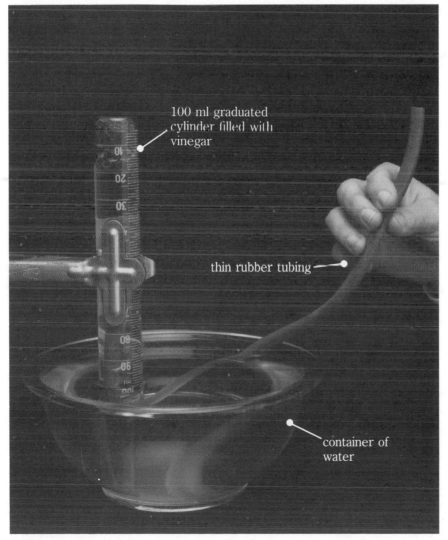

100 ml graduated cylinder filled with vinegar

thin rubber tubing

container of water

Mass Changes

In Exploration 6, you noticed that a candle has less mass after burning for a while. This decrease in mass is a clue that a chemical change has occurred. You also saw that, after steel wool is touched to a flame, it increases in mass. This gain in mass is also a clue that a chemical change has occurred.

But what would you find if you were able to compare the mass of all the reactants of a reaction to the mass of all the products of the reaction? How would the masses of the reactants and products in each of the reactions below compare?

$$\text{candle} + \text{oxygen} \rightarrow \text{carbon dioxide} + \text{water}$$
$$\text{Reactants} \text{Products}$$

$$\text{Iron} + \text{oxygen} \rightarrow \text{iron oxide}$$
$$\text{Reactants} \text{Product}$$

Does the mass of the reactants equal the mass of the products? How could you find out?

In groups of three, examine the ways in which some other Grade 9 students answered these questions. Evaluate the approach used by each group — you may wish to try some of them.

Ravi's Group

Ravi remembered that when vinegar is added to milk, a chemical change occurs: The milk curdles. His group decided to do the following:

1. Find the mass of a container of vinegar.

2. Find the mass of a container of milk.

3. Add the vinegar to the milk.

4. Find the mass of both containers and the curdled milk.

Do you think this approach worked? What did Ravi's group discover?

Dunja's Group

Dunja and her group followed a similar procedure, except that they decided to add water to baking powder. What did they find out?

Trina's Group

This group came up with a clever plan. Trina was a diabetic, so she knew all about syringes. Here is their procedure.

1. Place one-eighth of an Alka Seltzer tablet in a test tube. Stop the tube with a one-holed stopper.
2. Place 5 mL of water in a large syringe, and insert the end of the syringe into the one-holed stopper.
3. Find the mass of this "closed system".
4. Push the water into the test tube. As the reaction occurs, the plunger of the syringe will be forced outwards.
5. As the reaction occurs, the set-up remains on the balance.

What conclusions would Trina's group arrive at? What is the main difference between Trina's plan and Dunja's plan? What do you think of this approach?

Excerpt from Alasdair's Science Log

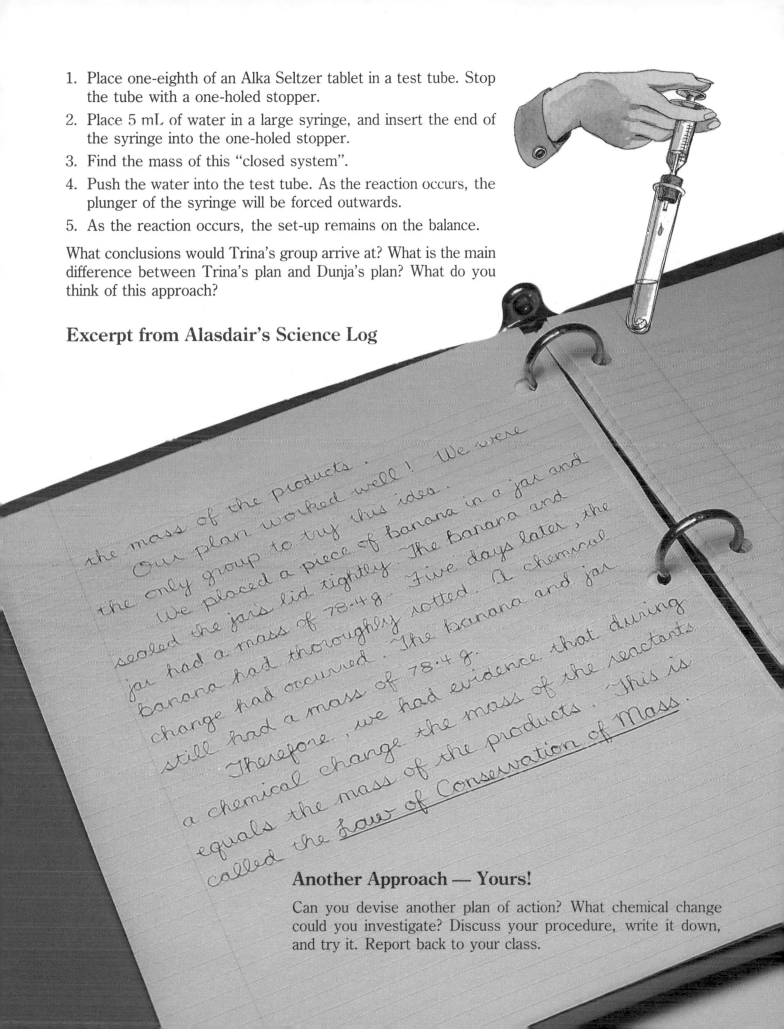

the mass of the products.

Our plan worked well! We were the only group to try this idea. We placed a piece of banana in a jar and sealed the jar's lid tightly. The banana and jar had a mass of 78.4 g. Five days later, the banana had thoroughly rotted. A chemical change had occurred. The banana and jar still had a mass of 78.4 g.

Therefore, we had evidence that during a chemical change the mass of the reactants equals the mass of the products. This is called the <u>Law of Conservation of Mass</u>.

Another Approach — Yours!

Can you devise another plan of action? What chemical change could you investigate? Discuss your procedure, write it down, and try it. Report back to your class.

Chemical Changes and You

It has been fun learning about chemical changes. All living things depend on chemical changes — from the smallest bacteria to the largest tree. You use chemical changes to start a car, to settle an upset stomach, to cook food. Chemical changes create useful products — and jobs. The manufacture of products as diverse as cement, paper, heavy water, and shampoo uses chemical changes. In fact, the uses of chemical changes are so numerous that this unit need never end — and it shouldn't! Whether you like to cook, enjoy the outdoors, or will be employed in one of the countless occupations that make use of chemical changes — chemical changes are going to be important to you.

Opinion Please!

This unit started by asking your opinion of chemicals. It will close by examing your opinion about chemical changes.

In groups of three, choose one of the statements below. These are direct quotes from this unit. In your group, form an argument in support of the statement. Your argument can consist of observations, findings, examples from the unit, or observations and examples from your everyday experience. Later, you will share your argument with the class.

"I think chemicals are everything around us."

"If my baking soda reacts with vinegar, then everyone else's will do the same."

"Our class concluded that there are some clues which show when a chemical change occurs:

• A new colour appears.

• Heat or light is given off.

• Bubbles form.

• The change is not easily reversible."

"The only problem is that you can't use the same clues for each chemical change! Life certainly is complicated!"

"What kinds of people do chemicals and their changes affect? Almost everyone!"

"In every chemical change, new substances are formed. These new substances are called the products of the chemical change."

"All chemicals or subtances can be classified as elements or as compounds."

"During a chemical change, the mass of the reactants equals the mass of the products."

Brain Teasers

1. Potatoes exposed to sunshine turn green. Is this a chemical change?

2. Cut apples and potatoes exposed to the air turn brown. Is this a chemical change? Put some pieces in a freezer bag and suck the air out with a straw. Do they still turn brown? Explain what you observe. Now do the same thing with some other pieces, but this time put the airless freezer bag in the freezer. Also try storing pieces underwater.

3. Limestone is found in many parts of Atlantic Canada. In the Annapolis Valley of Nova Scotia a strange landscape with many holes and gullies has formed where limestone deposits are located. This landscape is called a *karst landscape*. How to you think it was formed? (**Hint**: Review the experiment you performed on chalk in Exploration 1, Part 2.)

Karst landscape

4. The following are a few of the kitchen chemicals encountered in this unit:

   sugar   salt   baking soda   baking powder   starch

   On the basis of what you know about the changes that occur when using the reactants iodine, water, and vinegar, develop a system that would allow you to identify any one of these kitchen chemicals without tasting.

5. (a) Baking powder is essentially baking soda (sodium bicarbonate) with starch added to it. This is why it turns black when iodine solution is added. But why does it bubble when water is added? (**Hint**: Mix some baking soda with cream of tartar. Now add water.)

   (b) Why is starch added to the baking powder?

6. Use the clues to complete the crossword puzzle.

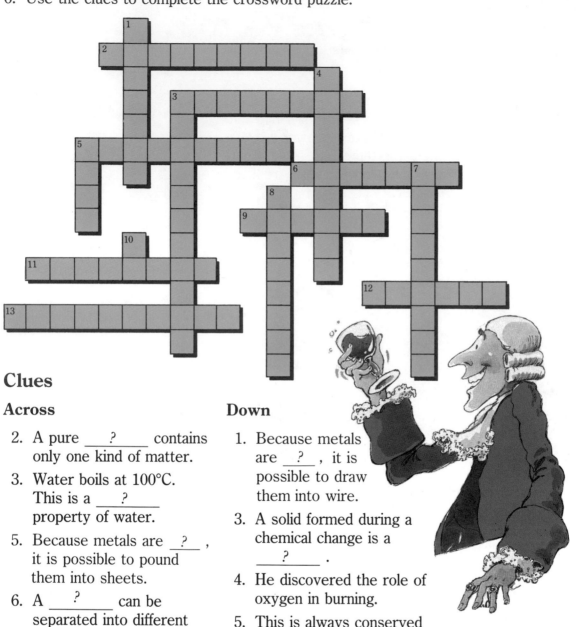

Clues

Across

2. A pure ___?___ contains only one kind of matter.

3. Water boils at 100°C. This is a ___?___ property of water.

5. Because metals are ___?___ , it is possible to pound them into sheets.

6. A ___?___ can be separated into different substances by physical means.

9. This element is used to test for starch.

11. The chemicals formed in a chemical change are ___?___ .

12. Water can exist in three ___?___ of matter.

13. Stahl thought that all materials which burned contained ___?___ .

Down

1. Because metals are ___?___ , it is possible to draw them into wire.

3. A solid formed during a chemical change is a ___?___ .

4. He discovered the role of oxygen in burning.

5. This is always conserved in a chemical change.

7. The chemicals used to start a chemical change are called ___?___ .

8. A substance that can be broken down by a chemical change.

10. The chemical symbol for gold.

7. From the descriptions below, would you expect each change to be chemical or physical? If it is difficult to judge, explain why.

   (a) A white substance exposed to light turns dark.

   (b) A colourless liquid disappears when heated.

   (c) As a liquid is heated, crystals appear at the bottom.

   (d) A colourless liquid turns yellow when heated.

   (e) A flash of light occurs.

   (f) Two liquids are mixed, and their temperature rises by 10°C.

   (g) Two liquids are mixed and become milky.

   (h) A liquid is cooled, and a solid forms on the bottom of the beaker.

   (i) A bar turns black when heated.

   (j) A bar, when heated, remains the same colour, but becomes 2 mm longer.

   (k) A yellow solid is heated, and the room is filled with choking fumes.

   (l) A sweet substance is stirred into a colourless liquid. The liquid remains colourless but tastes sweet.

   (m) A blue solid is dropped into water, and the water turns blue in colour.

8. How would you prove the following statements are true?

   (a) A burning match produces carbon dioxide.

   (b) Water is given off when blue copper sulphate is heated.

   (c) A plant leaf gives off water. (Which side?)

   (d) The bubbles given off by soda water and the bubbles found in ordinary water are made up of different substances

9. Definitions

   An element is a pure substance made up of itself.

   A compound is a pure substance made up of two or more elements.

   Discuss with a classmate what these statements mean.

10. The Great Fizz Race
    What are four ways in which you can change the rate at which
    Alka Seltzer tablets react with water? Break an Alka Seltzer
    tablet into four parts, and time your suggestions.

11. Nita took part in the Great Fizz Race. Here are her four
    trials. What do you think Nita did in Trials 2, 3, and 4?

Trials	What She Did	Time It Took
1	Placed ¼ tablet in water at room temperature.	30 s
2		50 s
3		15 s
4		20 s

12. A dramatic, unexpected colour change occurs in the presence
    of Vitamin C. Here is how to see it: Stir 1 mL of corn starch
    into 100 mL of warm water. Add one or two drops of iodine
    solution. The mixture turns black. Separate the mixture into
    several containers. Drop a small bit of food that you think
    may contain Vitamin C into 15 mL samples of the starch/
    iodine mixture. The foods containing Vitamin C will destroy
    the black iodine-starch complex.

    Test various foods around your home for Vitamin C, and
    report to your class. You can try different fruit juices, a piece
    of potato, *etc.*

13. Is aspirin an acid? Find out by using the litmus test. Will a
    Tums or Alka Seltzer tablet neutralize this acid? (Dissolve
    the aspirin in 10 mL of water first.)

14. Lift an ice cube with salt. Is what happens the result of a chemical change or a physical change?

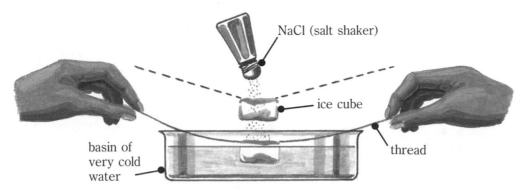

NaCl (salt shaker)

ice cube

basin of very cold water

thread

Wait a minute, then lift the thread slowly.

15. Instructions for a coffee maker: "Every month or so, vinegar should be passed through the coffee maker instead of water." Why do you think this is suggested?

16. After someone takes a bath, a scummy film or "bath tub ring" is often seen on the side of the bath tub. Is it a result of a chemical change? How could you prove whether it is?

17. Wayne placed a piece of phosphorus into a bottle containing a small amount of water. The system weighed 254 g.

    Sunlight shining on the flask caused the phosphorus to ignite, producing white smoke. The smoke dissolved in the water. What will the flask weigh now? Explain why.

sunlight

phosphorus

water

18. Sandra has been given five bottles labelled P, Q, R, S, and T, with colourless liquids in each. She is told that two of the liquids are dilute acids, one is a base, and the other two are water. She is also given the liquid acid/base indicator, phenolphthalein.

    Write down some instructions for Sandra to help her find out whether each liquid is an acid, a base, or water. She can use test tubes, droppers, *etc*.

19. Does boiling ink cause a chemical change? Wayne's sister Terri, who was in Grade 7, was attempting this change. She placed ink into a test tube and heated the test tube with an alcohol burner. A clear liquid dripped from the end of the tube into the beaker.

    Did a chemical change occur? Suggest a way to prove your answer.

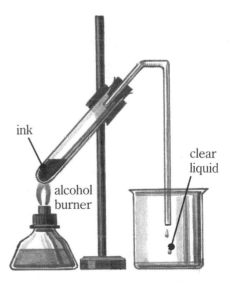

ink

alcohol burner

clear liquid

Science Teaching
Junior Secondary Level

John MacLennan teaches science to Grade 7, 8, and 9 students.

Q: What aspect of teaching do you enjoy most?

John: I think just working in the classroom with the students and helping them learn is the most enjoyable aspect. It is stimulating to have them discover things for themselves and to help them understand new ideas.

Q: Are there any frustrations in teaching?

John: Yes. The most frustrating thing would be the lack of time to prepare adequately for classes. Another would be the lack of interest and response by some students.

Q: As a teacher, you constantly have to be learning yourself. What opportunities do you get for doing so?

John: Well, I have taken part in many courses and workshops. Recently, for example, I received a fellowship that enabled me to spend a summer studying geology. The course work was conducted at the University of Western Ontario, and from there we traveled to different parts of Ontario on field trips, collecting samples of geological specimens. It was very interesting.

Q: Are there any socially important issues that you believe require special attention in science teaching?

John: I think one of the major issues of social importance is the environment, the need to live in harmony with nature. One of the objectives of education is to make people more aware of the need to protect the environment. While laws are needed, the main way of attacking the problem of environmental degradation is through education.

Q: What abilities and skills are most important in teaching?

John: Being able to relate well with people is the most important skill for any teacher. Also important, and closely related to this, is the ability to express your ideas clearly, to teach in a way that the students will understand.

A teacher should also be a well-organized person. Teaching involves a lot of preparation and planning.

I think it is also useful for a teacher to know when to be quiet, when to let the kids learn for themselves, rather than tell them everything you want them to learn: to help them find out for themselves, to create the environment and get the materials, but let them do the work.

Senior Secondary Level

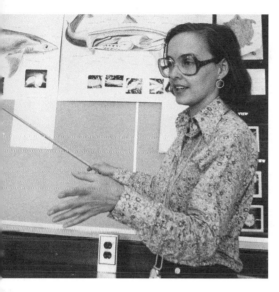

Susan Harrigan is a high school biology teacher.

Q: How did you become interested in teaching?

Susan: I didn't decide to become a teacher until I had already completed three years of university study, but my mother tells me that as a child I used to play school a lot and, apparently, I always had to be the teacher. In any case, as soon as I started my first week of practice teaching as part of studying for the Bachelor of Education degree, I knew I had really found my niche. I liked it from the first time!

Influences in this direction came from examples of good teaching by my own teachers. In particular, I had a university physics teacher who taught a class with well over 100 students and still seemed to have the knack of making each of us believe that he was really

interested in each of us. I try to do the same with my students — helping to remove some of the fears they may have about what biology or science in general is all about.

Q: What characteristic do you believe is particularly important for teaching?

Susan: I think people who want to be teachers, in particular teachers of science, must have a profound interest in the subject. They must find it exciting, so they can communicate their excitement to the students.

It is also important to continue to learn and to improve your teaching. There is always something new to be learned. You should be prepared to change the way you teach a concept. I find that I spend a lot of time with chemistry, physics, and math teachers discussing ways I can improve my own knowledge and teaching.

Q: Is there any particularly socially important message that you try to get across in your teaching?

Susan: For one thing, I take every opportunity I can to discourage students from smoking. It is a personal commitment to the health of the students. I know they simply don't know all the implications of smoking, and I feel that, as a biology teacher and an adult, I owe it to them to at least present them with all the facts.

Some Project Ideas

Seek the advice and assistance of a teacher for these projects.

1. Start up a science club for younger children in your neighbourhood or at an elementary school. Your task, like that of a teacher, is to plan and organize the activities of the club so that the younger children learn something useful. You might wish to work on this project with one or two of your friends.
2. Pick a topic in which you have a great interest, and propose to your teacher that you conduct a class on it.

The Chemical Industry

"Tom! What are you doing in the basement?"

"Be careful you don't hurt yourself!"

"Can't you find something to do outside? Something safe?"

"Clean up that mess! You know your father doesn't want you using his tools."

In 1875, when he was 15 years old, Thomas L. Willson was asked by his family to remove his "lab" from his home. He relocated it in the loft of John Rogers' blacksmith shop in Hamilton, Ontario. There Willson applied his curiosity and his inventive mind to making discoveries and inventions.

At first, Willson tried to convert sooty carbon into sparkling diamond. Had he succeeded, he would have become a very rich man. Failing that, he tried to find a way to change lime to calcium. Although not nearly as glamorous as making diamonds, a cheap way of producing calcium would have been a major achievement. His method involved mixing lime and coal tar, which he placed in an electric arc. However, instead of calcium, Willson got calcium carbide!

Willson soon made another discovery. He found that when a chip of calcium carbide fell in water, a gas bubbled up. In contact with the very hot calcium carbide still in the electric arc, this gas burned with a smoky flame. Willson had found a cheap way to produce acetylene gas as well as calcium carbide! Both substances have many important uses. In particular, oxyacetylene torches are used to weld metals. The acetylene in these torches burns at about 3000°C, high enough to fuse metal.

These first discoveries of Willson's, and those which followed, contributed to the thriving chemical industry in Canada and the United States. This industry is based on the fact that one substance can be converted to another by means of a chemical change. Thus, the chemical industry takes large quantities of raw materials and converts them into new materials which are useful to people.

Until recently, the raw materials for the chemical industry have been different natural resources— petroleum, coal, lumber, and various mineral ores. Because Canada is rich in resources, our chemical industry has enormous potential. Now the chemical industry is increasingly using waste products from other industries as raw materials, in addition to natural resources.

Find out which chemical industries are located in your province. Do the parents of any of your friends work in the chemical industry or in an industry where chemical processes are important? If so, ask them about their work. What does the industry produce, and what chemical changes are involved in making this product? Try to arrange a visit to a chemical plant to observe production processes.

The beads in this bag soak up oil.

Biotechnology

Some types of living things which are so small that you need a microscope to see them can bring about chemical changes. These living things, known as *micro-organisms*, are able to convert materials of one kind into another. An example of such a chemical change is *fermentation*, in which sugar is converted to alcohol.

Micro-organisms are also used in the manufacture of many medicines. Other micro-organisms that can digest rocks are used to mine ores.

Advances in our knowledge of the chemistry of life processes is leading to the creation of many new materials and to better ways of producing familiar ones. The techniques used to do these things are part of a new field called *biotechnology*. What industries in your province are based on biotechnology? Studying one of them, perhaps even making a visit, would make an interesting project.

Hazardous Wastes

Chemical changes, although very useful, can sometimes also produce hazardous materials. The sulphur dioxide gas that results from the smelting of ores is an example. However, many hazardous materials can be changed chemically into harmless ones. For instance, sulphur dioxide gas can be removed from factory smoke by being mixed with waste in a scrubber.

Some wastes can be incinerated, producing safe carbon dioxide and water vapour. *Biodegradable* wastes can be rendered harmless by the action of bacteria. All these methods change the waste chemically. Non-chemical methods include recycling wastes, or storing them safely.

Are there any hazardous wastes polluting the environment in your community? A worthwhile project would be to identify a hazardous waste problem and come up with a solution. Which of the methods mentioned above would be best for the hazardous waste problem you are investigating? Consider both safety and cost.

Sources of Information

- University departments of chemistry and chemical engineering

- Environment Canada

- Provincial departments of industrial development, commerce and technology

- Ontario Waste Management Corporation (OWMC)

- Your library

HEAT TRAVEL

How Heat Travels

Heat Travel Needs Help

Dozens of times every day you can see or experience heat moving from one place to another. Sometimes you want to help it on its way. Sometimes you want to slow it down. Let's talk about it!

In the kitchen, for instance, you want heat to move from the stove to the food in the pot. But you do not want heat to move from the pot through the handle to your hands.

In winter, you want heat to move from the radiators, hot air registers, or heaters throughout the room. However, you do not want the same heat to move outside through the windows and walls.

On a sunny winter's day, the Sun's rays heat the rooms through the windows, but at night the curtains and drapes are pulled to keep in heat.

When you go outside in winter, you bundle up in a hat, scarf, and gloves to keep the cold out and the heat in. In the summer, you tend to wear light-coloured clothes to reflect the Sun's rays (or heat), and you may also use suntan lotion to avoid burning.

Whenever heat travels (or flows), it always travels from one substance to another substance which is at a lower temperature.

How is the "flow" of heat like the "flow" of water? Look at the illustration for clues. How is it different?

What do you think the expression "a temperature hill" means?

Heat can travel through solids, liquids, gases, and empty space. The way it travels through solids is generally quite different from the way it travels through liquids or gases. And the way it travels through empty space is different from the way it travels through solids, liquids, or gases.

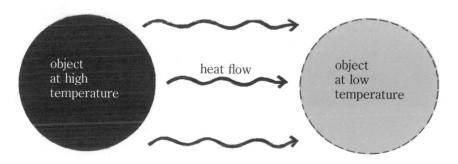

object at high temperature   heat flow   object at low temperature

How Heat Flows

These three experiments investigate the three different ways in which heat flows. Observe how heat travels in each of the experiments. In your notebook, write down the differences you saw among the three ways that heat travelled.

Experiment 1

You Will Need

- container of water
- metal spoon
- popsicle stick

What To Do

Boil the water. Put the spoon and stick in the boiling water.

After 30 s, feel the tops of the spoon and the stick. What do you observe? How do you explain your observations?

Experiment 2

You Will Need

- a spoonful of instant coffee granules
- 2 thermometers
- container of water
- spirit burner

What To Do

Arrange the experiment as shown in the illustration.

Watch the granules.

Watch the thermometer readings.

What is happening? How do you explain your observations?

Experiment 3

You Will Need

- lamp
- square of glass
- square of cardboard the same size as the glass

What To Do

Arrange the experiment as shown in the illustration.

Do you feel the heat of the light bulb through the glass and the cardboard?

Remove the cardboard. Do you feel the heat now?

Does the glass get hot? Have you an explanation for your observations?

Conduction, Convection, or Radiation?

In each of the experiments you did, heat travelled in a different way:

(a) Heat travelled through a solid material. This method of heat travel is called **conduction**.

(b) Heat travelled through a liquid, by means of the movement of the liquid being heated. This method of heat travel is called **convection**. (Heat can also travel through a gas by convection — can you think of an example?)

(c) Heat travelled through empty space or a transparent material, without heating the empty space or the transparent material between the heat source and the heated object. This method of heat travel is called **radiation**.

Now apply these ideas to your everyday experience. How does the food in the cooking pot become warm? By conduction? By convection? Or by radiation? How do other items in the kitchen — oven, toaster, microwave — give warmth?

How does your bed become warm? How is the hot water produced for your bath or shower?

Can you think of other examples where heat flows?

A Problem for Mike and Sue

Here is another way to look at the three methods of heat travel.

Mike, at the front of the bus, wants to pass a parcel (called HEAT) to Sue, at the back of the bus. However, Mike is blocked by people standing. How can Mike get the parcel to Sue?

In this case, there are no passengers between Mike and Sue. How can Mike get the parcel to Sue?

Now, the aisle between Mike and Sue is roped off. How can Mike get the parcel to Sue?

Which cartoon represents

(a) heat travel by convection?

(b) heat travel by radiation?

(c) heat travel by conduction?

Heat Travel Through Solids — Conduction

Scientists think that all matter is made of very, very small particles. The travel of heat along (or through) solid material, from one particle to the next, is conduction. Does this remind you of Mike and Sue's first situation? Each passenger was like a particle in a solid.

Watching Heat Travel Along (or Through) a Solid: A Demonstration

1. Cut a strip of aluminum from an aluminum pie plate.

2. With a burning candle, make a line of wax along the strip.

3. Hold the aluminum strip with a clothespin. Apply the heat of the candle to one end.

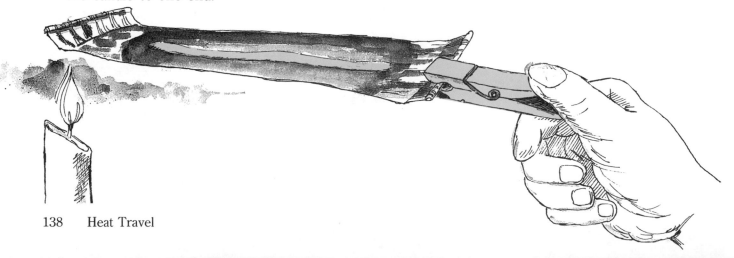

How Fast Does Heat Travel?

Dip a spoon into a cup of hot chocolate. Notice how quickly the heat travels from the hot chocolate up the spoon. Put on a pair of oven mitts, then remove a hot pan from the oven. The heat still travels, from the pan to your fingers, but not as quickly this time — otherwise you would burn yourself lifting the pan!

Heat travels at different rates. What factors affect the speed of heat travel in a solid?

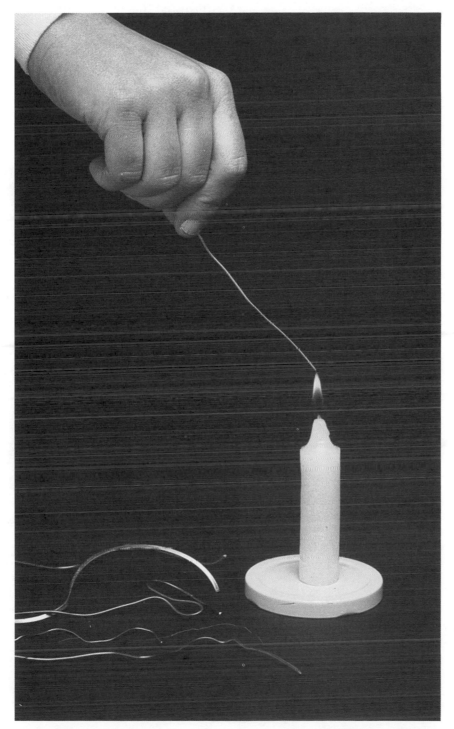

Testing for Speed of Heat Travel

You can carry out an inquiry into this problem in a simple way.

You Will Need

- candle
- watch with a second hand
- ruler
- a variety of wires

What To Do

First, do a trial run. Take any wire and hold it in the flame. Measure how long it takes before the wire becomes uncomfortably hot (the "ouch point").

It thirty different people do this, chances are that they will get thirty different "ouch points". Why? Well, some might have more sensitive fingers than others. Some will have held the wire closer to the flame than others. There might be other reasons as well. Your first task, therefore, is to make a list of the factors that might affect the speed of heat travel. For example:

(a) Does the length of wire have an effect?

(b) Does it matter whether the wire is bent?

(c) Does the angle of the wire to the flame make a difference?

Can you think of other things that might affect the speed? Make a list of them. These factors are called "variables".

Now that you have identified the variables, choose one to study in detail. How can you show that the variable you select does or does not make a difference? (**Hint:** To test this variable fairly, you should keep all other variables constant.)

Conduction Through Different Materials and Thicknesses

A Closer Look at Conduction

Spend ten minutes at each of the three stations described here.

In your notebook, record your observations, then answer the questions for each station.

For each station, write one sentence describing your discovery.

Station 1

Does the material make a difference?

You Will Need

- four rods, one each of copper, brass, glass, iron
- candle
- thumb tacks
- styrofoam coffee cup

What To Do

Attach the thumb tacks to the rods with candle wax. Then arrange the apparatus as shown.

Time how long it takes the thumb tack to drop.

Repeat, using another rod made of glass, brass, or iron. Do all materials conduct heat at the same rate?

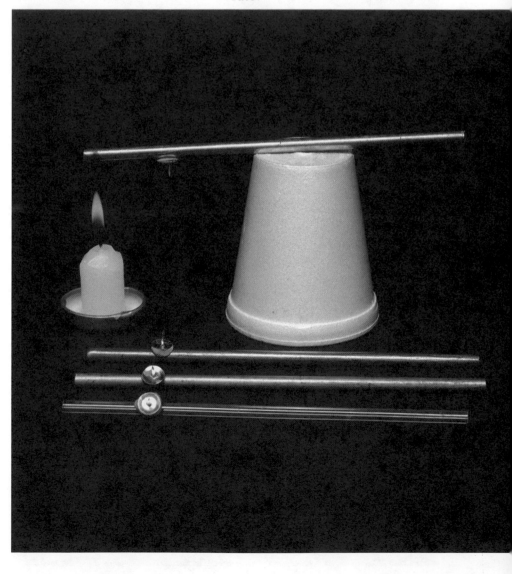

Station 2

Does the thickness of the material make a difference?

You Will Need

- 2 iron rods, of different thicknesses
- 2 styrofoam cups
- 2 candles
- 2 thumb tacks

What To Do

Before you start, take a guess. Do you think heat will travel faster along a thick rod or a thin rod? Now try it and find out.

Station 3

Can you make a thirty-second timer?

You are on a desert island and the battery in your watch is dying. But you do have a supply of candles, thumb tacks, styrofoam cups, and all sorts of metal rods.

Compare your timer with those of your classmates.

Thinking About and Using Your Findings

Here are some questions to help you check your understanding. Try them all!

1. On the basis of your observations, which substances are *good conductors* of heat? Which substances are *poor conductors* of heat?

2. How can you apply your findings to explain the construction of cooking utensils? What material would you make a pot from? How about the handle?

3. Ten similar rods made of different materials are placed for one minute in water at 70°C. Then the top of each is felt. Here are the results:

straw	cold
copper	hot
wood	cold
plastic	cold
brass	hot
rubber	cold
iron	hot
lead	hot
glass	cold
aluminum	hot

   (a) Which kind of material appears to be a good conductor of heat?

   (b) There are many everyday products which make use of this kind of material. Can you name five that you have used?

4. A friend has just made some instant coffee by pouring boiling water into each of these cups. Which cup would you prefer to hold as you drink your coffee? Will the thickness of the cup make a difference? What other factors might make a difference? Now list the cups in order of preference. To make sure you've made the right choices, test your guesses at home.

5. Woolly sweaters, fur, and feathers are very light and full of small air holes. Why do you think these materials are so warm? By the way, very poor conductors are called *insulators*.

6. To measure conduction rates, Pat made a clever device from a large juice can. She placed rods and bars of different materials, lengths, and thicknesses through a tripod made from the can, so that the ends touched in the centre.

She used some candle wax to attach a thumb tack to the other end of each rod. Then she placed a spirit lamp under the tripod so it would heat the inner edge of each rod and bar equally.

Why would these two small lambs need plastic coats to keep warm?

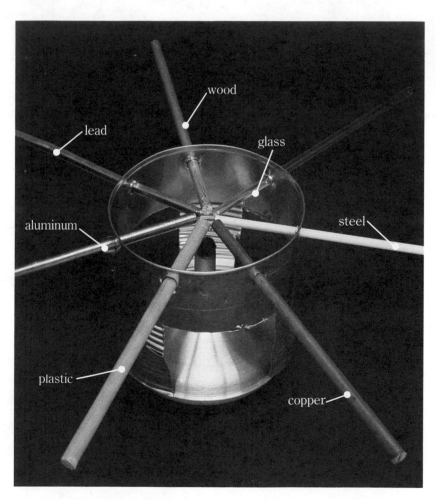

She had many difficulties, and her teacher said the class could not rely on Pat's results. Can you improve Pat's experiment?

Mysterious Events

The Mystery of the Scorching Paper

Join a copper rod or pipe and a wooden rod of the same diameter together by wrapping one layer of paper or masking tape around them. Heat the joint very slowly over a spirit burner until the paper is scorched. Which side of the paper is scorched?

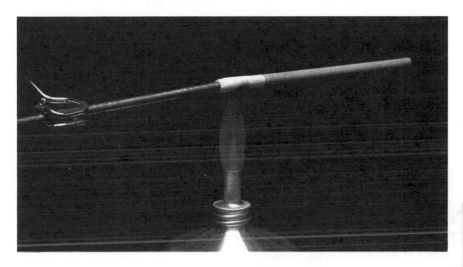

The Mystery of the Extinguished Candle

Strip about 30 cm of the insulation from some electrical wire about 40 cm long. Make the stripped part into a closely spiralling coil, and hold onto the insulated part. Place the coil over a lighted candle. What happens? Light the candle again, but this time hold the coil above the flame until it glows. Now slowly lower it . . . Explain the results.

Terrific Tricks to Try

Lower a piece of aluminum screen slowly over the flame. What happens? Why?

Place a wooden match between two prongs of a fork. Light the match. Can you get the whole match to burn?

Now try other matches, placing them in different positions between the prongs.

After observing what happens, can you explain the "trick"?

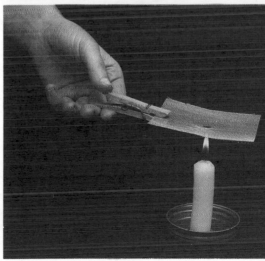

Believe It or Not: The Same Temperature?

This looks quite simple. There doesn't seem to be much to it at all! It will be a challenge, however.

A Classroom Demonstration

Leave a number of objects made of different materials in the classroom for a while. They should all be at the same temperature now. For instance, you might use

- glass (cup or beaker)
- foamed plastic (styrofoam cup)
- ordinary plastic (pencil case)
- metal (tin can)
- paper (textbook or notebook)

To make sure that they are all at the same temperature, you might strap a thermometer to each one.

EXPLORATION 4

Explaining the Temperature Mystery

Your Problem: How can you test your explanation?

What To Do

Design an experiment. Collect the materials you need. Perform the experiment.

Good luck!

Now hold each object against your cheek. Do some feel warmer than others? How is it that some of the objects *feel* warmer even though the thermometer shows they are all at the same temperature?

Insulators

A Competition: Save the Ice Cube!

Who can prevent an ice cube from melting for the longest time?

Use a cube from an ordinary tray. If you don't have one, make your ice cube in a small coffee cream container (20 mL).

Now devise a way to protect your ice cube. Use any materials you wish.

Your teacher will give you a Certificate to complete. In it, record your materials, the methods you used, and the length of time for which you kept your ice cube from melting.

Certificate

'Save the Ice Cube'

I hereby certify that

_____ at _____ hours
NAME   TIME

on _____ wrapped an ice cube the size of:
   DATE

_____
SIZE

and entrusted the same to me for safe-keeping.
The last time I witnessed any ice present was on:

_____ at _____ hours
                                        TIME

on _____
   DATE

Signed _____

Home Insulation Project

Brian Jones and Sandy MacDonald of Acadia Junior High School were highly commended for their exhibit at the National Science Fair. The annual fair, which opened in Toronto on Saturday, displayed the work of 330 hopeful contestants. All contestants had previously been successful in the regional competitions held from coast to coast.

Brian and Sandy's project, entitled "Home Insulation: An Investigation", examined the effectiveness of a variety of building materials. Awarding them their prize, the Ontario Premier said, "The judges were impressed that these two grade eight students should tackle a problem so closely related to energy conservation."

Unlike many of the other entries, their basic apparatus was extremely simple — cardboard boxes (sides 50 cm) with a thermometer inserted through the top of each one.

They tested the effects of various insulation materials, double glazing, and drafts.

In their experiments, the boys covered the boxes with different insulation materials, filled them with warm house air, and took them outside. Then they prepared graphs of temperature against time.

Asked whether they planned to continue with their project, Brian and Sandy said they were already redesigning the apparatus. Now on the drawing board they have an apparatus which uses an electric light bulb to keep the inside of the box at 20°C. Instead of measuring temperature fall, they plan to record how long the light bulb stays on to maintain the 20° C.

Congratulations, Brian and Sandy!

A Chart Prepared by Brian and Sandy

Time (in minutes)	2	4	6	8	10	12	14	16	18	20
Temperature of air, 5 cm fibreglass all over (in °C)	24	23	20	17	13	9	5	2	0	$-1\frac{1}{2}$	-3
Same, but with no insulation on roof (in °C)	24	20	14	9	5	2	0	-2	-4	-6	-9

House air temperature = 24°C   Outside air temperature = −9°C

Commended

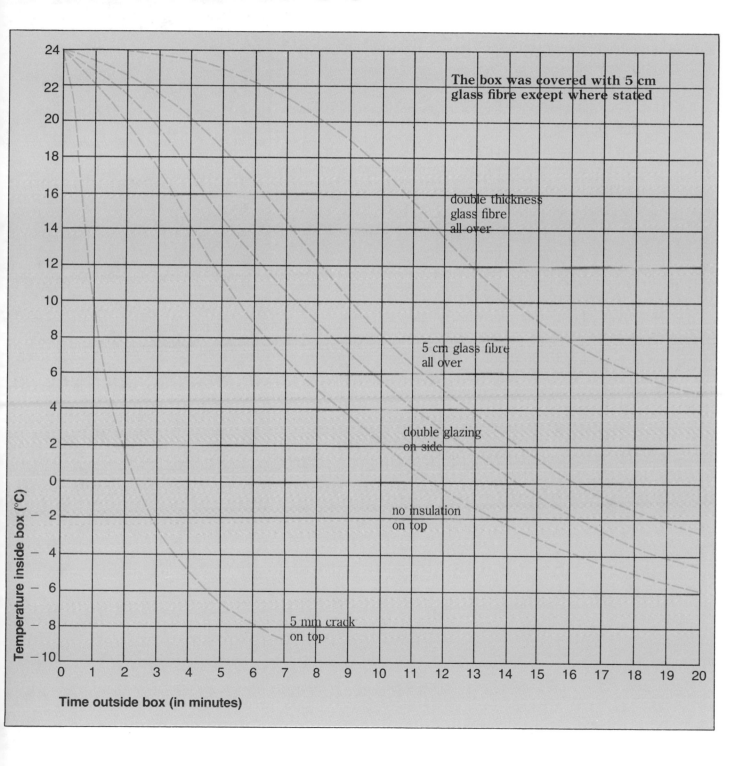

The box was covered with 5 cm glass fibre except where stated

double thickness
glass fibre
all over

5 cm glass fibre
all over

double glazing
on side

no insulation
on top

5 mm crack
on top

Temperature inside box (°C)

Time outside box (in minutes)

In Brian and Sandy's Shoes! (Problems to Ponder)

Here are some of the questions the judges asked Brian and Sandy. How would you have responded?

1. About your apparatus: What errors and problems did you encounter?

2. About your chart: What do these figures tell you? (How long did it take each sample to fall to 9°C? What were the temperatures inside the boxes after 10 min?) Why did you decide to graph the results?

3. About your graphs:
   (a) How long did it take for each sample to fall to 8°C? What did this tell you?
   (b) What was the temperature inside each box after 10 min?
   (c) Why did you join up the points to make curves, rather than straight lines?

4. What are your conclusions?

5. What other factors (materials or conditions) might you have tried?

6. More about your apparatus:
   (a) Why are you going to redesign it?
   (b) How does the new design work?
   (c) What sort of results do you expect to get?
   (d) Are you going to do different experiments or the same ones?

Try It at Home — Baked Alaska

Imagine the scene: Delmonico's, a high society restaurant in New York City. The guests, in full evening dress dripping with diamonds and gold, await their dessert. The master chef brings in his creation. It looks like any other cake. The glistening white meringue topping is delicately touched with gold. A hint of steam still hovers over the oven-fresh dish. The master chef places the platter on the table, ceremonially picks up a silver knife, and with a flourish cuts the cake to reveal the ice cream centre still perfectly frozen. "Mesdames, Messieurs — Baked Alaska."

If you would like to make Baked Alaska, ask one of your parents or another member of your family to help you.

You Will Need

- 1 small sponge cake (Two thicknesses of bread 10 cm square will do if you can't make or get sponge cake.)
- white of an egg
- 1 large spoonful of sugar (about 15 mL)
- 1 spoonful of your favourite jam
- 1 scoop of ice cream about 5 cm across
- pinch of salt

What To Do

1. Set the oven at 250°C to let it warm up. Many ovens use the Fahrenheit scale. If yours does, set it at 500°F.

2. Now to prepare the meringue: Crack an egg. Carefully separate the white from the yolk. Beat the white until it holds its shape. Add the sugar and a pinch of salt, then whisk until the mixture becomes very stiff.

3. Put the sponge cake on a piece of wooden board covered with aluminum foil. Spread the jam over the sponge cake.

4. Check whether the oven has reached the right temperature.

5. Ready! Get the ice cream from the fridge. Put it on the middle of the sponge cake. Smooth the meringue mixture over the ice cream, covering it completely.

6. Bake for 3 to 5 min, until the meringue just turns brown.

7. Take from the oven and serve immediately.

How did you do? Was your Baked Alaska tasty?

Now here is the science: Did the ice cream stay frozen? If so, why do you think it stayed frozen? If not, why not?

Do your classmates agree with you? Can you design an experiment to test your explanations?

Caution: Beware of hungry family members and friends!

Heat Travel By Currents — Convection

Look back at A Problem for Mike and Sue, on page 137. Find the cartoon that represents heat travel by convection. In the Exploration that follows, you will discover more about convection.

EXPLORATION 6

Some Convection Experiments

Form into groups. Choose one of the experiments. Practise it. Figure out how it works. Then present it to the other groups. Ask them questions until they understand how it works.

Experiment 1

You Will Need

• large beaker or clear bowl of cold water
• small bottle filled with hot, coloured water
• two-holed stopper with 2 glass tubes inserted — one tube should almost touch the bottom of the bottle (your teacher will push the tubes into the stoppers)

What To Do

Carefully lower the small bottle into the cold water, keeping your fingers over the ends of the glass tubes as in the illustration. Take your fingers away. Trace the direction of any currents formed. Why do you think these currents exist?

Experiment 2

You Will Need

- large pop bottle
- small candle
- T-shaped piece of aluminum foil
- 10 cm length of rope
- watch with a second hand
- wire

What To Do

With a wire, lower a burning candle into the bottle. Measure how long the candle burns.

Put new air in the bottle. (You will need to think of a way to do this.) Repeat, with the foil placed in the mouth of the bottle as in the photos. Insert the foil quickly after the lighted candle is inserted.

Check for currents at points A and B with a smoking rope.

Experiment 3

You Will Need

- circular piece of aluminum foil, 15 cm in diameter
- thread
- candle

What To Do

Make a pinhole in the centre of the foil, then cut it in a spiral. Hang the spiral from a knotted thread.

Place the spiral in several locations: over a candle (not too close!), to the side of the candle, above a lighted light bulb, over a radiator, near the bottom of a window, in different places in the room, in the schoolyard.

Experiment 4

You Will Need

- 2 beakers of water
- 2 coloured ice cubes
- wire

What To Do

Make sure to use lots of food colouring when making the ice cubes.

Wrap the wire around one of the ice cubes. Place each ice cube into a beaker at the same time. Observe how the colour spreads. Draw pictures of the currents.

Experiment 5

You Will Need

- metal and glass chimney box
- candle
- 2 corks
- 10 cm length of rope

What To Do

Arrange the apparatus as shown.

Observe the candle flame and the direction of smoke as you remove one or two corks. Try different combinations of open holes. This experiment shows one of the most important principles in the formation of convection currents.

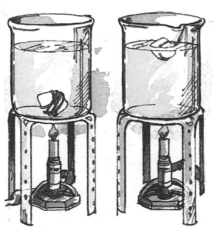

Experiment 6

You Will Need

- 2 ice cubes
- 2 beakers of water
- wire
- 2 Bunsen burners

What To Do

Wrap some wire around one ice cube, to make it sink. Look at the diagram — predict which ice cube will melt first. Now set up the experiment and try it. How do you explain what happens?

Experiment 7

You Will Need

- 2 tin cans
- scotch tape
- wooden dowel
- string
- board with a nail in the end
- textbook
- candle

What To Do

Make a simple balance: Support two upside-down open tin cans by a thread through a hole in the bottom of each can secured with scotch tape. Move the cans in and out until they balance. With a candle, heat the air in one can. Remove the candle. What happens? Let the balance stand for a few moments. Now heat the air under the other can. What happens? Why?

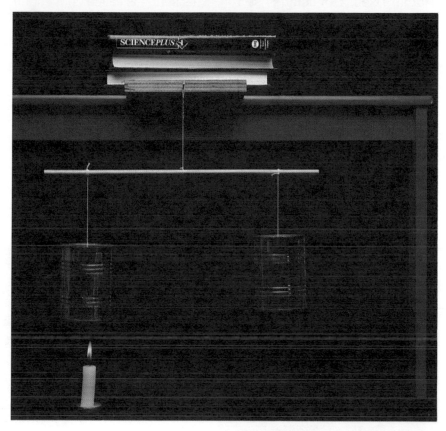

Experiment 8

You Will Need

- candle
- matches

What To Do

Light the candle. Hold your hand 20 cm above it, then hold your hand 20 cm to the side. What do you feel at each position?

Try this variation. How close can you put the head of a match to the flame before it catches fire? (Careful — don't burn your fingers!) Hold matches at different positions around the flame. What is your explanation for what you observe?

Draw a large diagram of the candle flame. Around it, draw a dotted line showing where the matches caught fire.

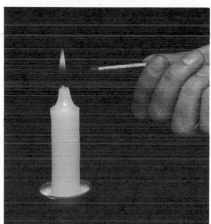

Analysis Please!

Hot air rises. Hot liquids rise too. This action is called convection. You can't always see it happening, however. Here are some problems to help you review what you observed in the experiments.

1. Using longer arrows to show faster flow and shorter arrows to show slower flow, draw in your notebook what you think is the air flow around a lighted candle. Test your guess by using a smoking string to reveal the air currents.

2. In this diagram, the air above the ground takes its temperature from the ground, while the air above the water takes its temperature from the water. Copy the diagram into your notebook, and use arrows to show the currents that might occur. What might happen to a sailor after sunset?

3. Carlo's Trick

   Carlo told his audience that all four bottles contained water, two of them with blue food colouring added. Then he slipped the cards from between the bottles. Abracadabra!

   How might he arrange this trick? In what other way could he have arranged this trick?

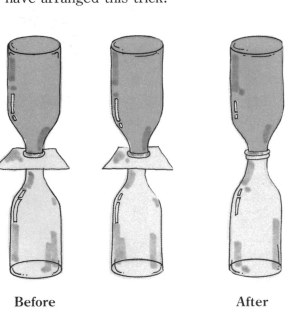

Before   **After**

4. Here is a model hot water heating system which doesn't need a circulating pump. How does it work?

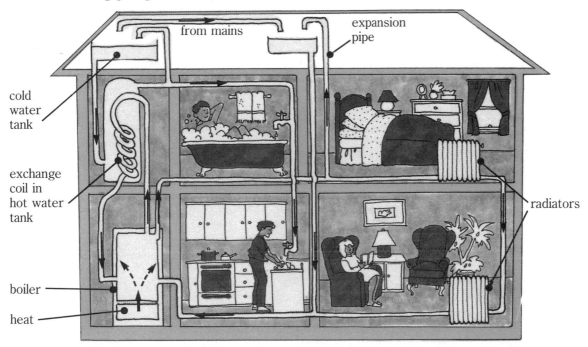

5. Study how this Magic Lamp works. How would you explain what is happening to your younger brother or sister?

6. Which is the better buy: a vertical freezer chest or a horizontal one?

7. Where would you install an air conditioning unit: near the floor or near the ceiling?

8. There's a story in this picture. Can you describe it? What would you do to improve the situation?

Convection in a Car

Ask a garage mechanic to explain the water cooling system of an automobile. Then sketch a diagram showing where and how the water is circulated through the radiator, around the motor, and through the heater of the car.

Become a Home Energy Consultant

Your family is worried about rising fuel costs. Can you help? This section will help you understand how heat energy is lost from your home and help you prepare a home energy report for your family.

Where Does the Heat Go?

The illustration gives the range of heat loss for fairly modern homes. Even if your house or apartment building was built before 1961, it has probably been upgraded to these standards. What does the diagram tell you?

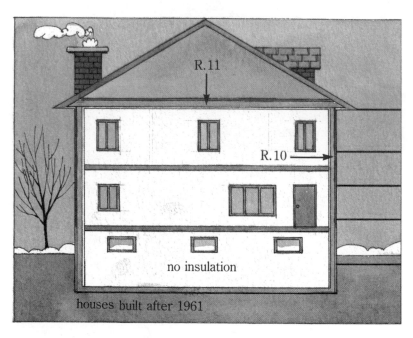

Heat loss from a house

air exchange	20 – 30%
ceiling	10 – 15%
walls	10 – 20%
double-glazed windows, doors	15 – 20%
single-glazed windows, doors	23 – 25%
basement	20 – 25%

- What percentage of heat is lost by air exchange?
- How does outside air enter the house?
- How does inside air leave the house?

- What percentage of heat escapes through the ceiling? Through the walls?
- How does heat travel through the walls and ceilings — by conduction or by convection?

- What percentage of heat passes through doors and windows?
- How do double windows or double glazing and storm doors help?

- What percentage of heat is lost in the basement? How could you reduce this loss?

Thermal Resistance of Some Common Building Materials

Material	RSI-Value/cm
Brick or concrete	0.01
Gypsum board	0.04
Wood	0.08
Glass fibre or rockwool	0.21
Cellulose fibre	0.25
Expanded polystyrene ("Beadboard")	0.25–0.28
Extruded polystyrene ("Styrofoam")	0.32

Most heat is lost from houses through air exchange. This occurs from leaks through gaps around doors, windows, attic entrances, and electrical outlets, and cracks in ceilings and walls. As well, air actually enters and exits through walls and ceilings which are not cracked. In Exploration 7, you can check out your own home for gaps and cracks.

Even if your ceilings and walls have no cracks in them, heat can still get through by conduction. We use insulating materials like glass fibre and polystyrene foam to reduce the heat loss. Do you know of any others?

The *thermal resistance* of insulating materials — called the RSI-value — measures just how good they are at stopping heat

Thermal photograph showing heat loss from house. (built after 1961)

getting through them. Most common insulating materials have an RSI-value of about 0.2 for every centimetre of thickness. Some plastic foams have higher RSI-values. The lower the thermal resistance of a material, the more easily heat travels through it. For instance twice as much heat escapes through a wall whose RSI-value is 1.5 than through a wall whose RSI-value is 3.0. If you visit your building supplier you will see the RSI-value of insulation products stamped on the packages.

- Which has the higher thermal resistance (RSI-value), 20 cm of concrete or 1 cm of glass fibre?

- What is the approximate RSI-value of a wall made of metal siding attached to 1 cm (half inch) plywood with 10 cm of glass fibre insulation in the middle and 1 cm (half inch) gypsum board on the inside? (**Hint:** Use the table to calculate the RSI-value of each part and simply add the RSI-values together.)

How much insulation should you have in ceilings and walls? Too little and you would waste lots of heat. Too much and you would spend a fortune on insulation! Architects in Canada have been trying to find the best balance. Here are their recommendations:

Recommended Insulation Levels

Parts of house	Recommended RSI-values	
	in warmer parts of Canada	in colder parts of Canada
Ceiling or roof	5.6	6.3
Walls	3.0	3.5
Basement (below ground)	2.1	2.1

- Why do you think the recommended RSI-values for ceilings, walls and basements are different?

- How many centimetres of glass fibre would you hope to find in the roof of your home?

In Exploration 8 you can check out your own home to see if it meets these recommendations.

Many homes, especially older ones, do not match these recommendations. The recommendations were only made in 1978 after the price of oil had skyrocketted. But your family may be able to do something about it. You might be able to add some insulation to your home. In Exploration 9 you can check out the best buys. Perhaps you will have some important recommendations to make to your family.

Find Those Gaps!

A convection current can find every crack in your home, even small cracks that you didn't know existed! About a quarter of the total heat loss in your home is from air exchange, and a quarter of *that* is from those gaps around doors and windows.

This means that, if your family were to use 4000 L of oil each year for heating, you could save 250 L simply by sealing these gaps. So home is a good place to start your energy survey.

What To Do

Make a simple draft gauge from a sandwich bag and a clothes hanger. Choose a cold day and look for those gaps!

Any gaps you find can easily be fixed with weatherstripping (between moving parts) or with caulking.

Before you prepare your report, check the cost of weatherstripping and caulking.

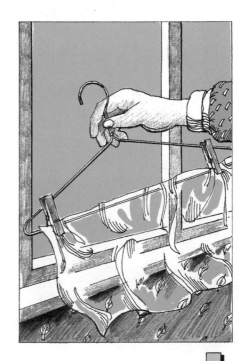

Is Your Home Well Insulated?

Ask an older member of your family to help you with this survey. You will need to look

- in the attic (Don't put your foot through the ceiling!),
- in the walls (You can often see inside if you unscrew the covers to electrical fittings. This must be done by an adult — you could get a nasty shock.)
- and in the basement.

Make a note of the type and thickness (cm) of the insulation in each place. Use a table like the one shown to record your results.

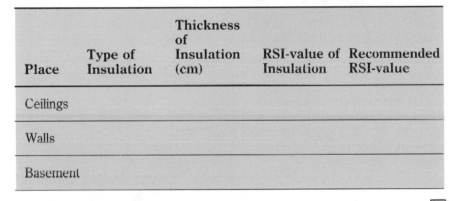

Place	Type of Insulation	Thickness of Insulation (cm)	RSI-value of Insulation	Recommended RSI-value
Ceilings				
Walls				
Basement				

Best Buys in Insulation?

Get together with some of your classmates and make a display of common insulation materials: glass fibre batts of different thicknesses, loose fills of different sorts, foamed plastics of different types — as many as you can find. Try your friendly builder or supplier. Label each sample. Don't forget to include the cost and the RSI-value on each label. Which is the best buy?

Fast Heat Travel — Radiation

Your Chance to Edit!

Newspaper editors know that a good headline should be interesting and have just two or three words. Pretend you are a newspaper editor. Read this article carefully, then think of a good headline for each paragraph. The article will tell you about the most important example of radiation.

Energy From a Star

(adapted from "Whence Energy" by Roy Bishop, Acadia University)

_____? (1)

We live on a blue and white planet, a small round turquoise gem nestled in the black velvet of space. The energy we have available for heat was either present when the Earth was formed or has been received from space since that time.

_____? (2)

Energy reaches the Earth from space in several ways. Meteors, streak down through the atmosphere, burning up with great flashes of fire. Cosmic rays bring pockets of energy that have travelled far through the universe. At night, we can see the stars sending their light energy to us.

_____? (3)

In particular, it is the nearest star that contributes most of the energy we receive from space. Because of its closeness, our Sun overwhelms the other stars, so we sometimes forget it is also a star.

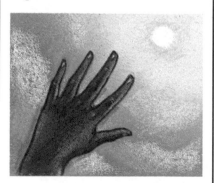

_____? (4)

On a clear sunny day, one square metre on the Earth receives from the Sun the same amount of energy that is given out by a 1000 W electric heater. If you hold your hand up to the heat of the Sun, it receives about five watts of energy.

_____? (5)

The most important immediate use of the Sun's energy is the warmth we receive from it. Thanks to sunlight, the _average_ outdoor temperature in Canada is about 2°C. Without the heat of the Sun the temperature of the Earth would be about 270°C lower, or approximately the temperature of the space between the stars: −269°C.

_____? (6)

We also use the Sun's energy for heat in indirect forms, but only after some delay. It can take weeks for the effect of sunlight to be transformed into a source of energy that can be used to heat our homes. For instance, sunlight evaporates moisture into the air, resulting in rainfall. This rainfall is channelled into streams and rivers. The rivers are dammed, and the water is forced through turbines, producing electricity. This electricity is used for many purposes: to run motors, produce light, and heat our homes, among others.

_____?_____ (7)

When plants use sunlight to grow, the delay is longer, lasting several months. Plants are the source of food for many animals. We use both plants and animals as sources of food. People need a constant energy input of about 100 W.

_____?_____ (8)

When we burn oil, gas, or coal, we are using energy from the Sun that was stored long ago. 100 000 000 a (years) ago, energy from the Sun was captured by huge living plants. It was stored in the form of fossil fuels. Recently, people have become aware that this particular source of energy will not last forever. Indeed, there are fears that most of this energy will be completely used within the next century, if not sooner.

_____?_____ (9)

And all this energy from the Sun, so much of which is in the form of heat, travels from the Sun to the Earth in just eight minutes. This is heat travel by radiation. As the Sun's energy falls on the Earth, some heat is reflected into space. But some of the energy is absorbed by the Earth, and everything on the surface is warmed and heated. Then, when darkness comes with the setting of the Sun, much of this heat is radiated back, or reradiated, into space.

The Greenhouse Effect

Heat travels from the Sun to the Earth, penetrating the Earth's atmosphere. Objects on Earth absorb some of this heat, becoming warmer as a result. These heated objects then radiate heat themselves. But their radiant heat may be a little different from the Sun's radiant heat. It may no longer be able to penetrate the Earth's atmosphere. Carbon dioxide in the air holds back some of this radiation. Therefore, much of the radiant heat never leaves the Earth. The carbon dioxide behaves like the glass in a greenhouse. For this reason, scientists call this phenomenon the "Greenhouse Effect".

During the past two centuries or so, the amount of industry has been steadily increasing. One result is that the amount of carbon dioxide in the air has also increased. Some scientists are afraid that this could, in turn, increase the Greenhouse Effect and cause overheating of the Earth. This is a controversial issue. Do research, and read some articles or books about it. Be sure to consider all sides of the issue. As you read, keep in mind these questions:

1. How serious do scientists consider an increase in the Greenhouse Effect to be today?

2. Is it getting worse?

3. What are some problems that an increase would cause? Specifically, how would it affect agriculture? The climate? The oceans?

4. What are some possible solutions to an increase in the Greenhouse Effect?

Heat Magic: A Puzzle

Scan the article Energy From a Star once again, then, in your notebook, try this puzzle without looking at the article.

Match the items in lists I and II, then enter the best combination of letter/number pairs in the Magic Square.

Add the numbers in each horizontal, vertical, and diagonal row to find the "magic number"!

List I

A. The star that gives us the most heat.

B. How this heat travels to us.

C. Heated objects do this.

D. Provides almost all of our heat.

F. Energy need of your body.

G. Time for Sun's energy to travel to Earth.

H. A form of short-term storage of solar energy.

I. A form of long-term storage of solar energy.

List II

1. conduct

2. radiation

3. oil

4. direct solar heat

5. eight minutes

6. two degrees Celsius

7. radiate heat

8. one hundred watts

9. Sun

10. running water

11. five watts

Magic Square

A	B	C
D	E	F
G	H	I

Reflectors, Absorbers, and Radiators

Heat Travel — Some Questions

Choose one or two questions to investigate, then share your results with your classmates.

Question 1

Do light bulbs and other hot objects radiate heat?

You Will Need

• lamp

What To Do

Turn on the lamp. Do you feel heat immediately? Turn off the lamp. What do you feel? Can you explain this?

Turn the lamp on again. Put your hand closer to it. What do you feel now? Can you explain this?

Could the heat be travelling by convection? (**Hint:** Compare what happens when you put your hand above the bulb, below the bulb, and to the side of the bulb.)

Try this activity at home with a hot iron. But be careful: Turn the steam off, and do not touch the iron!

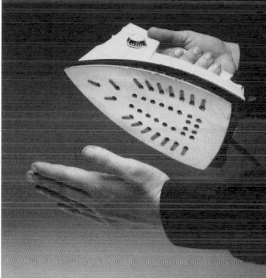

Question 2

Can radiant heat be reflected?

You Will Need

- lamp
- cardboard square
- mirror
- thermometer taped to cardboard

What To Do

Hold your hand about 15 cm from the lamp. Now try to reflect more heat onto your hand by using a mirror. Do you notice a difference? Are you sure? Check with the thermometer.

Next, arrange the lamp, cardboard square, and mirror as shown. Do you feel the reflected radiant heat?

Question 3

Can radiant heat be focused?

You Will Need

- lamp
- large (thick) lens
- thermometer taped to cardboard
- clothespin
- crumpled tissue paper

What To Do

Move the lens backward and forward, until you can see the image of the light bulb on the cardboard. Once you can see the image, does the temperature of the cardboard rise? Can you explain your observations?

Hold the tissue paper in the clothespin. Try to focus the Sun's rays so that the paper catches fire. CAUTION! — This is how some forest fires start.

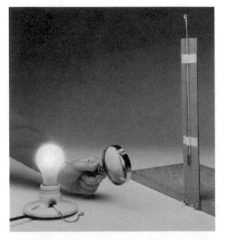

Question 4

Which colours are able to absorb the most radiant heat? the least?

You Will Need

- pop bottle painted white
- pop bottle painted black
- 2 balloons
- lamp
- variety of differently coloured cards
- thermometer
- 5 ice cubes
- square each of red, green, white, and black paper, and aluminum foil

What To Do

Put a balloon over the mouth of each bottle. Place a lamp halfway between the bottles (or, if it is a hot sunny day, put the bottles outside for a while). Observe the balloons. How do you explain what happens?

Strap a thermometer to a coloured card, then hold it up to the lamp. Repeat, using all the other cards. Remember to keep them the same distance from the lamp. (How long will you wait before reading the thermometer?) In your notebook, record the temperature of each card.

Put an ice cube on each square of paper and aluminum foil. Place them in sunlight. Record in your notebook the order in which the ice cubes melt.

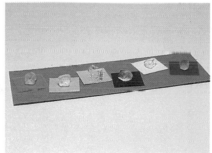

Question 5

Which colours radiate the most heat?

You Will Need

- 3 tin cans of the same size, one painted white, one painted black, and the other one unpainted.
- 3 cardboard covers to fit over the tin cans
- 3 thermometers
- hot water

What To Do

Fill each container with the same amount of hot water. Record the temperature at three-minute intervals.

Thinking About Your Discoveries

Answer these questions on the crossword puzzle your teacher gives you.

1. The heat below an electric light bulb travels to your hand by ____A____, while most of the heat above the light bulb probably travels by ____B____.

2. Heat travels fastest by *C (conduction, convection, radiation)*.

3. Ninety percent of the Earth's heat comes from the ____D____ by ____E____.

4. Radiant heat can be concentrated to a point by a ____F____ to produce a ____G____ temperature. Radiant heat can be felt after ____H____ by a mirror.

5. *I (dark, pale)* substances, when cool, are the poorest absorbers of heat.

6. *J (dark, pale)* substances, when hot, are the best radiators of heat.

7. A black cloth and a white cloth are placed on snow on a sunny day. The snow will melt least under the ____K____ cloth because it is the better *L (absorber, reflector)* of radiant heat.

If you can do this puzzle within ten minutes, you really radiate brightness and you have absorbed some real science!

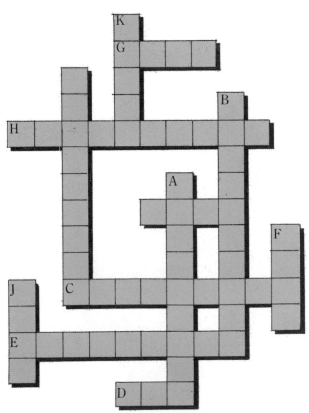

Problems to Ponder

Here are ten problems to ponder. Apply what you have learned about absorption, reflection, and radiation.

1. Why is white clothing so popular in tropical countries?

2. The inside of a thermos bottle is shiny. Why?

3. Why do some gardeners mix soot with garden soil?

4. Kettles are generally made of light-coloured, shiny metal. Why?

5. The car radiator through which water circulates is black in colour. Why?

6. Whitewash is placed on glass roofs to maintain a constant temperature in the house. Why?

7. Why is it sometimes cooler on clear nights than it is on cloudy nights?

8. Baked potatoes are often served to you wrapped in aluminum foil. Why?

9. How would you design a space suit for use on the Moon? The temperature of a lunar day is over 100°C; the temperature of a lunar night is below −150°C.

10. On hot summer days, a home should reflect heat. On cold winter nights houses radiate heat. What colour should a house be painted: green, red, black, white, or pink?

Solar Heat

A Solar Still

Make a solar still. Explain to your classmates how it works.

You Will Need

- cardboard box like the one in the illustration
- pane of glass slightly larger than the top of the box
- 2 pans: one to contain the dirty or salty water you want to purify; the other to collect the pure water
- 2 wooden sticks to put under the front edge of the glass
- tape

What To Do

Assemble the still to look like the one shown in the photograph.

Decide what colour(s) you should paint the inside and outside of the box and the pan.

Explain why the box is slanted, and why the two sticks are placed under the front edge of the glass.

Place the still in the sunlight until you get results.

Bear River Couple Has Solar Heated Home

Heating Canadian homes in winter is costly business. The Hamiltons, of Bear River, Nova Scotia, think that they have solved this problem by building a solar home. The savings in their fuel bill will pay for the solar heating unit in ten years. Their solar heating system should maintain a temperature of fifteen degrees Celsius even in the winter time. An oil furnace will bring the temperature up to a more comfortable twenty degrees Celsius. The aluminum collecting panel covers the south side of their house. When the temperature of the panel is two to three degrees Celsius higher than the temperature of water housed in tanks beneath the house, pumps turn on that lift the water to the top of the heat collecting panels. Here the water is heated before being returned to a storage tank where it is used to heat the house. The system can function for three to four days without sunshine which means there should be sufficient fair weather the year around to warrant it.

This house was built with energy conservation in mind. It is extremely well insulated and has a large number of windows, especially on the south side.

Article in the Halifax Chronicle-Herald, November 4, 1978.

Here are some questions that you may want to answer after reading about the Hamiltons' solar home.

Questions

1. Are you looking at the north or south side of the house?

2. Have the Hamiltons chosen the right shape for their roof?

3. Why weren't the solar panels on top of a flat roof placed facing directly upward?

4. Which colour should the aluminum collecting panel be painted: white, green, or black? Or should it be left shiny?

5. What would be the effect of increasing the size of the water tanks?

6. How could the large windows save energy?

Building a Model Solar Heat Collector

It costs a lot of money to build a solar heat collector. To make sure their product will work, designers often build a prototype, or model, first, and test it. You can make a model solar heat collector from materials found around your home and school.

You Will Need

- cardboard box, about 40 cm × 40 cm × 10 cm
- masking tape
- nine 30 cm lengths of glass (or copper) tubing
- rubber tubing
- thermometer
- 2 clamps
- clear plastic wrap
- funnel
- pail of water

What To Do

Using corrugated cardboard, make a box 40 cm long, 40 cm wide, and 10 cm deep. A discarded cardboard box is a good source of corrugated cardboard. The sides and bottom of the box can be held together with masking tape.

Fasten the nine lengths of glass tubing together with the short pieces of rubber tubing. Arrange the glass tubing in the bottom of the box as in the illustration.

Measure the water temperature. Attach a funnel to one end of the outlets, then fill the glass tubing with water. (Why should you wait to clamp the other outlet until the tubing is filled?) Cover the heat collector with clear plastic wrap. You are ready to investigate some of the problems related to solar heat.

Now to test the heat collector. Place it in sunlight or near a lamp for 15 min. Drain the water into a measuring cylinder. Measure the water temperature again. Do you recall that 4.2 J (joules) is the amount of energy needed to raise the temperature of one gram of water by 1°C? Calculate the number of joules of heat absorbed by your solar heat collector.

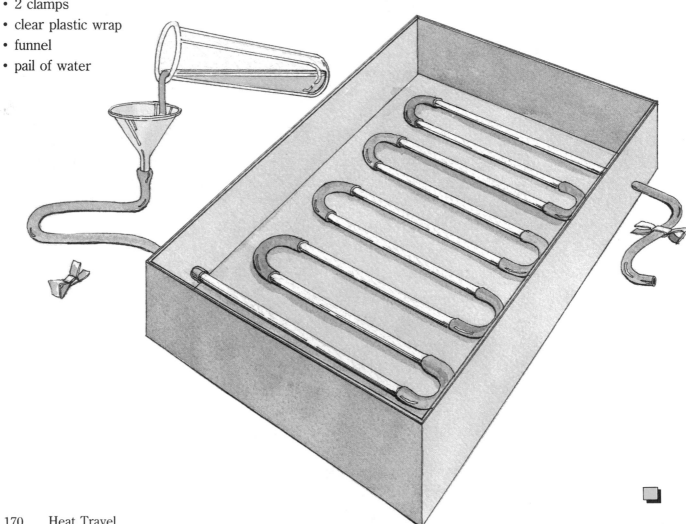

Design Features of Solar Heat Collectors

As you can probably imagine, there are many variables to consider when designing a solar heat collector. Scientists and technicians have gradually developed reliable collectors for houses and offices. Here are two specific problems. The first should be easy to solve, but the second one will make you do a little work!

1. What is the best colour for a collector?
2. What is the best angle for a collector?

Reviewing the experiments in Exploration 10 will help you decide on the best colour. But what is the best angle? Should the collector face straight upward or be slanted?

If you did Exploration 11, your results should confirm that your collector absorbs the most heat when it faces the Sun directly. But choosing the best angle is a tricky problem. Look at the table at right, which shows the Sun's altitude (angle from the horizon) at mid-day at latitude 52° (about halfway between Calgary and Edmonton). At which angle would you put your heat collector? Why?

Mid-day Altitude of Sun at Latitude 52°	
January 21st	18°
February 23rd	28°
March 21st	38°
April 16th	48°
May 21st	58°
June 22nd	63°
July 24th	58°
August 28th	48°
September 23rd	38°
October 20th	28°
November 22nd	18°
December 22nd	14°

This solar heat collector rotates so it always faces the Sun.

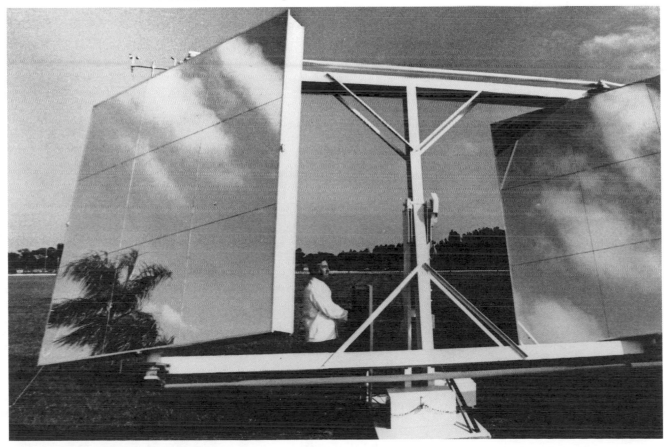

Nuclear Winter

The thought of nuclear war is horrifying. Many, many people would die — those close to an explosion and those living in the track of fallout from the nuclear cloud.

Then, in the 1970s and early 1980s, scientists began to worry that things could be worse still. They began to fear that the climate of our planet might be changed dramatically by the dust produced by the explosions and the smoke from tremendous fires. Scientists gave these effects the name "nuclear winter".

You can begin to understand why they arrived at this conclusion if you carry out a simple demonstration like the one illustrated.

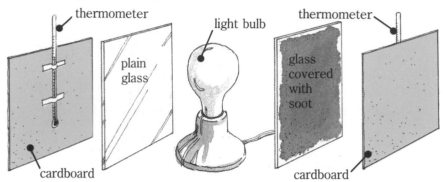

The lamp is like the Sun. The glass represents the Earth's atmosphere. The soot on the glass acts like the smoke layer. The brown card represents the Earth. What did you observe? Was there any difference in the temperatures recorded by the two thermometers?

There is a great difference between our model of the Sun and the Earth and the real thing, of course. But scientists tried hard to close the gap. There were many questions they needed to answer: How much smoke would there be? How much dust would be carried up into the atmosphere by an explosion? How would the wind spread the dust and smoke? How fast would the dust and smoke settle? There were many more; can you think of some of them?

What the Scientists Discovered

Once they had tentative answers to these questions, the researchers put their computers to work. In 1983, Carl Sagan, a well-known astronomer and writer, and his colleagues published the graphs at the top of the next page. They plotted "average land temperature" against "time after war". The blue dotted line on top (ambient temperature) shows the average temperature of the land if no war had taken place.

Studying the graph will help you answer the questions that follow.

Carl Sagan

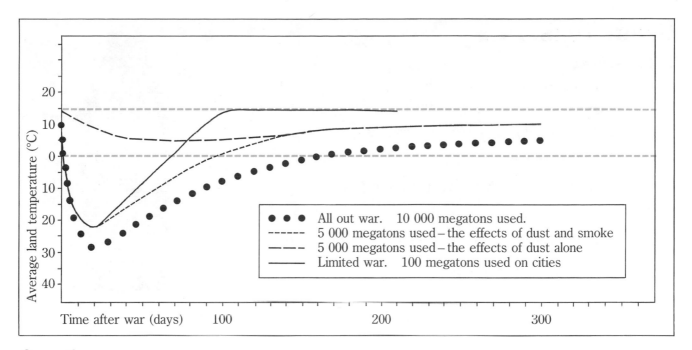

Questions

1. If a war took place in the summer, what would be the temperature of the land one month later?

2. If a war took place in the summer, how long would the lakes stay frozen?

3. How long would it take for the climate to return to normal?

4. What do you think would be the effects on crops (the food supply)? To answer this question, you need to know the ambient temperature when most crops are planted (in May).

5. On the basis of their studies, the researchers concluded that even a so-called "limited nuclear war" could have very serious effects. If a limited war took place on another continent, Canadians would probably escape the explosion and the fallout, but *not* nuclear winter. Do you think most people realize this? What can you do about preventing nuclear winter?

Suggestions

1. Design and conduct a survey about what people know and how they feel.

2. Write a letter to the editor of your local newspaper explaining your viewpoint.

3. Make a poster about nuclear winter.

4. Invite a politician to come and answer some of your questions. (If this isn't possible, write a letter to this person asking for some answers.)

5. Your Choice.

Brain Teasers

1. Some Design!

   In your notebook, fill in the blanks. Imagine going to all this trouble just to keep your drink hot!

   The plastic cup reduces heat travel by __?__ .

   The cork reduces heat travel by __?__ .

   The double-walled glass bottle reduces heat travel by __?__ .

   The vacuum reduces heat travel by __?__ .

   The silvered surfaces cause heat travel by __?__ .

   The air reduces heat travel by __?__ .

   The plastic case reduces heat travel by __?__ .

2. Explanations, Please!

   (a) If a car is parked in the sunlight with the windows closed, you become too warm. Yet the glass windows feel cool.

   (b) When you make toast with the end of the loaf, the crusty side feels hotter. Is it really hotter?

   (c) Glider pilots experience uplift when they pass over ploughed fields and houses, but drop when going over trees and ponds.

   (d) A thermometer taken out on a sunny day does not give a good measurement of the temperature of the air.

   (e) A motorbike engine has fins around it.

   (f) You can wrap ice cream in a sweater to keep it cold!

   (g) On a windy day, people feel warmer when they wear their fur coats inside out.

   (h) Aluminum foil is included in the wall insulation of many homes. The foil is placed on the inside face of the insulation.

   (i) A newspaper placed against the screen of a fireplace remains stuck to it. CAUTION! Don't try it! Fire hazard!

   (j) Sand added to the snow on a highway not only helps tire traction but also helps melt the snow.

   (k) As we leave the Earth and go into outer space, the temperature of the atmosphere drops.

   (l) Hot air registers are always placed near the floor.

   (m) In a room heated by a fireplace, the hot air in the room actually leaves the room and goes up the chimney, yet people in the room feel warm.

(n) A smudge pot is a small container that burns oil and produces very thick smoke. Fruit growers put smudge pots in their orchards overnight when they fear frost. The pots are far apart and cannot supply enough heat to keep the fruit warm. Why do the fruit growers put out smudge pots, then?

(o) The soil in small pots in which tree seedlings are grown is covered with a thin layer of white sand.

3. Hot Dog!

Can you cook a hot dog by conduction? convection? radiation? Sketch how you would do it by each method.

4. Consumer Research

How does this fuel-saving energy grate work? Would the fan attachment be worth buying?

5. Predictions Please!

(a) You are going to bake potatoes in aluminum foil. Aluminum foil has a shiny side and a dull side. Would it make any difference which side is next to the potatoes?

(b) Some people prefer their coffee black, others prefer it with cream only, others with sugar only, and still others with both cream and sugar. Of these mixtures, which would cool the fastest?

(c) What do you think would happen to the water levels if this apparatus were placed in sunlight?

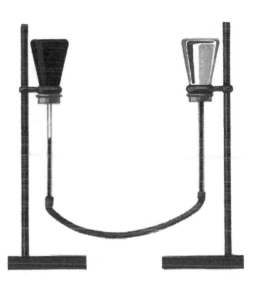

(d) This box has eight holes which can be plugged with corks. It contains four candles, and one side is covered by plastic wrap. What do you think will happen to the candles as different openings are plugged or unplugged? (For instance, what would happen if all the holes on the right side were plugged, or if all the holes on the left side were plugged?) Consider several possibilities.

6. Professor Duncer's Experiments

Can you improve these conduction experiments which Professor Duncer performed? What is wrong with Professor Duncer's conclusions?

Experiment 1

To test the *conducting rates* of two metals.

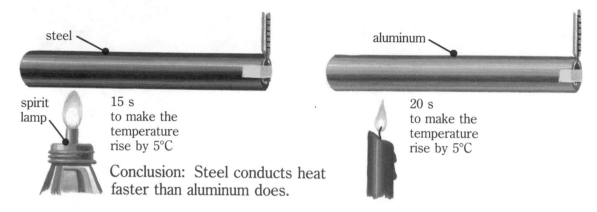

steel

spirit lamp

15 s to make the temperature rise by 5°C

Conclusion: Steel conducts heat faster than aluminum does.

aluminum

20 s to make the temperature rise by 5°C

Experiment 2

To test the effect of the *length* of a metal rod on *time of heat travel* from one end to the other.

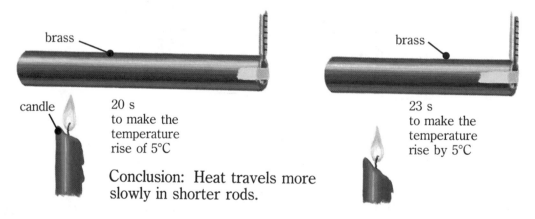

brass

candle

20 s to make the temperature rise of 5°C

Conclusion: Heat travels more slowly in shorter rods.

brass

23 s to make the temperature rise by 5°C

Experiment 3

To test the effect of *diameter* on *time of heat travel* from one end to the other.

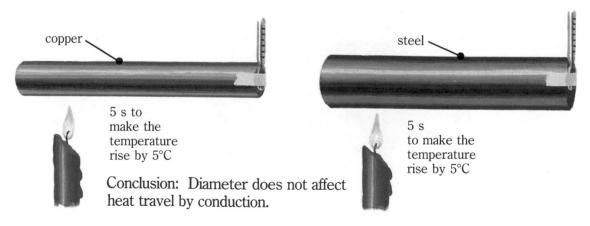

copper

5 s to make the temperature rise by 5°C

Conclusion: Diameter does not affect heat travel by conduction.

steel

5 s to make the temperature rise by 5°C

Reinforce Yourself

Cover the right-hand column with a piece of paper. Expose the answers only after you have tried to complete the blanks.

1. Room temperature is closest to _____?_____ (0°C, 20°C, 50°C, 70°C).

2. The coldest and warmest temperatures recorded on Earth are about _____?_____ (−20°C, 20°C; −40°C, 40°C; −60°C, 60°C; −80°C, 80°C).

3. The temperatures often used to calibrate thermometers are _____?_____ °C, the freezing point of _____?_____ , and _____?_____ °C, the _____?_____ of water.

4. Mercury is used in thermometers because when it is heated it _____?_____ . A bimetallic strip may be used to measure temperature because when heated it _____?_____ . A coiled bimetallic strip is used in a _____?_____ .

5. If you place your hand in cold water and then transfer it to lukewarm water, the lukewarm water will appear to be _____?_____ .

6.

    1. 20°C

    2. −60°C, 60°C

    3. 0°
       water
       100°
       boiling point

    4. expands
       bends (curves)
       thermostat

    5. hot

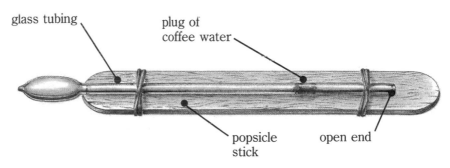

glass tubing · plug of coffee water · popsicle stick · open end

In this home-made thermometer, the _____?_____ expands to indicate a change in temperature.

7. A problem with air thermometers is that the temperature appears to change with a change in air ___?___ .

6. air

8. All of the following persons *except one* developed a kind of thermometer: Galileo, Newton, Fahrenheit, Réamur, Celsius, Sanctorio. Which one?

7. pressure

9. A clinical thermometer used by doctors stays at the ___?___ temperature measured because of a ___?___ in the fine tube containing the mercury.

8. Newton

10. The maximum daily temperature reading is recorded on a thermometer constructed like a ___?___ thermometer. To reuse the thermometer it is necessary to ___?___ the mercury.

9. highest
   kink (constriction)

11. In a minimum thermometer, the liquid commonly used is ___?___ . When the thermometer goes to the lowest temperature on a given day, the liquid shrinks toward the bulb, and the surface hauls the ___?___ with it. This indicates the lowest or ___?___ temperature reading on a given day.

10. clinical
   shakedown

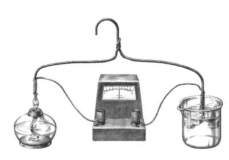

12. Two different metals connected at two points can measure temperature. Such a device is called a ___?___ ; it measures temperature by the amount of ___?___ which flows when the two points of connection of the wires are at different temperatures.

11. alcohol
   index
   minimum

13. The temperature of stars can be determined by the ___?___ of the light coming from them.

12. thermocouple
   electricity

14. Gases, liquids, and solids all expand when heated. These materials, arranged in order of amount of expansion from small to great for a given temperature increase, are as follows:
___?___ , ___?___ , ___?___ .

13. colour

15. Heat and temperature are not the same. Which words fit best in these questions? Is there enough ___?___ from the match to boil water? What is the ___?___ of boiling water?

14. solids
    liquids
    gases

16. Which requires more heat: (a) to raise the temperature of 10 mL of water from 20°C to 25°C, or (b) to raise the temperature of 5 mL of water from 20°C to 25°C?

15. heat
    temperature

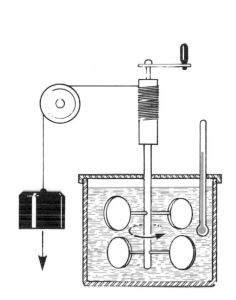

17. James Prescott ___?___ , a British scientist, showed that every time 4.2 J of mechanical work were used to stir 1 g of water, the temperature of the water rose by ___?___ °C.

16. (a)

18. Heat is a form of ___?___ , and is measured in a unit called ___?___ . The heat required to raise the temperature of 1 mL or (1 g) of water through 1°C is about ___?___ J.

17. Joule
    1

19. The heat needed to raise the temperature of 20 mL of water from 25°C to 30°C is ___?___ (the same as, less than, more than) the heat needed to raise the temperature of 20 mL of water from 30°C to 35°C.

18. energy
    joule
    4

20. The amount of heat in a material depends not only on its ___?___ but also on the ___?___ of the material.

19. the same as

21. When heat is placed into a material, the temperature ___?___ (rises, falls). The number of degrees it (rises or falls) depends on the ___?___ of the material.

20. temperature
    amount (or mass or volume)

22. When heat leaves a material, its temperature ___?___ *(rises, falls)*. The number of degrees it (rises or falls) depends on the ___?___ of the material.

23. The heat required to raise the temperature of 30 mL of water from 20°C to 25°C is ___?___ *(the same as, less than, more than)* the heat required to raise the temperature of 15 mL of water from 20°C to 30°C.

24. A finger placed for two seconds in a glass of water at 50°C feels ___?___ *(colder than, the same as, hotter than)* when placed in a bath tub of hot water at 50°C for two seconds.

25. 20 mL of water at 40°C are mixed with 20 mL of water at 10°C. The temperature of the mixture is likely to be close to ___?___ *(10°C, 20°C, 25°C, 30°C, 40°C)*.

26. 40 mL of water at 40°C are mixed with 20 mL of water at 10°C. The temperature of the mixture is likely to be close to ___?___ *(10°C, 20°C, 25°C, 30°C, 40°C)*.

27. 100 mL of water at 65°C are mixed with 200 mL of water at 5°C; the temperature of the mixture will likely be near ___?___

28. The energy content of foods is measured in a unit called the ___?___ , whose symbol is ___?___ .

21. rises

amount (or mass or volume)

22. falls

amount (or mass or volume)

23. the same as

24. the same as

25. 25°C

26. 30°C

27. 25°C

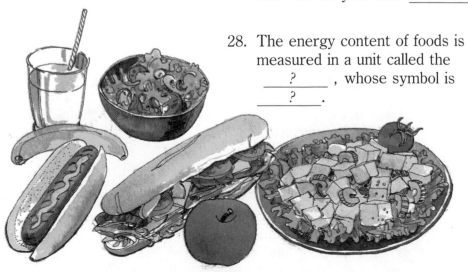

29. The energy required by you daily is closest to ____?____ kJ *(80, 800, 8000, 80 000)*.

30. A peanut, when burned, produces about 40 kJ or 40 000 J of energy. This would be enough energy to raise the temperature of 200 mL of water from 20°C to ____?____ °C.

28. kilojoule
    kJ

29. 8000 kJ

30. 70

Civil Engineering

Designing structures such as bridges, wharves, industrial plants, dams, and roads is the task of a civil engineer. Genanne Sims is a civil engineer who has been engaged in many such jobs.

Q: What do you like most about your work?

Genanne: I like the variety and challenge. Every job is different. Each project has its unique phases and I think that is really fine. The job I have now is stimulating because I spend a fair bit of the time both in the field and at my desk.

Q: What do you do?

Genanne: I am responsible for 45 marine structures along the coast, including many wharves. My work runs the whole gamut from identification of a problem through design of a solution to supervision of construction. This brings me in contact with fishermen, contractors, and people in various government departments.

Q: What event of your working life particularly stands out?

Genanne: There are many, including wharves falling down, getting a helicopter ten minutes later, and setting up tents at the site within an hour. But the event that especially stands out is the first time I went to a large wharf which I had helped design. We spent a complete day touring the site and facilities. It was overwhelming — just awesome to see what you had designed.

Q: How did you get interested in engineering?

Genanne: For one thing, in school I really liked the lab work in science, and I used to love math. I would sit back for hours on end and do it for fun.

Q: What courses would you advise young people to take in school if they might want to do the kind of work you are doing?

Genanne: Keep all your options open. Don't close any doors, because if you change your mind two or three years later it can be too late. Obviously, math and science are very important, particularly math. Among the sciences, physics, chemistry, and geology are especially important to my field of work. Also, communications skills are really important. Any work you can do in the English language, communications, drama — anything to improve how you express yourself — is critical. The greatest design solution to the most complicated problem is useless if it isn't communicated well to the boss or the client.

Q: What skill is most important to an engineer?

Genanne: The biggest asset in engineering is the ability to think in an organized fashion, to think a problem through from beginning to end.

Q: What personal characteristics are important?

Genanne: Engineering involves team work, and you also need stamina and enthusiasm. It comes back to getting along with everyone.

Q: What issues that concern the community arise in your field of work?

Genanne: Safety is a major issue. The National Building Code of Canada requires that a designer of any project must do site supervision. However, if your client doesn't pay for it or ask you to do it, you may have no way of knowing whether what you have designed has been built as you designed it. What happens, then, if there is a failure and people are killed?

Q: That is a challenging question. Are there other issues that concern you as an engineer?

Genanne: What do engineers do when they have clients who want them to do work which the engineers feel is not in the best interests of society, for example, projects that would add to the acid rain problem?

There are also everyday, nittygritty problems, such as a project to close a wharf by consolidating two wharves into one. These tiny wharves may concern only two fishermen, but the consolidation changes their whole lives, how they work, and how they operate.

A Project Idea

What structures could be built in your community to make life better for the local people? Perhaps a sidewalk, or a foot bridge across a ravine, or a playground for children? Maybe a wharf for recreational boating, if you live near water? Ask your neighbours what improvements they would like to see. You will then have plenty of project ideas.

The engineering side of such a project includes the selection of materials and the design. Doing the actual construction might not be practical, but you could produce a model from your design.

Some of the questions you should consider include these: Would the structure built on the basis of your design or model be safe? Would it last? What materials should be used in the construction, considering both cost and the requirements of the project?

Advice can be obtained from civil engineers in your community. They work for engineering consulting firms, Public Works, and transportation departments of government, among other agencies. Industrial arts teachers, building supply companies, builders, and contractors can also be very helpful.

Mechanical Engineering

Mechanical engineering involves machines and equipment, particularly engines of all sorts. Engineers like Brian King apply both scientific and practical knowledge to the tasks of designing, selecting, building, or repairing machinery. Some of this knowledge is gained in school, particularly through the study of physics and chemistry. Further knowledge is acquired in university, where Brian King, for example, completed a Bachelor of Engineering Degree. After university, practical experience and continuing study of new technology are the most important ways of gaining knowledge.

Q: How did you become interested in mechanical engineering?

Brian: One answer to that would be that I was very brutal on toys, bikes, and cars as a youngster. I had to develop the ability to repair things as well as break them. This developed a mechanical bent and also an electrical one, since many of the toys were electric, or had electric motors.

My parents bought me things like Meccano sets, where you connect parts together to make model cranes, ships, and things like that, including motor-driven vehicles. Also, I was very keen on model aircraft. Trying to get some of those things to fly correctly would have needed better engineering abilities than that required by most people who build big aircraft. So I was never particularly successful at it.

Q: What kind of education should young people who might be interested in your profession obtain?

Brian: Education should be an eye-opener. You need good exposure to the arts as well as the sciences. Prospective engineers must expect their working lives to cover a multitude of disciplines and subjects. Of course, physics and chemistry are the school topics most related to engineering.

Q: What is the main idea in science that is important to engineering?

Brian: I guess the most fundamental lesson for practical engineering purposes is that energy and matter are neither created nor destroyed. Take heat energy, for example, and turn it into work to drive an automobile. You have not created energy. All you have done is used it in one form and turned it into another. The total energy in the world is still the same.

Q: What skills and abilities are particularly important in engineering?

Brian: It is important to be able to reduce problems to fundamentals. A complicated problem has to be reduced to items that can be addressed singly and then collectively. A broad background of knowledge is important for this purpose.

Q: Is there an important social issue connected with your work that you would single out?

Brian: Yes. The economic welfare of society should be everybody's concern. Everyone should know how the economy works. There is really no such thing as a free lunch. Somebody worked to provide that lunch and somebody worked to pay for it. Work has to be done, and it has to be paid for.

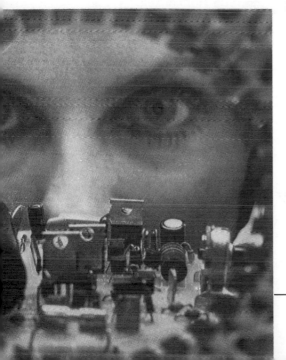

Some Project Ideas

Mechanical engineers can be found in engineering consulting firms and most larger industrial plants and companies. You might also try the Mechanical Engineering Department at a university. Other assistance can be obtained from industrial arts teachers, science teachers, and mechanics (automobile, airplane, and various specialties).

1. Designing a labour-saving device is a challenging and potentially rewarding project. Such a project begins with the identification of a problem. You might start by observing and listing various tasks performed by people around your home or school. Which tasks might be done more easily or better if an appropriate device or piece of equipment were created? You have now defined a problem. Design a solution and, if feasible, construct it.

2. Can you think of something that you or others would enjoy doing if only a device existed to allow you to do it? Begin by identifying such an activity. This defines a problem requiring a solution. Can you come up with a practical solution? If so, design it. If possible, construct it, and if it is safe, try it out.

3. There are many possible, valuable research projects concerning combustion that you might do. Which materials give the most heat at the least cost? You can't deal with all parts of this question, but you can try a small part. For example, how does wood compare with coal, or coal with oil? How do different grades of the same materials compare? What conditions are required for good combustion? Can a wood furnace be designed and built so that creosote does not form? The possibilities for research projects on combustion are unlimited. Needless to say, the results might be very important to society. Before you proceed, however, get good advice about how such research can be done safely.

Energy Sources

Ready for a big challenge? Here is one the future of the world depends on: finding sources of energy and using them wisely. No single person will solve this problem. But you can contribute even if it is to satisfy your own needs for energy at the lowest possible cost.

You can begin right now. Do some research on one of the topics suggested below, and share your results with others by creating an exhibit. If your classmates do the same, the result could be something like a trade fair.

If you've ever been to a trade fair, you know that it is an exhibition in which companies, government departments, and/or individuals have a chance to show their products and ideas to each other. A trade fair on energy resources would include exhibits on energy from hydroelectricity, oil, gas, coal, and uranium. It might also include exhibits on alternate energy sources such as solar energy, wind, geothermal energy, biomass and tidal energy.

A model trade fair on energy resources would be an important event at your school or in your community. It can help educate the public about energy. If a model trade fair is not possible, enter your exhibit in a science fair, or simply display it at your school.

Exhibits on Energy Resources

Imagine that you are a representative of an actual company which extracts and sells an energy resource such as petroleum, coal, or uranium. Find out all you can about the importance of this resource to Canada. How important is it today? How important will it be in the future? Does it provide a significant number of jobs? How is it used to provide energy? Develop an exhibit that will help convince the public of the value of your industry. Include charts and diagrams. Consult *The Canadian Encyclopedia* and other materials in your library. The company you choose to represent is also likely to be very helpful in supplying information and materials you can use in your exhibit.

Exhibits on Means of Producing Energy

Means of producing energy include hydroelectric generating stations, nuclear power plants, thermo-electric generating plants, and gas combustion engines, among other things. Find out the basic operating principles of the device or plant which interests you, and build a model of it. For the trade fair, take the role of a representative of a company that designs or makes the station or machine you have modelled. For information, you can consult not only your library, but also the company you will represent. It might be an engineering firm, a power corporation, or a manufacturer.

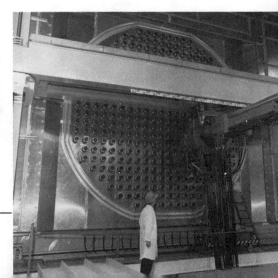

Exhibits on the Wise Use of Energy Resources

On a *per capita* (per person) basis, Canadians are among the highest users of energy in the world. Why is this so? How do our geography and climate affect our energy use? Why is wise energy use so important to Canadians?

Which sources of energy are *renewable*; which are *non-renewable*? Which sources may be used up in your lifetime? What steps can and should be taken to regulate energy use? What dangers to the environment arise from the way energy resources are used? How can these risks be eliminated or reduced?

For this kind of exhibit, imagine that you represent a government department (either a branch of Energy, Mines and Resources Canada or an energy-related branch of your provincial government) or an environmental group. In addition to using the library, get information for your exhibit from the government department or environmental organization you will represent.

Exhibits on Alternate Energy Sources

Most of the energy for home and commercial use comes from oil and gas, coal and coke, hydro-electric dams and nuclear fission. The future may see increasing use of solar and wind energy, which are renewable resources, and geothermal and biomass energy, which can be renewable. Energy from the fusion of hydrogen atoms may also someday be harnessed safely and cheaply. To learn what is being done in Canada in these fields, refer to topics like "biomass energy", "geothermal energy", "nuclear energy", "nuclear fusion", "solar energy", "tidal energy", or "wind energy" in *The Canadian Encyclopedia*. Also contact the National Research Council, the Solar Energy Society of Canada, the physics and engineering departments at a university, and/or companies which specialize in alternate energy. Exhibit the information you obtain as if you were a representative of one of these agencies or organizations.

Good luck on a successful and interesting exhibition!

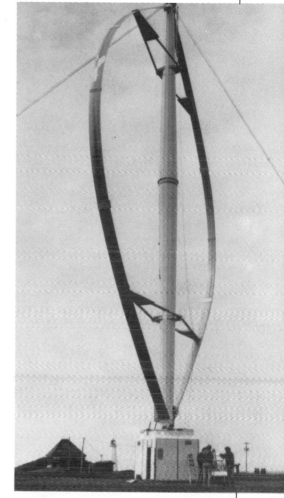

The Annapolis Tidal Power Generating Station on the Bay of Fundy converts tidal power to electricity.

FLUIDS

The Nature of Fluids

A World of Fluids

How do downhill skiers or racing cyclists improve their performance? How can a force applied at point A be felt at point B a kilometre away without any electrical contacts? Why does an extremely large object like a semi-submersible oil rig float while a pin sinks? These questions have at least one thing in common: their answers have something to do with the characteristics of fluids.

Fluids blanket the Earth. We live and move through a fluid—the atmosphere. Water, which covers more of the Earth's surface than does land and is the home of many plants and animals, is also a fluid.

The atmosphere is made up of many gases. In fact, all gases are fluids. Water is an example of a liquid and all liquids are fluids. Fluids are different from solids in that they are able to flow. The word "fluid" means "flow". Would you not consider that air and water are the most important fluids for living things?

Human beings have developed technologies that make use of the characteristics of fluids to allow us to move on or through fluids efficiently. Other technologies use fluid characteristics to perform tasks that would normally be beyond our capabilities.

This unit will help you to make sense of the world of fluids around you.

In Explorations 1 and 2 you will be examining a number of problems, each of which demonstrates a characteristic or application of fluids. Your understanding of these problems will increase as you proceed through the unit.

Fluid Problems

Part 1
Sports Technologies

Skiing and bicycle racing are two sports that involve moving through a fluid at high speed. Downhill skiers race at speeds that may exceed 100 km/h. The average velocity of a racing cyclist is considerably slower, although a speed record of 210.3 km/h was set in 1982.

Make a list of ways in which skiers and cyclists could increase their speed. Do fluids have anything to do with your suggestions? If so, what?

Part 2
Needed — An Invention

Here is the scenario. John would like to have a hot pot of coffee ready in the morning. Unfortunately he never knows what time of day he is going to get up and there is no one else to turn the coffee maker on for him. He adds coffee and water to his coffee maker and then devises a system so that he can push the on/off button from his bedroom around the corner and down the hall. His system does not use electrical energy. In your groups discuss this problem and suggest a solution. As with many problems, there are probably a number of solutions. What is the "best" solution suggested by your classmates? Do any of your solutions have something to do with fluids?

Part 3
An Impossible Task

You Will Need

- 2 L plastic soft drink bottle
- balloon

What To Do

1. Insert the balloon into the bottle as illustrated in the diagram.

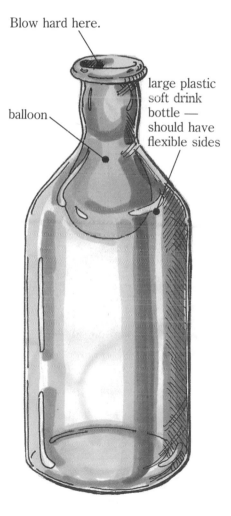

Blow hard here.

balloon

large plastic soft drink bottle — should have flexible sides

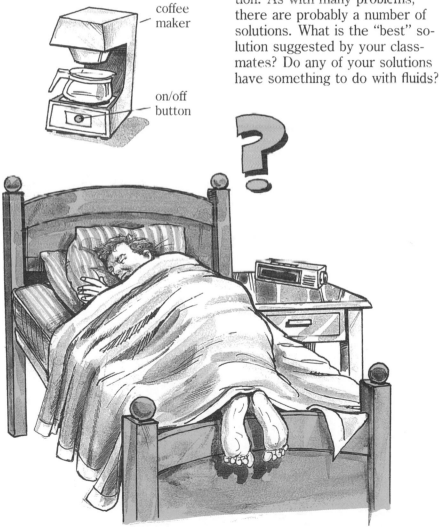

coffee maker

on/off button

2. Gently squeeze the sides of the bottle. What happens?

3. Now try blowing up the balloon. Why is this an impossible task?

Part 4
Floaters and Sinkers

You Will Need

• 3 beakers
• 200 mL of alcohol
• egg
• ice cube
• 20 g of salt

What To Do

1. Add 200 mL of water to one beaker, 200 mL of alcohol to the second, and 200 mL of water and 20 g of salt to the third. Stir the water in the third beaker to dissolve the salt.

2. Now place the egg in the first beaker. Record what you observe by drawing a picture in your notebook, showing the egg as either sinking or floating. Repeat for each of the other two beakers.

3. Remove the egg and place the ice cube in each of the beakers in turn. Once again record your observations in diagram form.

Why do some objects sink in one fluid but float in another?

Summing Up

In your groups, describe the characteristics of fluids that were demonstrated in each part of this Exploration.

More fluid characteristics are examined in the next Exploration.

A Fluid Circus

For each station, describe what you observe and state the characteristic of the fluid being observed. Perhaps a table like this one may help you organize your findings.

STATION	OBSERVATIONS	FLUID CHARACTERISTIC
#1		
#2		
etc.		

Station One

You Will Need

• water
• large plastic syringe

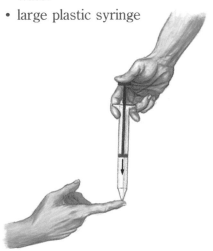

What To Do

1. Fill the syringe with air. Now, with your finger over the end, determine how far you can push the plunger down. Release the plunger.

2. Fill the syringe with water. Again try to push the plunger down while holding a finger over the end of the syringe. What characteristics of the fluids — air and water — are being demonstrated?

Station Two

You Will Need

• ice-cream container, two-thirds full of water
• plastic cup

What To Do

Place the cup bottom end down in the water, as shown. Now gently push the cup until it is partially submerged. Release the cup. What did you feel as you pushed the cup deeper into the water? What happened when you released the cup? What characteristic of the fluid does this demonstrate?

Station Three

You Will Need

- ice-cream container
- large beaker
- birthday candle
- 30 mL of baking soda
- 30 mL of vinegar
- plasticine

vinegar

baking soda

candle

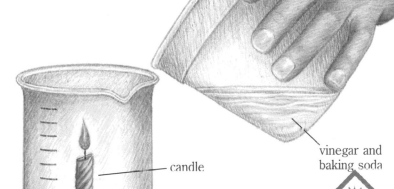

vinegar and
baking soda

What To Do

1. Place the candle in the beaker, holding it upright with plasticine. Light the candle.

2. Add the baking soda to the ice-cream container. Now add the vinegar. What happens?

3. After one minute try pouring the gas produced in the container over the candle. (Be careful not to pour any liquid onto the candle.) What happens to the candle? What characteristic or property of fluids is illustrated by this activity?

Station Four

You Will Need

- 4 large test tubes with stoppers
- marbles that will fit into the test tubes
- three of these liquids — alcohol, water, glycerine, or cooking oil

What To Do

1. Fill three of the test tubes with three of the fluids listed above (one fluid per test tube). The fluid in the fourth test tube is air.

2. Put a marble in each test tube and stopper each one. Compare the rates at which the marbles sink through each fluid. Repeat the test by turning all of the test tubes upside down at the same time. Through which fluid did the marble require the least time to sink? the most time? How would you explain your observations?

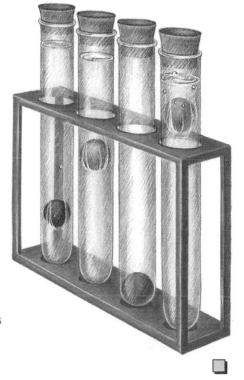

Fluid Fun

What characteristics or properties of fluids are illustrated in each of these drawings? After doing the next section, make a drawing of your own that illustrates a characteristic or property of fluids.

Match Your Observations

Here is a description of some characteristics of fluids you may have identified in Explorations 1 and 2. Which description best fits the observations?

(a) Fluids exert pressure. Pressure is something you experience everyday when you increase the pressure in your bicycle tires, use a pressure cooker, change the pressure in a garden hose by adjusting the nozzle, ride in the pressurized cabin of a jet, or obtain water from a tap.

Suggest another example from around the home of how you experience fluid pressure.

How does a hovercraft use fluid pressure to move?

(b) Fluids exert an upward force on objects placed in them. This is called buoyant force. If the buoyant force is equal to the gravitational force acting downward on the object, the object floats. Wood floats on water; hot air balloons float in air. If the buoyant force is less than the gravitational force on the object, it will sink. Suggest two examples of inventions or technology that use the buoyant force of fluids.

Why does an iceberg float?

(c) Fluids flow. Earlier you read that the word "fluid" means "flow". This property enables fluids to move around objects and objects to move through fluids. Pipelines are used to transfer large volumes of fluids—both liquids and gases. Flowing water is used to create electrical energy. What other applications of fluids can you think of that are based on this characteristic of fluids?

Why are these called fluids?

(d) Some fluids are compressible and others are not noticeably so. Gases are compressible and can be transported under high pressures. The ride on most land vehicles is cushioned by compressed air in the tires. Although liquids are slightly compressible, the effect is so small that it can be detected only with special instruments. Give examples from your everyday life that demonstrate the degree of compressibility of gaseous and liquid fluids.

(e) Fluids vary in their viscosity. Viscosity is the ease with which a fluid will flow. You may associate viscosity with the "thickness" of the fluid. "As slow as molasses" is a saying that is based on this characteristic. What does it mean? Often the viscosity of the fluid determines its use. How is this true for fluids such as oil?

What characteristics of fluids are illustrated in these photographs?

Floaters

An Oil Rig and a Pin

An Oil Rig	
Height	91 m (30 story building)
Mass	13 600 t
Area	deck 15 000 m² (two football fields)
Crew	about 84
Ability to Float	good to excellent
Function	drilling for oil

A Pin
2.5 cm
0.08 g
0.000 003 m²
none
poor
holding fabrics

Why does a pin sink, when a mountain of steel, such as an oil rig, will float? How does an oil rig control its depth in water? Can a pin be a floater? Can an oil rig sink? How many pins would it take to provide enough steel to make an oil rig?

The *Ocean Ranger*

Perhaps questions like these were in the minds of all Canadians on February 16, 1982, when we were stunned by the headline:

84 DROWNED IN OIL RIG DISASTER

The data table at the beginning of this unit describes the *Ocean Ranger*, a semi-submersible oil drilling rig. Its sinking was the worst sea disaster off the east coast of Canada since the ferry *Caribou* was sunk by a German submarine during World War II.

Now read on about the *Ocean Ranger*. Following this article, you will be provided with a design problem that will increase your understanding of the science of sinking and floating.

The *Ocean Ranger* was the world's largest semi-submersible oil rig. It was designed to handle conditions too dangerous and waters too deep for other types of drilling rigs. It floated half-sub-merged, using anchors and thrusters to keep it in position. Each one of its twelve anchors weighed over 10 t.

The rig had been lowered to its desired depth by allowing water to enter its hollow legs and pontoons. The amount of water (ballast) had to be carefully calculated to keep the *Ocean Ranger* level regardless of weather conditions and the loads which might be placed on its deck platform. Only if the ballast was correct would the vessel have the right amount of buoyancy and balance.

Properly monitored, the *Ocean Ranger* was designed to withstand winds blowing 185 km/h and waves 37 m high. It was thought to be un-sinkable. But, like the *Titanic*, which also met its end off Newfoundland, a combination of environmental conditions and human error caused it to list (lean over) 10° to 15° and topple into the cold waters of the Atlantic Ocean.

Design a Model Oil Rig

Oil rigs were designed as a solution to a problem—how to drill for oil that may lie below the ocean floor. If the water is not too deep, the rig may rest on the ocean floor. For greater depths, the oil rig may be a semi-submersible; that is, it floats. Such oil rigs must be strong enough to survive waves and storms, stable enough not to tip over, and able to carry a large cargo that includes the drilling equipment, pipes, and helicopters. They also have to be able to alter their depth up and down in the water.

This is your challenge—to build a model that satisfies these requirements.

You Will Need

- building materials, selected according to your design
- a large plastic garbage container for testing the models

What To Do

1. Discuss the criteria by which different groups will evaluate the designs. Perhaps your criteria will be similar to the ideas suggested here.
   (a) The model must float without resting on the bottom of the container.
   (b) adjustability: you should be able to alter its depth in the water.
   (c) size: small enough to fit into the available container, in this case, a plastic garbage container.
   (d) Stability will be a factor in the evaluation of the design.
   (e) The model should be able to carry at least 500 g of cargo.

2. Prepare a drawing of your final design for exhibition in the classroom.

3. Build your model. What ideas did you change from your initial plan?

4. Demonstrate your model to other groups. When you explain how and why it works, try to use such terms as "ballast", "semi-submersible", and "buoyancy".

5. How well does your model work compared to others? How would you improve on your design now that you have tested it?

Solving a technological problem

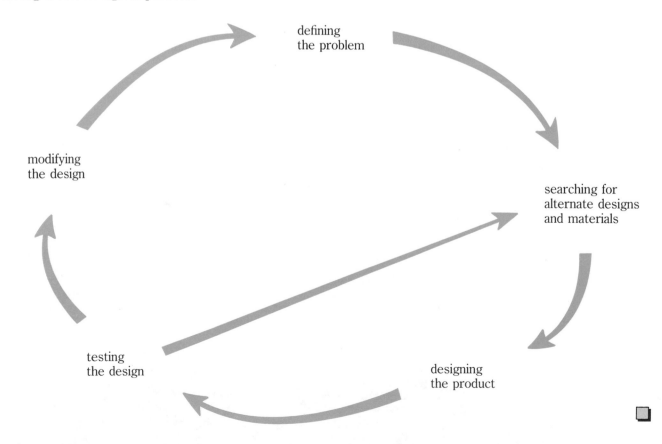

Displacing Water

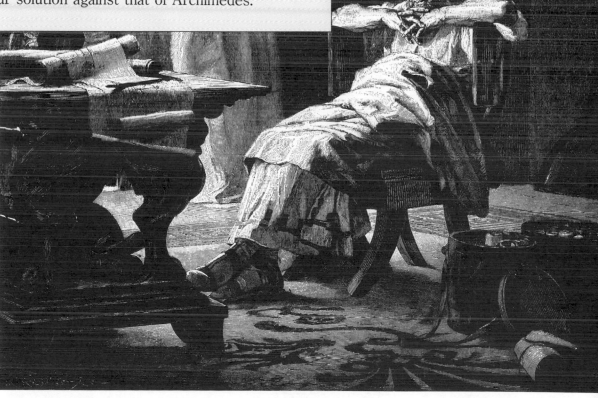

Archimedes' Problem — Is It Gold or Not?

There is an amusing tale about a Greek mathematician and physicist named Archimedes. He was born in the town of Syracuse, on the island of Sicily, in about 287 BC. Hiero II, the ruler of Syracuse, had a fantastic crown of gold made for himself. But Hiero did not trust the goldsmith who made the crown. After the crown was made, he wanted to make sure that it was pure gold and not alloyed (mixed) with silver by the goldsmith. Hiero asked Archimedes to find out without destroying the beautiful crown. But how was he to do this?

At first Archimedes was baffled by the problem. Then, one day while he was at the baths, he noticed that the water rose in the bath as he lowered himself into the water. When he lifted himself out of the water, the level fell. In an instant Archimedes realized that he knew how to solve the king's problem. So excited was he that he ran home naked through the streets of Syracuse shouting, "Eureka! Eureka!" — Greek for "I have found it!"

What do you think Archimedes' solution was? Put yourself in Archimedes' place, and write a letter to King Hiero outlining your solution and offering your services. Later in this unit you will be able to check your solution against that of Archimedes.

Water Displacement

The story about Archimedes illustrates that major break-throughs in scientific thought sometimes result from observing very common occurrences. You, too, may have noticed that floating and sinking objects displace water. When you tested your model oil rig, how much water did it displace? How could you find out? What happened when you added cargo to the deck of the rig? In this and the following Explorations you will investigate further how water is displaced by floating and sinking objects. In doing so, you will make the same discovery that Archimedes did over 2000 years ago.

In this Exploration you will examine ways in which you can measure the amount of water displaced by objects placed in fluids.

Container ship with cargo

Part 1 Using the Overflow Can

This method can be used to measure the volume of larger objects.

You Will Need

- overflow can
- rectangular blocks of wood that will fit into the overflow can
- graduated cylinder
- ruler

What To Do

1. Measure the length, width, and height of a block of wood in centimetres.
2. Use this formula to calculate the volume of the block in cubic centimetres.

volume = length × width × height

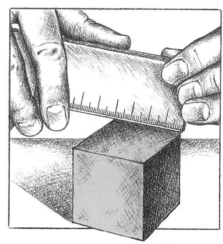

What is the volume of this block in cubic centimetres?

Part 2
Another Method

3. Follow these steps to determine the volume of water the wood displaces if it is submerged in water. This volume will be measured in millilitres.

   (a) Set the overflow can on the edge of a flat desk. Fill it with water so that the water flows out of the spout. Be sure to catch the overflow. (Do not use the graduated cylinder.)

   (b) Stick a pin firmly into the wooden block. Hold the wood by the pin and completely submerge it in the water in the overflow can. Avoid getting your fingers in the water. (Why?)

   (c) Collect all of the water that overflows in a graduated cylinder. What volume of water did the submerged block displace? What is the volume of the block?

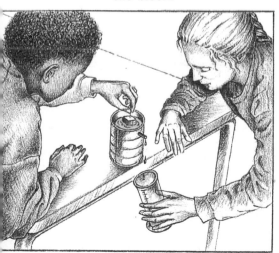

4. Compare the volume of the block in cubic centimetres and in millilitres.

For smaller objects a more accurate measure of the water displaced, and therefore of the volume of the object, may be determined in the following way.

You Will Need

• a small object, such as a bolt
• graduated cylinder

What To Do

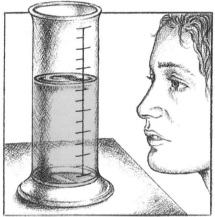

1. Read the level of the water on the scale of the graduated cylinder.

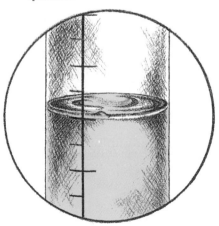

Note: To read volume, locate the double-layered curve at the top of the liquid. (This surface is called the meniscus.) Read at eye level the value at the lowest point of the curve.

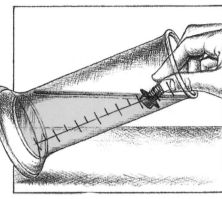

2. Carefully slide the bolt into the water.

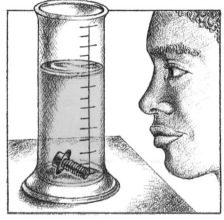

3. Read the new water level. This reading is the volume of the bolt and the water together. What is the volume of the bolt?

Why Boats Float
Part 1

Make a prediction! Which displaces more water—a piece of clay which floats, or the same piece of clay which sinks? Now, test your prediction.

You Will Need

- graduated cylinder
- balance
- overflow can
- ice-cream container
- 20 g of clay

What To Do

1. Prepare a data table. Make it large enough to include the results of your classmates.

Mass of Clay	Water Displaced by the Floating Clay		Water Displaced by the Sinking Clay	
(g)	(mL)	(g)	(mL)	(g)

2. Set the overflow can on the edge of a flat surface. Fill it with water and discard the water that comes out of the spout.

3. Record the mass of the clay in the data table. Shape the clay into a boat and determine whether it floats by placing it in an ice-cream container of water.

4. Carefully add the clay boat to the overflow can in such a way that it floats. Collect the water which it displaces. Record the volume of the displaced water in the data table.

5. Refill the overflow can and place the clay boat into the water bow first, so that it sinks. Collect, measure, and record the volume of water displaced.

6. Add your classmates' results to your table.

The Results

1. What did you discover? Does the floating clay or the sinking clay displace more water?

2. Suggest a rule for predicting how much water floating objects displace.

3. "Boats float because . . . " How would you finish this sentence?

4. Now return to the oil rig problem at the start of this lesson. Do your results in this Exploration suggest a way to determine the quantity of water displaced by extra cargo added to an oil rig? Doing Part 2 of this Exploration will help you answer this question.

Part 2

Make a prediction! How much water will be displaced when a cargo is added to a boat? Here is a way to test your prediction.

You Will Need

- graduated cylinder
- aluminum foil
- 10 pennies
- balance
- overflow can
- ice-cream container

What To Do

1. Fill the overflow can with water.

2. This time, make a boat from a 10 cm by 10 cm piece of aluminum foil. Float the boat in the overflow can. Dispose of the water which overflows.

3. Find the mass of 10 pennies. Place the 10 pennies in the aluminum boat, collecting in a dry container the water which overflows. Measure the volume of water displaced.

pennies

4. What is the volume of the water overflow? What is the mass? How does this figure compare with the mass of the pennies?

5. When cargo is added to an oil rig, it sinks deeper. What is the volume of water displaced by the cargo on the floating oil rig?

A Scientific Riddle

A boat containing a rock is floating in a swimming pool. The rock is thrown overboard. What happens to the water level in the swimming pool? Does it become higher or lower, or remain the same?

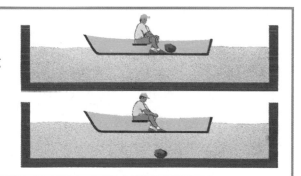

Archimedes' Principle

Forces—Up and Down

In Exploration 5 you discovered that the mass of a floater, such as a boat, is equal to the mass of the water it displaces.

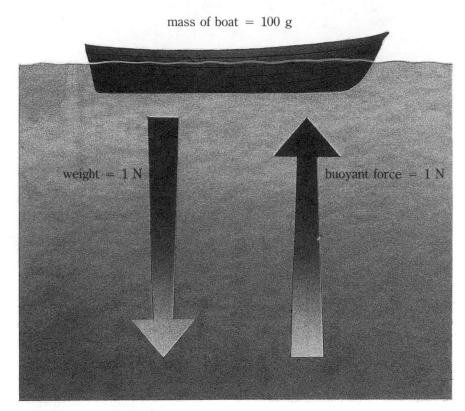

mass of boat = 100 g

weight = 1 N

buoyant force = 1 N

For example, a 100 g clay boat displaces 100 g of water. Since a mass of 100 g has a weight of approximately 1 N on Earth, a clay boat whose weight is 1 N displaces 1 N of water. The clay boat floats because there is lift, known as the buoyant force, exerted upward on the boat. This force completely offsets the weight of the boat. In this case, the buoyant force must be 1 N.

Do you see why the following statement is true? "The buoyant force on an object floating in water is equal to the weight of the water displaced by it." How does Exploration 5 support this statement?

Sinkers also displace water. Is there a relationship between the water displaced by a sinker and the buoyant force exerted on the object? Exploration 6 will look at this question.

Measuring Buoyant Force

Follow the procedure suggested in the four diagrams. Jeremy and Sue placed the data they obtained in a table like the one on page 207. Copy this table in your notebook, and add your results to theirs.

Remember: 100 g of water = 100 mL of water = 1 N of weight

1. Select an object

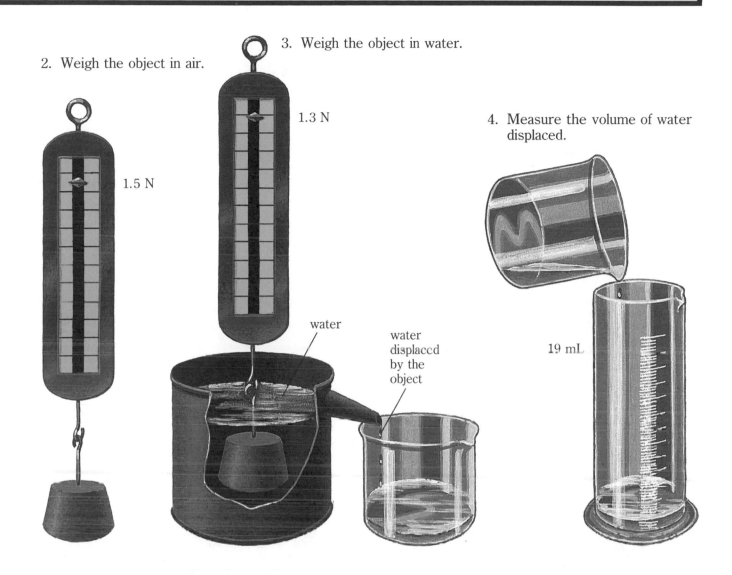

2. Weigh the object in air.

1.5 N

3. Weigh the object in water.

1.3 N

water

water displaced by the object

4. Measure the volume of water displaced.

19 mL

Jeremy's and Sue's Data Table

Exp't.	Weight of Object in Air	Apparent Weight of Object in Water	Buoyant Force of Water on Object	Weight of Water Displaced
1	1.5 N	1.3 N	(1.5 N − 1.3 N) = 0.2 N	(19 mL) 0.19 N
2	3.2 N	2.8 N	(3.2 N − 2.8 N) = 0.4 N	(42 mL) 0.42 N
3	0.7 N	0.4 N	(0.7 N − 0.4 N) = 0.3 N	(29 mL) 0.29 N
4	Your data . . .			

Your Analysis

After examining your own data in Exploration 6, as well as the results from Exploration 5, consider the following conclusions. For each conclusion, write a statement of proof in your notebook based on something you discovered by doing the Explorations.

Your Proof

1. All matter (including air) displaces water.   1. ?

2. The weight of the water displaced by a floating object equals the weight of the object.   2. ?

3. The weight of the water displaced by a sinking object equals the loss of weight of that object.   3. ?

4. The buoyant force exerted on the object equals the weight of water displaced by the object.   4. ?

If you agreed with and found proof for each statement, congratulations! You have rediscovered **Archimedes' Principle**!

"JUST DON'T FORGET WHO DISCOVERED IT FIRST!"

Archimedes' Principle

upward buoyant force = weight of the fluid displaced
(exerted on an   (by the object)
object by the fluid
in which it is placed)

Therefore,

for a floater:

    weight of floater = weight of the fluid displaced

for a sinker:

    apparent loss of weight = weight of the fluid displaced

What Archimedes Might Have Done

Now it is time to re-examine Archimedes' problem concerning King Hiero's crown. Was King Hiero cheated? Did the goldsmith alloy the gold with silver? After listening to Archimedes, you decide.

> *"Mmm," muttered Archimedes, "here's a crown that I cannot destroy, and here is an equal mass of gold. I'll put the crown into the overflow bucket. Now I'll place the water that is displaced by the crown on the left-hand pan of my equal arm balance. Good! I didn't spill any. Now the gold goes into the overflow bucket. If I place this displaced water on the right pan . . . by the sword of Damocles — the water displaced by the crown weighs more!"*

Why did the crown displace more water? Was the crown made of pure gold? Should the goldsmith flee?

What Archimedes Actually Did (So the Story Goes)

Archimedes placed his balance in a container of water so that it was totally submerged. The pans were balanced. Then he placed the crown on one pan and an equal mass of gold on the other pan. The pans no longer balanced — the pan containing the mass of pure gold was lower. Can you explain why?

More About Buoyant Force

Archimedes did not have spring scales to measure the buoyant force of water. We do, however. In the illustration, Angelo is using a spring scale to determine the buoyant force on a variety of objects. To record the data, he uses a downward-pointing arrow to indicate the weight of the object in air and in water, and an upward-pointing arrow to represent the buoyant force of water on the object. These arrows are called **force vectors**. The length of a vector indicates the size of the force it represents.

This is Angelo's record for one object:

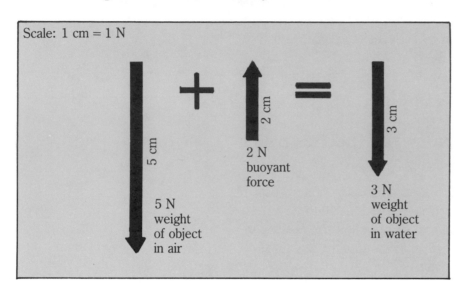

Scale: 1 cm = 1 N

5 cm — 5 N weight of object in air

2 cm — 2 N buoyant force

3 cm — 3 N weight of object in water

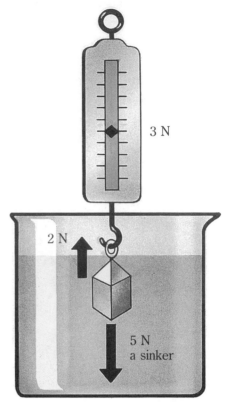

3 N

2 N

5 N a sinker

Your Turn

1. In Exploration 6, you determined the weight of several objects in air and in water. Record your findings, as Angelo did, by using arrows to represent the different forces involved and their sizes. Use both floaters and sinkers.

2. Angelo was interrupted, so he did not draw the arrows for part of his experiment. Copy what he did finish into your notebook, then complete it for him. Also indicate whether each object is a sinker or a floater, and explain why.

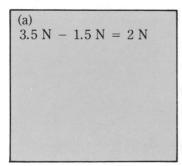

(a)
3.5 N − 1.5 N = 2 N

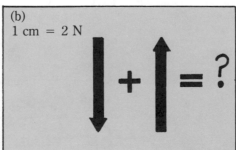

(b)
1 cm = 2 N

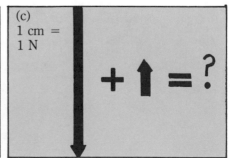

(c)
1 cm = 1 N

How a Submarine Works

The drawing shows a model submarine. Follow the instructions to make it, then determine why it goes up and down.

You Will Need

- eyedropper
- plastic soft drink bottle with cap

What To Do

Add enough water to the eyedropper so it just floats in a container of water. Transfer the eyedropper to a soft drink bottle full of water. Place the cap on the bottle.

Squeeze the sides of the bottle. Can you control the position of the submarine?

Questions

1. What is happening to make the dropper float? sink?
2. What is the ballast in the model submarine?
3. Use force vectors to describe the forces acting on the dropper to make it float or sink.
4. Write an explanation of how a real submarine works using terms such as "buoyant force" and "ballast".

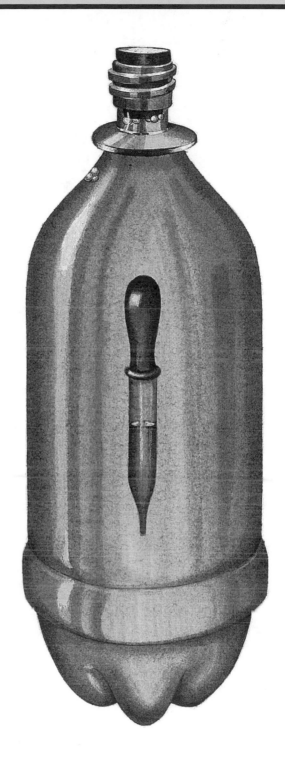

The Buoyancy of Air

Air has buoyancy too. However, it is less than that of water. But it clearly exists — the upward force is used by balloonists in their sport.

Can you apply Archimedes' Principle to air and explain why a large balloon can float in air?

Try this: Read the four statements that described Archimedes' Principle, found on page 208. Wherever water is mentioned, substitute air instead. Are you now able to give a better explanation of why hot air balloons float in air?

If a balloon is floating and not rising higher, which of the three sets of vectors is correct? Why? Label each arrow in the three diagrams.

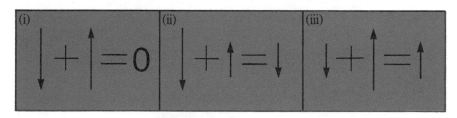

If a balloon is rising, which of the three sets of vectors is correct? Why?

A Last Bit of Research — How Are Sunken Ships Refloated?

With a friend, come up with an idea that you think will work. Be ready to explain why it will work. You may have read about the rediscovery of the *Titanic* off the coast of Newfoundland. There are plans to raise this famous ship. How might it be done?

Footnote — A News Report

Sunday, August 21, 1983

The drilling rig *Ocean Ranger* was floated today, with its pontoons pointing upward. The salvage company will haul it farther out to sea, where it will be dynamited and sunk in a thousand metres of water.

Density and Buoyancy

An Early Recipe for Pickled Vegetables. "Make a salt solution by adding salt to water until a potato floats. Add chopped vegetables to the brine solution."

• Why does a potato sink in ordinary water but float in a salt solution?

• Why does an ice cube float in water but sink in alcohol?

Can you explain the behaviour of the ice cube using the idea of buoyant force? Which fluid exerts a greater buoyant force against the ice cube, alcohol or water?

    Examine the diagram of the three candles in liquids A, B, and C. Now answer these questions.

A

B

C

1. In which container is the candle experiencing the least buoyant force?

2. In two containers the buoyant force experienced by the candle is the same. Which containers are these? Why is the buoyant force the same in the two containers?

3. Floaters displace an amount of fluid equal to the weight of the floater. In which container does the candle displace an amount of water less than the weight of the candle?

4. If a pin was used to submerge each candle in water, salt water, and alcohol, which liquid would now exert the largest buoyant force on the candle?

    In the final question, the volume of liquid displaced by the submerged candle was the same for each liquid. However, the mass, and therefore the weight, of liquid displaced was different. Can you prove that this is so?

Densities of Different Fluids

In this Exploration you will investigate one property of matter, that equal volumes often have different masses. This property is called density.

Part 1
Comparing Masses of Equal Volumes

You Will Need

- balance
- pill container
- alcohol
- water
- salt water

What To Do

Determine the mass of an equal volume of each liquid. This can be done by placing a mark on the pill container and filling the pill container to this mark with each liquid. Alternatively, you can fill the pill container to the top with each liquid.

Now answer these questions.

1. If density determines the mass of equal volumes of different kinds of matter, which one of the liquids investigated has the greatest density? the smallest density?

2. The liquids A, B, and C in the candle study were alcohol, salt water, and water. Which one was alcohol? water? salt water?

3. In Exploration 1 you added an egg and an ice cube to water, salt water, and alcohol. Cathy drew the following conclusions.

   "An ice cube sinks in alcohol but floats in water and salt water. Water and salt water must have densities greater than that of alcohol."

   "An egg sinks in water and alcohol but floats in salt water. Salt water must have a density greater than that of water."

   "I think that the density of an object that floats is less than that of the liquid it is floating in."

   (a) Did your findings in this Exploration support Cathy's conclusions?

   (b) Have you proved that Cathy's last statement is true? Is the egg less dense than salt water? Does the ice cube have a greater density than the alcohol it sank in? How could you find out?

5. If Cathy is right in concluding that floaters are less dense than the liquids that they float in, which of the liquids used in this Exploration will float on which other liquids? Make your prediction and then go on to Part 2 to check your prediction.

Part 2
Density and Floating

You Will Need

- 3 test tubes
- liquids used in Part 1
- 2 colours of food colouring
- clear straws

What To Do

Fill three test tubes halfway with each liquid. Add several drops of one food colouring to one test tube (A), and the second colour to the other tube (B.) Then try to form three separate layers of the liquids inside a clear plastic straw or glass tube, as shown in the drawings.

Step 1

Immerse the straw about 1 cm deep into test tube A allowing liquid A to enter the straw. Now cover the top of the straw securely with your finger.

Step 2

Transfer the straw with liquid A to test tube B, and lower it to a depth of 2 cm or more.

Step 3

Lift your finger off the top of the straw to let liquid B enter. Cover the top of the straw again. Remove the straw from test tube B. Repeat with liquid C.

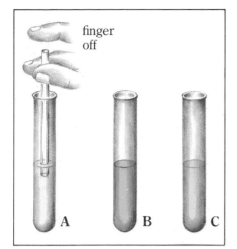

finger off

A   B   C

Step 1

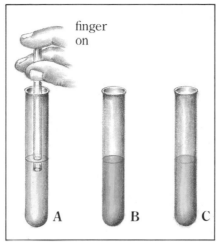

finger on

A   B   C

Questions

1. Compare the densities of liquids to their ability to float or sink in each other.

2. Now put the three liquids, an ice cube, and an egg in order of density from the smallest to the largest, using your observations of which float and which sink in each other.

3. How can a candle be used to compare the densities of different liquids?

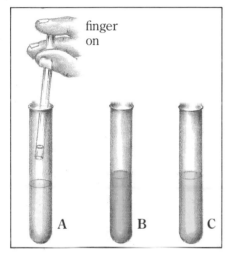

finger on

A   B   C

Step 2

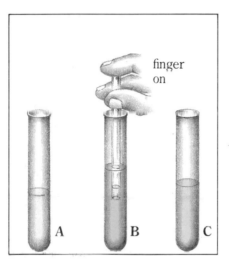

finger on

A   B   C

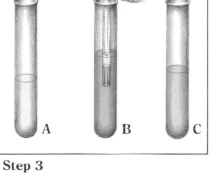

finger off

A   B   C

Step 3

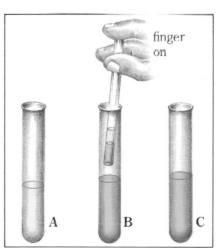

finger on

A   B   C

Making a Straw Hydrometer

Commercial instruments that are used to measure the densities of different fluids are called hydrometers. A candle can be used also as a hydrometer. In this Exploration you will make a better hydrometer from a drinking straw.

You Will Need

• plastic straw
• modelling clay
• test tube
• sand
• water
• salt
• alcohol

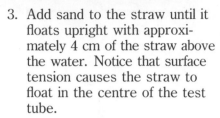

What To Do

1. First, cut the straw to a length of 10 cm. Plug one end of it with a piece of modelling clay.

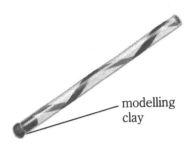

modelling clay

2. Fill a test tube with water until it bulges above the rim. This is due to surface tension.

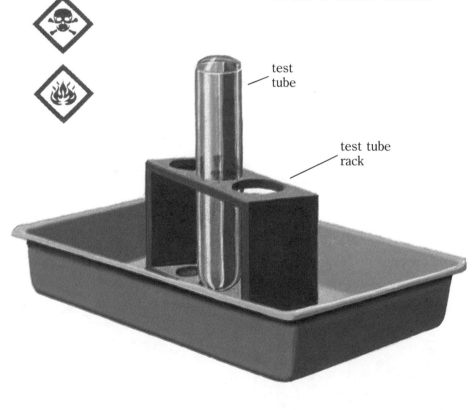

test tube

test tube rack

3. Add sand to the straw until it floats upright with approximately 4 cm of the straw above the water. Notice that surface tension causes the straw to float in the centre of the test tube.

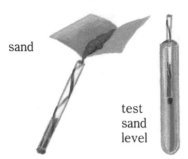

sand

test sand level

4. Plug the open end of the straw with clay. Your hydrometer is now ready for use.

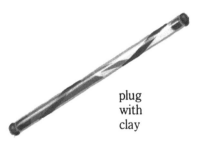

plug with clay

5. Place the hydrometer in liquids of different densities. Try salt water, alcohol, and water. Wipe off the hydrometer between uses.

Questions

1. How does the hydrometer behave when placed in a liquid less dense than water? Can the device be used to put liquids in order according to their densities? Explain.

2. How can you calibrate your straw hydrometer to give a numerical value for the densities of liquids?

3. Use the word "density" in explaining how hydrometers work.

More About Hydrometers — A Bit of Research

The photographs show some commercial hydrometers. Try to determine the purpose for each and explain how it works. Can you discover other kinds of commercial hydrometers and how they work?

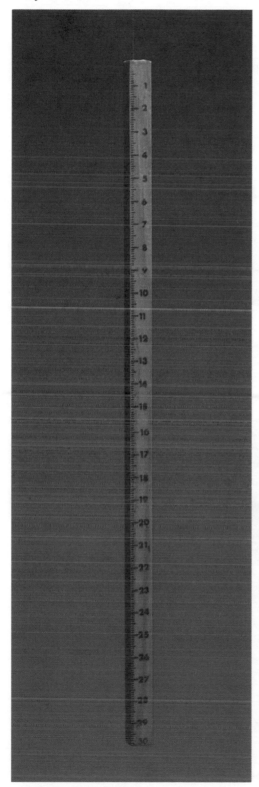

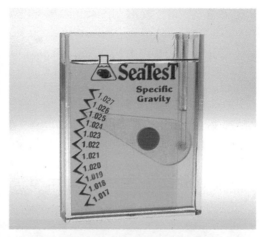

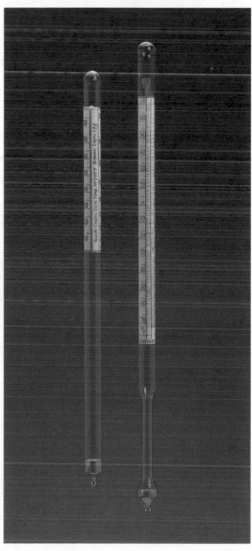

Pressure

Two Frontiers

Human beings live on a planet that has two fluids in great quantity — water and air. Have you ever noticed that when we refer to these fluids we often speak about their pressures? "The air pressure today is 102 kilopascals" or "The water pressure is a bit low". We know that to explore ocean bottoms, we use technologies that protect us against the great water pressure. To explore space, different technologies allow astronauts to carry normal atmosphere and pressure with them.

But what is pressure? How would you explain the concept of pressure to someone else? How would you go about measuring it? How important is fluid pressure in our technological society? What do we use it for? These questions will be explored in the following sections.

Three Problems for Your Consideration

It is not only fluids that exert pressure. The following are three non-fluid examples. Discuss each one with a classmate before continuing with the lesson.

"There is nothing like a bed of nails!"

Why can a person lie on a bed of nails without suffering harm, while stepping on a single nail causes a serious wound?

"If you knew what I know — you wouldn't be in there."

Why is it possible for a person to crawl across thin ice, while walking across is foolhardy?

"That hurts!"

When the woman in front of me stepped back suddenly, one of her feet landed squarely on my left toe. My friend said I was lucky the woman was not wearing high heels! Was my friend right? Why?

Excerpt from Susan's Science Log

"The secret to not breaking through the ice is to spread your weight over a large area. When I stand up, my whole weight is on the area directly beneath my feet. When I lie down, however, my weight is spread over a much larger area. So, when I lie down, the pressure on the ice is less than when I stand."

Can you use Susan's reasoning to explain the other two problems? From Susan's explanation, what do you think "pressure" is? The following section will help you to form a definition.

Demonstrating Pressure

Ms. Bellotti asked Class 9B to do a demonstration to show that they understood the meaning of pressure. The class was divided into groups of four for this task. What could they do? They thought of a number of excellent ideas. Form your own groups, then discuss each idea presented by Ms. Bellotti's class. You may wish to try their ideas in class. Then create your own pressure demonstration. Share your group's idea with the class.

Plan 1
John's Group

You Will Need

- block of clay 1 cm thick
- wooden dowels of different diameters
- brick

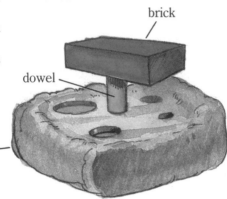

brick

dowel

clay

What To Do

"We observed how far the dowel penetrated the clay."

"We placed a piece of dowel on the clay block, then placed the brick on top."

"We repeated this process with the other pieces of dowel."

What was John's group trying to demonstrate? What is your conclusion to their experiment?

Plan 2
Helen's Group

You Will Need

- centicube or die
- books

What To Do

"I put my hand on my desk. Then we placed the centicube on the back of my hand. It didn't hurt at all. Then we placed a book on the centicube; it hurt a little. Two books on top of the centicube hurt a bit more. We decided that we had invented a pressure gauge."

How did their pressure gauge work?

Plan 3:
Corey's Group

You Will Need

- 100 g of sand
- newspaper

What To Do

"We weighed 1 N (100 g) of sand and spread the sand evenly over a newspaper on the floor. Then we folded the newspaper in half, and spread the sand evenly over this new area."

1 N of sand   1 N of sand

Discussion

1. Have you concluded from Exploration 10 that pressure can be changed in either of two ways?

   • by changing the size of the force applied to an area

   • by changing the size of the area receiving the force

   Use these two facts to suggest solutions for the situations described below. Include a statement explaining why each solution will work.

   Situation

   (a) You are standing. You want to double the pressure you exert against the floor.

   (b) You are making a fence by driving fence posts into the ground. What can you do to increase the pressure of each post against the ground, so that it goes in as far as possible? Suggest two solutions.

   (c) You have a can of soup, but no can opener. What could you use to open the can? Use the word "pressure" in your solution.

   (d) Suggest a pressure situation of your own. Have a classmate suggest a solution for your pressure situation.

2. The uses of many common objects are based on the concept of pressure. For each of the following, discuss how pressure is important for its use.

   Thumb tacks   Skis   Ice skates

3. How can different pressures be compared? One way is to give a numerical value to pressure.

   Suppose that you spread 1 N of sand over a piece of paper that measures 1 m × 1 m. Its area is therefore 1 m². This is similar to the activity Corey's group performed in Exploration 10. The pressure of the sand on the paper is 1 newton per square metre.

   $$1 \text{ N of sand}/1 \text{ m}^2 \text{ of area}$$

   Spread the same amount of sand over exactly half the paper. This doubles the pressure exerted by the sand on this smaller area.

   $$\text{Now the pressure is } \frac{1 \text{ N}}{0.5 \text{ m}^2} = \frac{2 \text{ N}}{1 \text{ m}^2}$$

   Use this idea to express the pressure illustrated in the following examples. In each case, give the pressure as the number of newtons per square metre (N/m²).

What did Corey's group want to demonstrate with this experiment? What is your conclusion for it?

Plan 4
Antonio's Group

"*For this demonstration we found pictures of different animals and researched their habitats.*"

"*We looked at the feet of animals that were adapted to walking on different surfaces, such as snow and hard ground.*"

What do you think Antonio's group discovered about pressure?

(a) 1 N of sand is spread over an area of 0.25 m².

(b) A 400 N (40 kg) person stands on snowshoes that have a total area of 1 m².

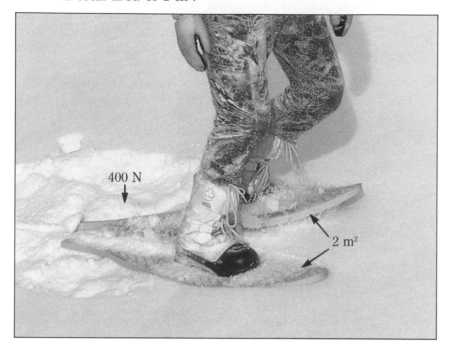

(c) A force of 5 N is applied to a thumb tack whose point has an area of 0.000 000 01 m². (No wonder a thumb tack can be pushed into wood so easily!)

(d) A 500 N (50 kg) woman stands on both feet. The total area of the woman's feet is 0.03 m².

(e) The woman in (d) stands on one foot.

(f) The same woman, now wearing high heels whose total area is 0.0001 m², is standing on your foot with her full weight.

4. Review the plan John's group made in Exploration 10. The brick weighed 20 N. First, estimate the area of the ends of each piece of dowel they used. Then calculate the pressure that each piece of dowel exerted against the clay. Do these numbers agree with the conclusion you wrote for their demonstration?

Estimate the areas of the ends of each of John's dowels. Express your answers in cm².

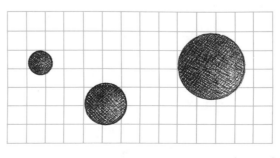

5. Blaise Pascal, born in France in 1623, was a child genius. He became a writer, religious philosopher, mathematician, inventor, and scientist. Among other things, Pascal invented a calculating machine, syringe, barometer (for measuring the pressure exerted by the atmosphere), and hydraulic press. In honour of his contribution to science, Pascal had a unit of pressure named after him.

Blaise Pascal

A **pascal** is defined as one newton of weight on an area of one square metre. The metric symbol for a pascal is "Pa."

$$\frac{1\ N}{m^2} = 1\ Pa$$

One thousand pascals are called a **kilopascal** (kPa).

Return to Question 3, and state each answer in "Pa" instead of "N/m²."

A Pressure Puzzle

This is a story of three people — Peter, Paul, and Mary. One day they decided to go snowshoeing. Mary sank deeper in the snow than Paul. Can you infer that Mary must weigh more than Paul? Explain.

Mary and Peter sank to the same depth in the snow. Could each of the following inferences be true?

• Mary weighs the same as Peter.

• Peter weighs more than Mary, but he wore larger snowshoes.

• Peter weighs less than Mary, but he wore smaller snowshoes.

The table below lists weight and snowshoe size for Peter, Paul, and Mary. Deduce which of the three is Person A, *etc*. (Do you have enough information to do so?)

	Weight	Snowshoe Size (Area)
Person A	500 N	1 m²
Person B	300 N	0.5 m²
Person C	600 N	1 m²

Fluid Systems and Pressure

John's System

Do you remember John and his design problem — to devise a way to start a coffee maker from the comfort of his bedroom? Did your design involve fluids? John's did. Examine the diagram of his system. How does it work?

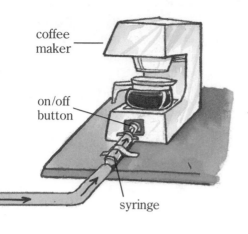

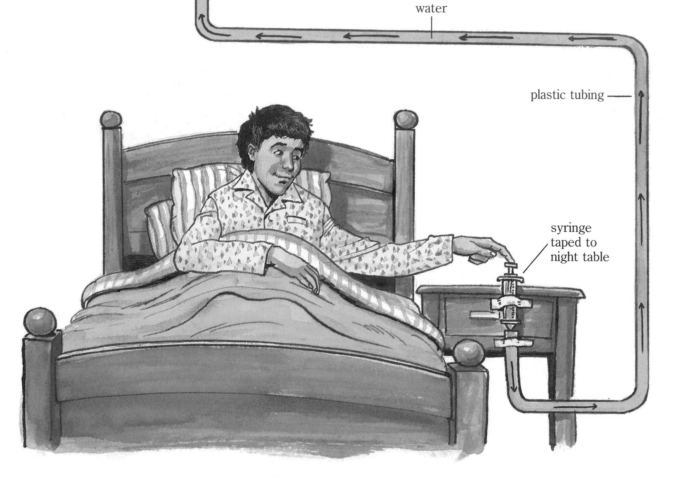

Now consider these questions.

1. What are the parts of this system? What is the function of each part?

2. Why does the system work? Try to use the idea of pressure in your explanation.

3. Could he have used air instead of water in the piping? Are there advantages to using water?

4. Examine the diagram of a brake system that uses fluid pressure.
   (a) How is it similar to John's design?
   (b) Where is the force first applied?
   (c) To where is the force transmitted?
   (d) How do the front brakes differ from the brakes on the rear wheels?
   (e) How would you use the idea of pressure in your explanation of how such brakes work?

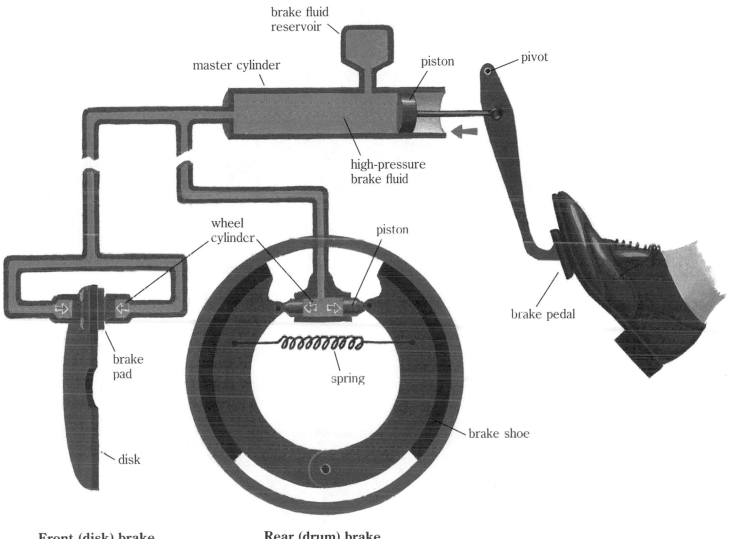

Front (disk) brake
(front wheels)

Rear (drum) brake
(rear wheels)

5. Suggest examples from your experience which use "fluid power"—either liquids or gases. After brainstorming a number of suggestions, perform the following Exploration. Perhaps it will suggest more examples of "fluid power".

Fluids at Work

Can you use fluids to do work? Can you lift a classmate with little effort? Archimedes reportedly said, "Give me a place to stand and a lever long enough, and I will lift the world." Could Archimedes have made a similar statement about fluid power?

Part 1
Finger Power

You Will Need

• large syringe or bicycle pump

What To Do

Have a friend push on the plunger of the syringe or pump while you hold the other end with your finger. Can you counteract with your finger the force exerted by your friend's push? How would you explain this?

Part 2
Putting Fluids To Work

You Will Need

• hot-water bottle
• one-hole stopper fitted with a short piece of plastic tubing
• 3 m of rubber tubing

What To Do

1. Assemble the materials as shown in the diagram. Be sure that the stopper is inserted into the hot-water bottle very tightly.

2. Invite a member of your class to stand on the hot-water bottle. While standing on a chair, start pouring water through the funnel and into the bottle.

3. What happens? How can you explain your observations?

4. Where else have you seen fluids used to raise or move objects?

Part 3
Equal Pressures

Study the following system, which shows a 1 N force counteracting a 10 N force. Answer the questions which follow.

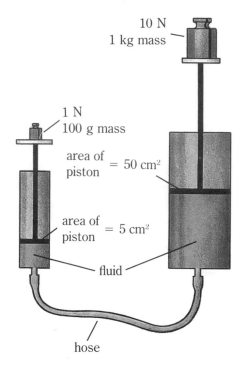

1. What are the parts of this system and what do they do?

2. Compare the forces exerted on each piston.

3. The pressure exerted on the fluid by the smaller piston can be calculated in the following way.

    P = force/area
    P = 1 N/5 cm²
    = 0.2 N/cm²

(a) Calculate the pressure exerted by the larger piston on the fluid. How does it compare with the pressure exerted by the smaller piston?

(b) What would happen to the larger piston if a 200 g mass was substituted for the 100 g mass on the smaller piston?

funnel

rubber tubing   one-hole stopper   plastic tubing   hot-water bottle

Pascal's Discovery

4. Find evidence from your study of this system that the following statements are true.
   - Pressure is transmitted throughout the liquid.
   - The pressure is the same in every direction.
   - Every part of the container experiences a force of the same size.

5. Describe how this picture experiment helps explain observations made in Parts 1 and 2.

6. If you can obtain two syringes of different sizes, set this situation up as a demonstration.

❑

If you have found evidence to support the statements found in Question 4 in Part 3 of Exploration 11, then you have rediscovered what Blaise Pascal discovered more than 300 years ago. He found that the pressure exerted on a fluid in a closed system is the same in every direction and that every part of the container experiences the same forces. This statement has become known as **Pascal's Law.**

Is Pascal's Law true for the system you examined in Part 3 of Exploration 11? What is the force being exerted on each square centimetre of that system?

Pascal's Law is applied in many systems that use fluids to transmit forces. Hydraulic systems use liquids, usually oil, to transmit forces. Pneumatic systems use gases, usually air, instead of liquids. Is there an advantage to using one fluid over another for a particular application? Is a bicycle pump an example of a hydraulic system or a pneumatic system?

Hydraulic systems increase the maneuverability of machines like this one.

Pascal's Law is applied to many hydraulic and pneumatic systems to help us do work. The type of hydraulic lift used in service stations is one example. Examine the diagram of a lift and try to explain to someone else why it can easily raise the great weight of a car for inspection. Did you use Pascal's Law in your explanation?

Now use the diagram to follow this sequence of events.

- Air is pumped into the master cylinder, which increases the pressure of the oil. (Which syringe in Part 3 of Exploration 11 does the master cylinder correspond to?)

- The high-pressure oil is forced into the base of the slave cylinder, where it forces up the piston carrying the car. (Which is greater, the pressure of the oil on the piston, or the pressure of the car and piston on the oil?)

- When the car has been raised to the desired height, the oil valve is closed, keeping the piston stationary and extended. (How does the pressure throughout the system compare now?)

A hydraulic lift

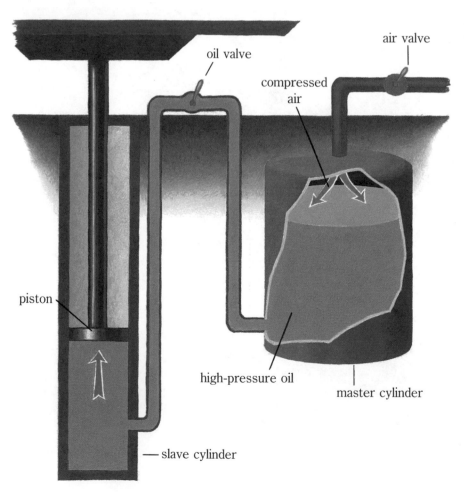

How Things Work

The following diagrams illustrate a few applications of how fluids are used in hydraulic and pneumatic systems. For each one, write a description of how it works. In your description, answer the following questions:

- What kind of fluid is used?
- Where is pressure applied to the fluid?
- What passageways do the fluids travel through?
- What work is the fluid doing?

Bicycle Pump

The bicycle pump is one of the more familiar fluid systems. Compare the operation of this pump with a syringe. How are they similar? How are they different?

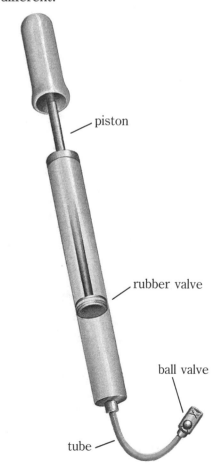

Dentist's Drill

This high-speed drill, which is used to cut into your teeth, is a descendant of the first windmill. Do you see why? How is its operation different from that of a windmill?

Shock Absorber

Shock absorbers are fixed between the wheel axle and the body of a car. They slow down the movement of the springs to prevent the car and its occupants from bouncing up and down excessively.

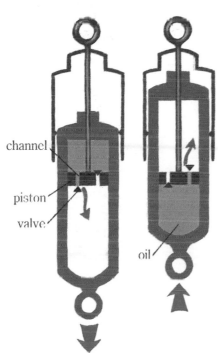

The Jackhammer

The next time you hear the ear-blasting roar produced by a jackhammer, you will realize that you are hearing fluids at work.

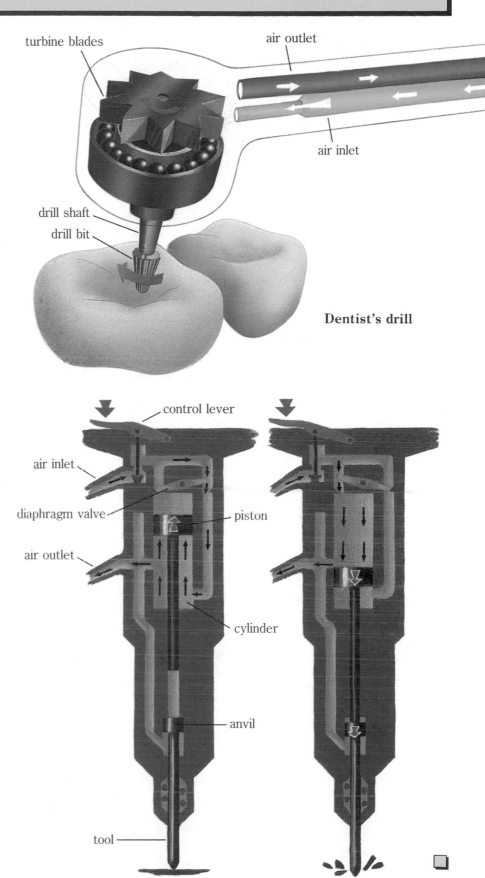

Dentist's drill

Moving Fluids

Early Technologies

How do we move water from where we find it to where we need it? Since people began farming and living in communities, they have been moving water to where it was needed. Irrigation was carried out with the assistance of gravity. This meant that the irrigation channels had to be lower than the water source, which was usually a river. How is this problem overcome today?

One early device for lifting water from a lower source was the shaduf. The shaduf is a long pole, with a counterweight at one end and a water bucket at the other. This technology is still used in some parts of the world. On what scientific principle is this invention based?

Still another early invention was the saqiya, which consists of a large wheel with buckets arranged around its periphery. Again, versions of this technology can still be found today.

Shaduf

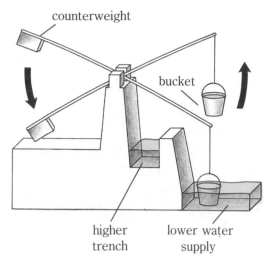

Saqiya

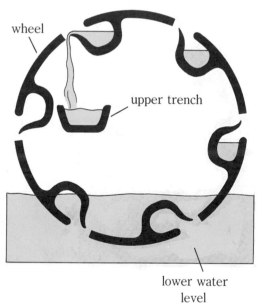

A saqiya in use today

Archimedes is thought to have invented the following device for irrigation. It is called **Archimedes' screw** and can be operated by a person or by an animal.

How does it work?

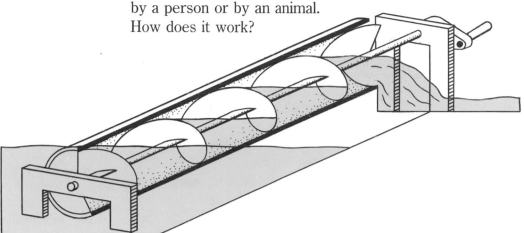

The Romans were masters at moving water. Some of the aqueducts that they built still stand today.

Pont du Gard, a Roman aqueduct in Nimes, France. This 2000-year-old aqueduct was used to carry spring water over a distance of 35 km to the town of Nimes.

Today, fluids are moved on a massive scale. Large tracts of land are irrigated with the help of pumps. Water diversion projects have changed the course of rivers so that water flows in new directions. Pipelines carry vast amounts of oil and natural gas to refineries and to consumers. Some of the examples mentioned here rely on gravity to move the fluid. For others, the technology of pumps and valves keeps the flow going.

Think of the fluids that are important to you. Where does the water in your home come from? How does it get from the source into your home? What is the source of the water pressure you experience when you turn on a tap? What science and technology is involved in moving fluids — both liquids and gases?

Designing a Water Tower

Throughout western Canada the water tower is a familiar sight against the skyline. Water is pumped into the tower and then distributed to the users. In choosing a design for a tower to serve a population of 10 000 people, what characteristics would be regarded as important?

- Would the storage capacity be a consideration?
- How about pressure and the rates of flow?

- Is the shape of the tower a factor?

The town of River Bend is inviting submissions for the design of a water tower. They have four criteria for determining the best design:

1. cost
2. appearance
3. volume of flow to meet needs of the community
4. maximum water pressure in the homes

Each proposal must be accompanied by a model and a written submission describing the results of tests on criteria 3 and 4. The River Bend Town Council will review the submissions at their next meeting and make a decision.

Trouble Shooting!

Jennifer's class decided to submit their ideas for a new water tower. Jennifer asked: "How can I measure the water pressure at the bottom of my tower? Does the pressure depend on the depth of water or the volume of water?"

Three suggestions were made by Jennifer's classmates.

Terri's Idea

"I will use different sizes of cans to investigate ways of obtaining the greatest pressure. I'll punch a hole near the bottom to represent the outlet of the tower. For each can I will measure the distance the water initially squirts out when the can is filled to different heights. If I allow the water to squirt into a large container such as a stream table, I can avoid making a mess. Part of my presentation will be graphs of the depth of the water and the distances the water squirted."

Depth of Water	Distance Water Squirted

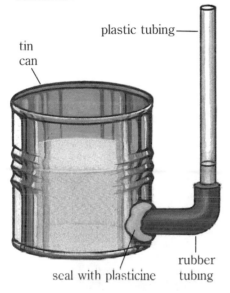

plastic tubing

tin can

rubber tubing

seal with plasticine

Share a problem that you encountered, as well as your solution, with classmates who are submitting design proposals for a water tower.

The Atmosphere Exerts Pressure, Too

Hilda's idea for measuring the pressure at the bottom of her tower is called a **manometer**. She concluded that the pressure at the bottom of the container depends on the depth of the liquid in the container. In fact, you could design a tower that actually holds more water than another but would deliver less pressure in the homes being served. What would such a design look like?

The atmosphere is also a fluid. Does the atmosphere behave like water? Does it exert a pressure? If so, does the pressure exerted by the atmosphere decrease with the depth of the atmosphere? Suggest an observation or experience that would imply that the atmosphere exerts a pressure and that this pressure decreases with depth.

Here are two suggestions. You may like to try the first one for yourself.

Lynn's experience: "If I fill a glass completely with water and place a piece of paper over its mouth, I can turn the glass over and the water will not fall out. I think it is the pressure of the atmosphere pushing against the paper that is holding the water in the glass."

Colin: "My uncle took me up in a small plane and I carried a balloon onto the plane. I was surprised to notice that the balloon became slightly bigger and harder as we climbed. I suppose that, higher up, the pressure of the atmosphere against the balloon is less than it was on the ground. This allowed the balloon to expand."

Barometers

Instruments that measure atmospheric pressure and changes in atmospheric pressure are called **barometers**. Colin's balloon was acting as a barometer since it indicated there is less pressure at high elevations than at lower ones.

The first barometer was invented by an Italian physicist and mathematician, Evangelista Torricelli (1608–1647). He did not do this in order to measure the pressure of the atmosphere, for this idea was not around at that time. He wanted to test the truth of a statement made by Aristotle, that "nature abhors a vacuum," that is, that matter will always move to fill an empty space, or vacuum.

Why was it that suction (vacuum) pumps used by miners to prevent flooding in mines at that time could not lift water any more than 10 m? Was this height a limit imposed by nature? Was this limit the same for all liquids?

Torricelli wondered what would happen if a liquid of greater density such as mercury was used instead of water. Mercury has a density 13.6 times larger than that of water. In 1644, he filled a 123 cm long tube with mercury and sealed it at one end. After he inverted the other end in a pool of mercury, some of the mercury drained out, leaving a vacuum in the space that remained.

Torricelli thought that the vacuum at the top of the tube sucked or pulled the liquid up into the tube and that this vacuum could only support a column of mercury about 76 cm high. Now we know that it is the atmospheric pressure on the surface of the pool of mercury that supports the column of mercury in the tube. If the atmospheric pressure changes, then so does the height of mercury in the tube supported by the atmosphere. Torricelli unintentionally devised the first instrument, the barometer, for measuring atmospheric pressure.

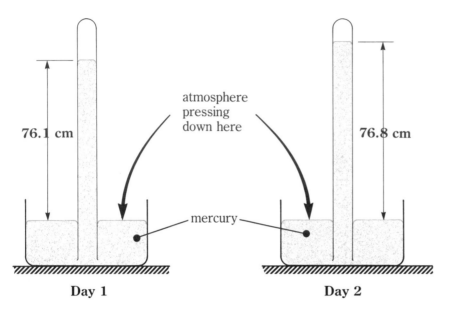

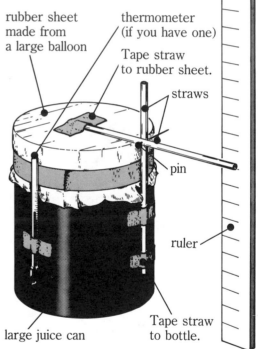

Water could be used in the barometer instead of mercury but you would need a column at least 10 m long! Why?

In the mid-1600s, the French scientist Blaise Pascal built mercury barometers to compare the atmospheric pressures in Paris and at the top of the Puy-de-Dome mountain. He, indeed, found that the pressure decreases with the depth of the atmosphere. Today, the mercury barometer is still the most sensitive instrument for measuring atmospheric pressure.

A second type of barometer, the **aneroid barometer**, does not use mercury. It contains hollow disks with thin, flexible sides. Inside these disks is a partial vacuum. The disks are attached to levers and a dial which records the pressure in kilopascals (kPa). If the atmospheric pressure increases, the sides of the disks move inward. This very small movement is amplified by the levers and is registered on the dial as a higher pressure. Although aneroid barometers are convenient to use, they are not as precise as mercury barometers.

Making Your Own Barometer: A Do-at-Home Project

You Will Need

- drinking straws
- large can
- balloon
- pin
- masking tape
- ruler
- thermometer

What To Do

Set up your apparatus as shown. Blow up the balloon a few hours ahead of time, so the rubber is well stretched. Cut out a piece of the stretched balloon and tape it firmly to the mouth of the can, making the opening airtight.

Changes in air pressure can be detected by observing the position of the straw pointer along the ruler. When the atmospheric pressure gets higher, will the reading on the ruler be higher or lower?

Place the barometer where the temperature does not vary. Why is it important to do so when using this barometer?

Using Your Barometer

In a weather table similar to the one shown below, record the daily changes in atmospheric pressure over a two-week period. You should also record the weather on each day.

Weather Table

	Change in Pressure	**Weather Conditions**
Day 1	rising	clear skies
Day 2	falling	clouding over
Day 3		
Day 4		
. . .		

After two weeks, bring your barometer and data to class. Working in groups of five, compare the information you gathered. Can you explain any differences that might occur in your data?

Finally, consider this important question. Is there any correlation (connection) between pressure changes and the weather conditions on each day?

Lifting Water

You have read about several early devices that raise water from one level to another. Today the most common water-raising device is the pump. The Romans are credited with the discovery of the first pump. One Roman pump was discovered in Bolsena, Italy, and is therefore known as the Bolsena Pump. It consists of a cylinder with a plunger in it, much like a very large syringe, and has two valves, one at either end of the cylinder.

Today, pumps are very much a part of everyday life. Your home probably contains at least three pumps. What might they be? What are pumps used for in your community? What is the "science" of pumps?

Here is a challenge. Use an empty ice-cream container to represent a water tower and a second water-filled container to represent a water source at a lower elevation. Devise a method to transfer water from the source to the tower. Be prepared to demonstrate your design.

Compare designs. Whose design is the most efficient? the most creative? the most unusual? What problems did you encounter in developing your design? How should the designs be evaluated?

Here are the rules.

1. The water cannot be carried in containers held by human hands.

2. The water must be elevated a distance of 0.5 m.

3. Commercial toy or model pumps cannot be used.

4. You can use such everyday things as syringes, balloons, plastic tubing, and plastic bottles.

Before starting on your design, you may wish to read about Elaine's model and how she overcame certain problems.

Elaine's Model Pump

Elaine is describing the model which she and her group made. "We used a large balloon, a plastic funnel, 0.5 m of rubber tubing, and an eyedropper. We knew that air pressure can be used to push a liquid up a tube so we looked for a way of creating a low-pressure area in a container above the liquid. We cut the end off a balloon and stretched the balloon over the top of a plastic funnel...."

Cut the neck off of the balloon. Save it for later.

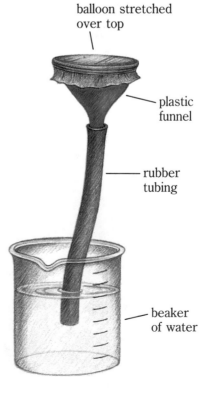

balloon stretched over top

plastic funnel

rubber tubing

beaker of water

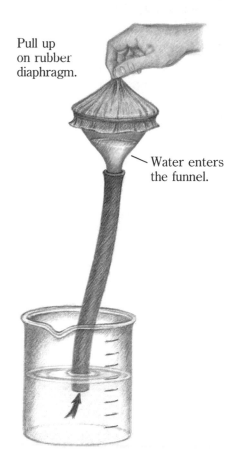

Pull up on rubber diaphragm.

Water enters the funnel.

"Pulling on the balloon caused water to be forced into the funnel. However, as soon as the balloon was released, the water returned to the beaker. We needed some way of keeping the water in the funnel. We tried to make a valve using a ball bearing—but the water leaked past it."

"Our solution was to make a valve from the end of an eyedropper. We cut a short section from the dropper, plugged the hole with plasticine and placed it in the funnel. Now, when we pull up on the rubber diaphragm, the water enters the funnel as before, but the eyedropper valve prevents it from returning. Since we had to ask someone else to cut the eyedropper, we are looking for another type of valve to use instead."

i)

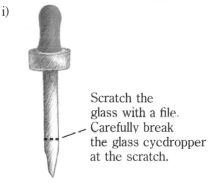

Scratch the glass with a file. Carefully break the glass eyedropper at the scratch.

ii)

eyedropper valve

iii)

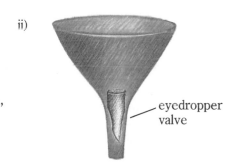

Make hole here.

"After making a hole in the side of the funnel, we had a place for the water to exit. But we noticed that when the hole was opened, air would come in, instead of the water coming up the tube and into the pump. We needed to find a way to stop air from coming in when the water was being drawn upward. So at first we used a finger as a valve, closing the hole when water was being drawn up and opening the hole to allow the water to exit the pump."

Questions

1. Explain the science behind Elaine's pump.

2. Elaine used the word "pump". What would be your definition of a pump? Is a siphon a pump? a saqiya?

3. Elaine would like to substitute something else for the glass valve in the funnel. Do you have any suggestions?

4. Elaine used her finger on the hole in the funnel as a valve.

She then thought of a better solution using the end of the balloon she cut off earlier. She noticed that she could blow air out through the end of the balloon, but she could not draw air in. The rubber would close, cutting off the air flow. Perhaps the end of the balloon would allow water to exit the pump and prevent air from entering.

Can you suggest another solution?

i) plastic eyedropper   balloon

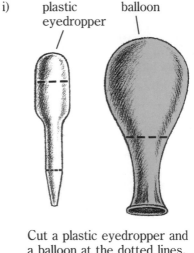

Cut a plastic eyedropper and a balloon at the dotted lines.

ii)

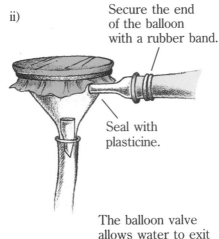

Secure the end of the balloon with a rubber band.

Seal with plasticine.

The balloon valve allows water to exit but prevents air from entering the funnel.

iii)

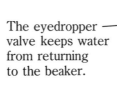

The eyedropper valve keeps water from returning to the beaker.

5. Elaine's pump was an example of a lift pump. It depends on differences in air pressure to push the liquid from a lower level to a higher one. However, lift pumps can only raise water a maximum distance of 10.3 m. A column of water in a pipe that is this high exerts the same pressure as the atmosphere.
   (a) Describe how air pressure is being used to lift water in Elaine's pump.
   (b) How would you improve Elaine's pump so that it could lift water a greater height?

Puzzling Pumps

If you could see inside of systems, it would be so much easier to determine how they work. In the following diagrams you are "seeing inside" various pumps. Determine how each one works. If you need help, perhaps there are others who can offer suggestions.

Start with the fluid inflow and then follow it to the outlet. Then retrace your steps to determine what creates the pressure that forces the fluid to flow.

Gear Pump

The oil that lubricates the engine of a car is forced through channels in the engine with this type of pump.

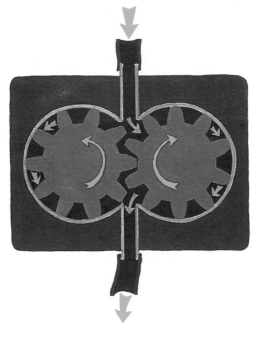

Centrifugal Pump

The cooling system of a car engine requires a steady flow of coolant. This pump raises the pressure of the coolant and forces it through the radiator and engine.

impeller

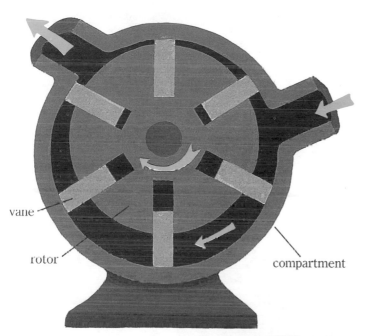

vane

rotor

compartment

Rotary Vane Pump

This type of pump is often used to deliver fuel at gas stations.

Peristaltic Pump

This pump has a special purpose — in devices such as heart-lung machines. This pump will not clog when it is used with a liquid which contains particles, such as blood. As well, other types of pumps would damage the blood cells.

flexible tube

Directing The Flow

One problem Elaine encountered was keeping the water in the funnel once it was raised to that position. Her solution was to use a valve made from an eyedropper. Later she constructed a valve from the end of a balloon. Is there another type of valve she could have used? In your design you may have encountered a similar problem.

What are valves? What are their purposes? How do they differ? You have already encountered several valves earlier in this unit. Try the following activities to learn more about this everyday technology for directing and controlling the flow of fluids.

1. The hydraulic and pneumatic systems investigated earlier also contain valves. Return to those diagrams and determine the location and purpose of each valve.

2. Your toilet tank contains two valves. Examine the float/valve system in your toilet tank at home. Where are the valves and what do they do? What is the purpose of the float?

3. Your water tap is a valve that controls the rate of flow of water. How does it operate?

4. Examine the valves that are part of a bicycle pump and of bicycle tires. What is the function of each? How do they work?

5. Musical instruments such as the coronet can play up to six different notes by using combinations of three pistons. Depressing the pistons opens up extra sections of tubing.

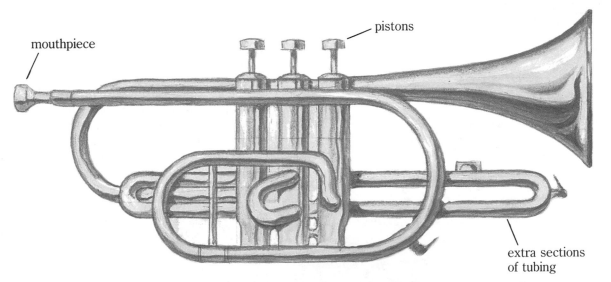

Valves play an important role in making music. Examine the following diagrams to answer these questions.

(a) What is the purpose of the spring?

(b) Where does the air go when the valve is closed?

(c) Where does the air go when the valve is open?

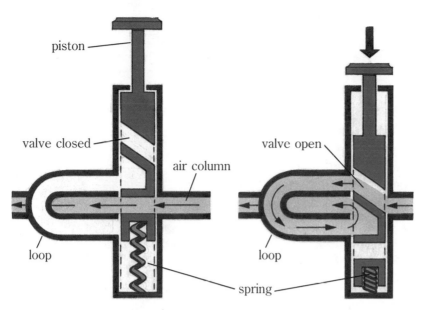

piston

valve closed

air column

valve open

loop

loop

spring

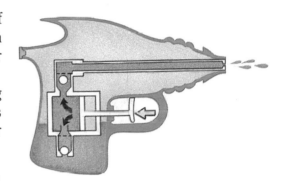

6. A valve is a device that opens or closes to control the flow of a fluid through a pipe, or in and out of a container. Valves often work one way to seal a container so that the fluid can enter but cannot escape.

How many valves can you find around the home? According to this definition, is the ball in a ballpoint pen a valve? Does an aerosol can contain a valve? Does a liquid soap dispenser contain a valve? Does a water pistol have a valve?

7. Here is Tara's design for a pump, which contains two valves. What is the purpose of each valve? Will this design work?

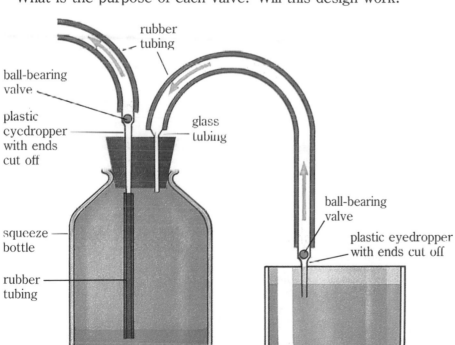

rubber tubing

ball-bearing valve

plastic eyedropper with ends cut off

glass tubing

ball-bearing valve

plastic eyedropper with ends cut off

squeeze bottle

rubber tubing

8. Finally, when you compare your inventions for raising water to the water tower, observe which ones contain a valve. How does each valve work?

The Most Important Pump of All — The Heart

"Except for his sharply focused blue eyes, Dr. Christopher Slade's face was covered by a green surgical mask as he leaned over the open chest cavity of the patient on the operating table.

An intense light was trained on the new heart Slade was suturing in place. It appeared to be a good, sound, healthy heart. The fit, while not perfect, was close enough after Slade had trimmed the circumference very slightly and adjusted the patient's aorta so it joined perfectly to the new heart. With extreme care he proceeded to complete his suturing."

from *A Gift of Life* by Henry Denker

The heart, once thought of as the seat of the emotions, is now known to be a very powerful pump. The heart never rests—beating at an average rate of about 75 beats per minute, or 4500 times an hour. How many times does the average heart beat in a day? in a year? in a lifetime? The blood flows through a network of tubes 16 000 km long called the *circulatory system*. The blood vessels bringing blood to the heart are called *veins*, while those carrying blood away from the heart are called *arteries*. The inside diameter of these vessels ranges from 0.25 mm to 25.0 mm.

Observe the diagram of the heart. How many separate chambers are there?

The heartbeat really consists of two pumping actions—the contracting of the upper chambers followed by the contracting of the lower chambers. These chambers are connected. How? Which of the two diagrams show the two atria (plural of atrium) contracted? expanded? Which of the two diagrams shows the two ventricles contracted? expanded?

Now locate the valves in the heart. There are four of them. One is identified. It is open and is between the right atrium and right ventricle. Locate the other three valves.

Valves play an important role in the function of the heart. They are made of tissue that lets blood flow in one direction only. Follow the flow in the diagram. When is each valve open and when is it closed?

In some people the heart valve may become defective. Blood may leak through the valve causing the heart to make a different sound, called a "heart murmur". Open heart surgery to replace defective valves with artificial ones is a fairly common operation.

The heart: the arrows show the direction of blood flow.

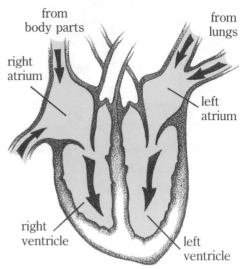

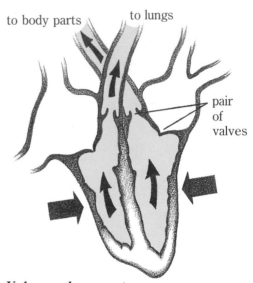

Valve replacement

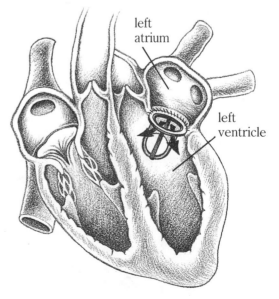

Ball-type artificial valve

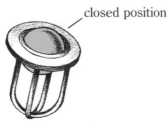

Blood Pressure

What is your blood pressure? 110/65? Good, that sounds normal! What do these numbers mean? They have something to do with pressure. Blood is similar to any other fluid that is acted on by a pump — it exerts a pressure.

In 1733 Stephen Hale performed the following experiment. He cut and tied off one end of a major artery of a horse. He tied the other end to a glass tube. The blood rose to a height of 251.5 cm in the tube. Through this experiment he proved that a pressure is exerted on blood within the body — or that there is such a thing as blood pressure.

Fortunately, you need not go through this process when having your blood pressure determined. An instrument called a sphygmomanometer is used. A cuff is wrapped around your arm. Two rubber tubes extend from this cuff. One tube is attached to a rubber bulb which inflates the cuff. The other is attached to a pressure gauge. The examiner places a stethoscope against the artery at the bend of the elbow and inflates the cuff using the bulb. Eventually the pressure of the cuff against the artery cuts off the blood flow and the pulse is no longer heard. The pressure at which this happens is read from the pressure gauge.

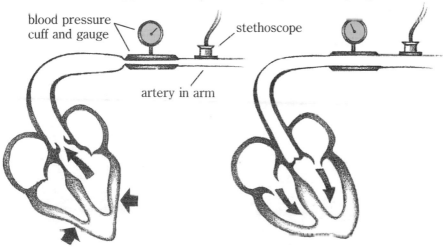

Heart during contraction (systole)   **Relaxed heart (diastole)**

The normal range for this reading, which is called the *systolic pressure*, is sufficient to support a column of mercury 120 to 150 mm high.

The examiner slowly releases the pressure in the cuff until the pulse cannot be heard. The reading taken at this point is called the *diastolic* pressure and usually has a range of 80 to 100 mm. It is customary to write the readings with the systolic pressure first, for example, 120/80.

Blood pressure increases with age. At birth, the blood pressure is about 75/40. Teenagers have blood pressure of about 100/60. At 65, men have a pressure up to 170/100 and women 175/100.

Extensions

1. Invite a nurse to class to talk about blood pressure and lifestyles. Ask the nurse to measure the blood pressure of class members. How do the readings vary? What effect does exercise have on blood pressure?

2. Artificial hearts have been used to replace defective hearts. Find out more about artificial hearts and the concerns that some doctors and citizens have about them.

3. Heart transplants save a number of Canadian lives every year. However, there is always a shortage of donors. What is being done to solve this problem? What could be done? Should accident victims be required to donate organs to help others?

4. Find out more about lifestyle and heart disease. What care should we be taking now to prevent health problems later in life?

Fluid Flow

Shape and Flow

How do downhill skiers and cyclists improve their performance? This is a question you were asked to think about at the beginning of this unit. The answer involves two ideas: that fluids flow and that different fluids have different viscosities. For objects moving through a fluid, the effects are the same as if the fluid was flowing over a stationary object. In the case of a skier, both may be happening. Have you ever skied while the wind was blowing?

How effectively objects such as planes, gliders, boats, submarines, birds, and whales move through fluids depends on their design or shape. How are the shapes of submarines and whales similar? What is the advantage of this shape? How does shape and design affect the speed that racing cyclists can obtain?

How are whales adapted for speed?

Sports Technology

Going faster than your competitors is the aim of all racers. One factor that limits the speed of objects moving through fluids is the retarding forces at work between the object and the fluid through which it is moving. What would be the retarding forces acting on a skier?

Skiers, like cyclists, experience three kinds of retarding force. First there is the direct push of air against the moving object. What can be done to reduce this retarding force?

Second, there are two frictional forces at work. There is the friction of the moving air against the racer as the racer moves through the fluid. This accounts for 90% of the retarding force on a bicycle at 50 km/h. Then there are frictional forces between the racer and the ground. What can be done to reduce these retarding forces acting on the skier and the cyclist?

Finally, there is a retarding force called drag. As the air flows around a moving object, a low pressure wake is created behind the moving object. This creates a force that tends to slow a skier or cyclist down. Wind tunnel studies have shown that a stream-lined shape creates less drag than an object of a different shape but with the same frontal area. The reason is that, at the speed travelled by the skier or cyclist, the size of the wake is reduced behind the streamlined shape. This results in a smaller low-pressure area and less drag.

The flow of air around a circular object creates a low-pressure wake.

A teardrop shape reduces the size of the wake, resulting in less drag.

Now answer these questions.

1. Both skiers and cyclists crouch when racing. What retarding forces are reduced using this technique?

2. Both type of racers wear tight, form-fitting outfits made of smooth rubberized plastic or other materials with the same characteristics. What retarding forces does this reduce?

3. Cyclists make use of lightweight alloys that decreases the mass of the bike. What retarding forces does this reduce? What do skiers do to reduce the same retarding forces?

4. Many racing bicycles are made of oval or teardrop-shaped tubing. Even the water bottles and helmets have this shape. What retarding forces does this reduce? Do skiers use equipment with a similar design?

Observing the Wake

You Will Need

- a large container, such as an ice-cream container
- pepper

What To Do

Add water to the container and then sprinkle the surface with pepper. Slowly move your finger through the fluid while observing the action of the pepper behind your finger.

1. What happens to the pepper behind your moving finger?

2. Explain your observations using the terms "wake", "low pressure", and "drag".

3. Draw and label a diagram that would explain your observations. The diagram should be similar to those on page 245. What labels would you place on the diagram that would help explain your observations to others?

4. How could you decrease the drag on objects moving through water?

Flow and Viscosity

If the shape of an object moving through air is an important consideration in reducing frictional forces and drag, it becomes even more important for objects moving through a fluid with a greater viscosity. Viscosity is a fluid's resistance to flow. In a viscous fluid, the particles of the fluids are attracted towards each other more strongly than in a less viscous one. Water is an example of a fluid that is more viscous than air. Many animals such as fish, whales, and dolphins have evolved with a streamlined shape. This allows them to move through water at greater speeds and with less effort. What forces have been reduced by this streamlined shape? If water had a viscosity similar to that of oil, would shape become a more, or a less, important factor in moving through the fluid?

An interesting project would be to design the most efficient shape for a boat or submarine for moving through or under water. Science on Your Own describes such a project.

And There's More

Other questions that would make interesting research are:

1. How can planes fly?

2. How is wing shape related to the speed of an airplane?

3. What are hydrofoils? How are hydrofoils similar to airplanes?

4. Why can sail boats travel in directions other than that of the wind?

5. How can an extremely fine spray of water be used as a cutting tool in industry and medicine?

As you examine the world of fluids, its characteristics and applications, there will be other questions that you may want answers to.

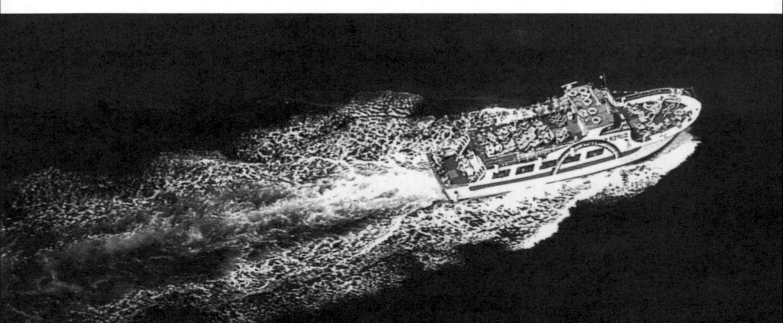

Brain Teasers

1. (a)

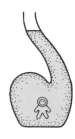 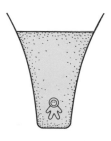  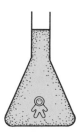

The pressure on the toy divers is the same. Why?

(b)

   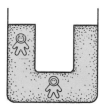

In each jar, which diver feels the greater pressure? Why?

2. An air shock contains both air and a liquid. Its advantage is that the pressure can be increased to accommodate heavier loads. Its disadvantage is that it is more likely to leak and lose pressure.

   (a) Examine the diagram and explain how an air shock works.

   (b) Discuss the science behind the advantage and the disadvantage mentioned above.

3. Examine the following diagram. What weight should be placed on the left piston so that it will balance the dog on the right?

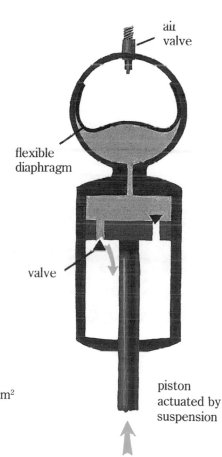

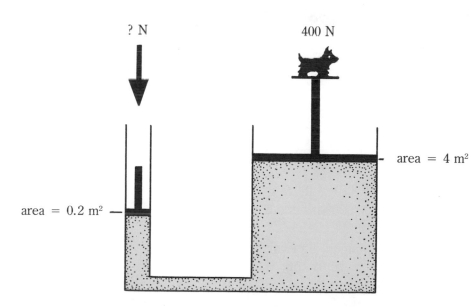

4. These are diagrams of three types of valves, but there are no explanations. Examine each valve carefully and provide an explanation of how it works.

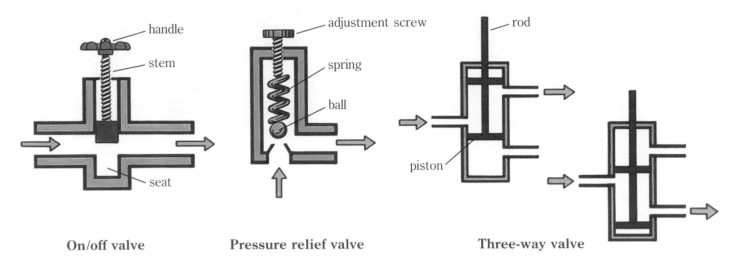

On/off valve   **Pressure relief valve**   **Three-way valve**

5. Another valve that is used in steam engines is the slide valve. Steam under pressure is injected into chamber P. What happens to the piston when A is open? when B is open?

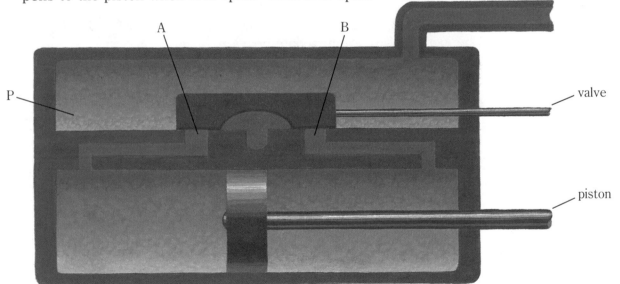

6. An automatic washing machine has inlets for hot and cold water, a way of adjusting the temperature of the water that is entering the machine, and a method of removing the water from the machine.

   (a) How many valves would you find? What is their purpose?

   (b) How does the machine know when the tub contains enough water? Would you expect to find a pump?

   (c) Make a diagram of what you think the piping and valve system would look like. Use symbols to represent the valves.

7. **Make a Plan**

"Do you mean that you can find the weight of a car using only a ruler and a pressure gauge? Impossible!" said Alicia. "No, it is possible," said Alicia's teacher. "Break into groups of three and decide how you could do it. Then we will go out into the parking lot and find the weight of my old Dodge using just a ruler and a pressure gauge."

(*Hint:* The pressure gauge is calibrated in kilopascals.)

8. Using a straw to drink will not work if the straw is too long. Why not?

9. Ms. Bradley asked her class to explain in writing how a syringe works. What comments should she add to each of these responses?

   (a) Orhan's response: "A vacuum will occur when the plunger is pulled which, in turn, will suck up the water into the empty space."

   (b) Mei-Ling's response: "The molecules in the syringe push water up the tube."

   (c) Jane's response: "A vacuum formed when the syringe was pulled. Water took the place of the air. No air could get in, so water took its place."

   (d) Max's response: "The water is pushed up the tube by air from the outside."

10. Set up this equipment as shown. You will need a ruler, a weight, a piece of chalk or dowel, and a beaker of water. Now adjust the ruler so that the end with the weight just touches the table top. Put two fingers into the beaker of water, without touching the bottom. Describe what happens, and why.

12 m is too long!

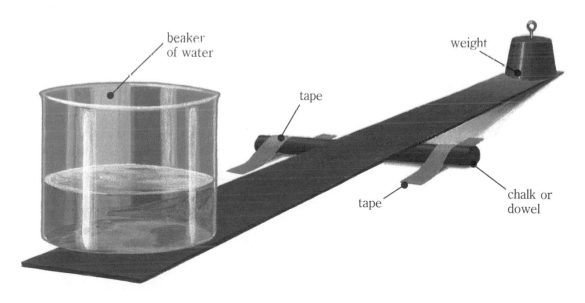

beaker of water

weight

tape

tape

chalk or dowel

11. What? No Fizz?

A legendary story of underwater festivities illustrates what happens when people drink under pressure.

A group of dignitaries met to celebrate the joining of two shafts of a tunnel under a river. (If one account is correct, the river was the Thames, and the year was 1827.) The champagne seemed to be flat when it was opened, so the dignitaries toasted the occasion in champagne which had no bubbles. But when they returned to the surface after the celebration was over, the champagne—now in their stomachs—became very bubbly indeed, and one man had to hurry back down to the tunnel to undergo champagne recompression.

The reason? Carbonated beverages are under pressure and contain gases dissolved in the liquid. When a bottle is opened, the gases bubble out of the solution, causing the familiar fizz. But when a bottle is opened where the air pressure is comparable to the pressure under which the beverage was bottled, the gases remain in solution and the beverage is flat, that is, until the drinkers return to normal air pressure.

How would the reading on a barometer in a tunnel compare with its reading on the surface? Why is there a difference?

12. Water Pumps

(a) Hand pumps were once a common way to draw water from wells. Use your knowledge of air pressure to describe how the pump works.

(b) In a mercury barometer, the atmosphere will support a column of mercury 0.76 m (76 cm) high. Mercury is 13.6 times more dense than water. How high a column of water would the atmosphere support?

(c) At what depth would the lift pump stop?

13. Tracking

The needle on the stereo skipped. To prevent it from happening again, Andre placed a nickel on the turntable arm. "Don't do that!" cried Nan. "You'll ruin your record. The added pressure is as much as that of a 50 kg woman wearing high heels standing on your foot!" Is Nan right? Explain.

For a real challenge, try this calculation. A nickel has a mass of about 5 g. Estimate the area of the tip of a stereo needle in square metres. Calculate the pressure exerted by the addition of the nickel to the arm of the turntable. Compare your answer to the pressure exerted by the 50 kg woman in high heels. (See page 222 and remember, the weight of a 100 g mass is 1 N.)

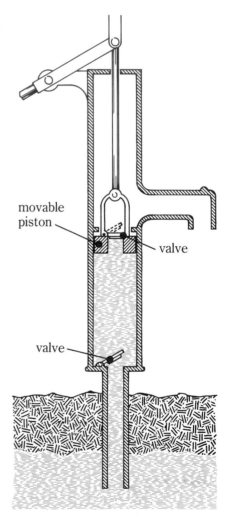

movable piston

valve

valve

14. Vancouver has a domed stadium with a collapsible roof, called B.C. Place. How does the roof retain its shape without collapsing?

15. How does a rubber suction cup support a thermometer on the window? Why do you moisten the suction cup before placing it on the window?

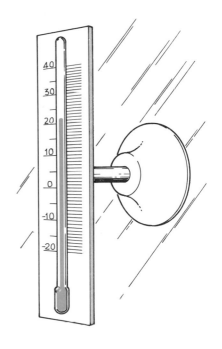

16. **A Question on Mr. Schofield's Test**

"Describe how to determine the height of a building using a barometer."

Hilda's answer:
"You tie a piece of string to the neck of the barometer and lower the barometer from the roof of the building to the ground. The length of the string plus the length of the barometer will equal the height of the building."

Hank's answer:
"Knock on the janitor's door and say to him, 'If you would like a new barometer, I will give you this one for telling me the height of the building.'"

Your answer:
(What answer do you think Mr. Schofield expected?)

17. Overnight, a rowboat made of wood fills completely with water. Does it sink?

18. Megan built a model boat with a mass of 320 g. When she tried it out, she found that it displaced 260 g of water. Did the boat sink or float?

19. A ship has a mass of 100 t. It takes on a cargo of 15 t. How much water is the ship now displacing?

20. A pail is filled to the brim with water and placed on one pan of a two-pan balance. An identical pail is filled to the brim with water, but it has a piece of wood floating in it. What will you observe when this pail is placed on the opposite pan? Explain.

21. You have a balance, a pill container, and two liquids of different densities. What is the fastest way of finding out which liquid has the greater density?

22. The next time you weigh yourself on the bathroom scale, remember that the weight indicated on the scale is not your true weight. Are you actually a little heavier, or a little lighter? Can you explain why?

Thank goodness this isn't my true weight....

23. In fresh water, an ice cube floats with about nine-tenths of its mass below the surface. Is this true for an iceberg in sea water? Explain.

Mechanical Engineering

Mechanical Engineering in Industry

Graham Smith is a manager in an industrial enterprise. He is responsible for developing new products and putting them into production. Graham has a Bachelor's and a Master's degree in mechanical engineering.

Q: What does your job involve?

Graham: As a senior program manager, I run projects. These projects take new products from the engineering stage, when they are designed and developed, to the production stage, when thousands are made. After the design is approved in the engineering stage, it is necessary to establish test equipment for checking the products and to locate sources for all the parts that will be required. This also involves organizing the machining of the tools that will be needed to make the products. Keeping costs to a minimum so that people can afford the product is an important part of the job. I co-ordinate all of this. Previously, I was manager of engineering and was responsible for the design and development stage of projects.

Q: When you were younger, what activities contributed most to developing your interest and aptitude for your work?

Graham: I did some model building which was helpful — model airplanes, model cars, that sort of thing. But I think more generally it was project work, even something as minor as mowing the lawn. Project work of all sorts was probably the most important childhood interest because it gave me the enjoyment of completing projects. It was the same sort of satisfaction that I get now from my job.

Q: What personal characteristics would you single out as important in your work?

Graham: Of course, the ability to work with other people is very important. Also, it is important to stand up for what you believe in. If you are a member of a task team developing a product, you represent some aspect of the work. You may be the quality engineer, the design person, the

draftsperson, or whatever. You have to stick up for the principles involved in the interests you represent.

I think young people in school should think through each problem they encounter to their own satisfaction. They should train themselves to gather all the data that are available, and draw their own conclusions only when they have reviewed all these data. In terms of personal characteristics I would say that integrity — sticking to your own guns and not being pushed around when you have an opinion — is important.

Q: What is the most stimulating part of your job?

Graham: It is satisfying to see the products, that I worked on, doing their job properly. I am an applied scientist; that is to say, basic research is not my field and is not what I like best. Getting the job done is what I really enjoy.

Some Project Ideas

1. Buoyant force has many engineering applications. One of the most ingenious is moving a massive object by floating it in a very small amount of water. This can work for an object with a large enough base area — for instance, an oil drum standing on its end or a huge oil tanker.

2. One of the aims in designing vessels that move through water or air is to reduce drag. The force required to move an object through a fluid at a constant speed is a measure of the drag. For a given design, find out whether drag changes with varying speeds. Then try various designs.

   Another aim in designing vessels is improving their stability — their ability to move in a straight line without rotation or wobble. Design a vessel which combines a minimum of drag with the desired stability.

3. A careful study of the operation of a manufacturing plant or other industrial operation could be a most interesting and valuable experience. This project could involve your entire class, a group of your friends, or yourself alone.

   Such a project depends on the level of interest and co-operation of the employees of the particular industry you select, as well as on your own interest. You might, for example, try to trace the product from the design stage, through production, and into the stages of marketing and use. Where do the required materials come from? What scientific ideas are being applied in the manufacture of the product, and in the product itself? What knowledge and skills are needed by the personnel working in various capacities in the industry? How is this industry likely to change in the future? Do you see any ways to improve the operation of the plant under study?

Robots are used at the Ford Motor Company to assemble cars.

Testing Models For Streamlined Performance

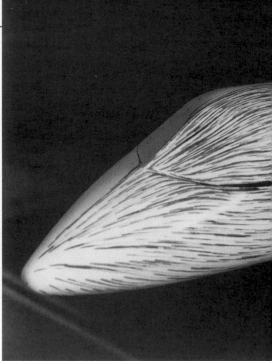

Wind tunnels are used to study the movement of air around objects. This model aircraft has been placed in a wind tunnel. The patterns made by the streaks of oil show how the wind moves around the model.

Submarines must be designed with streamlining in mind, as it is more difficult to move through water than air.

Some problems can be solved in your head, and the solution tested. You do this all the time, for example, when crossing a street safely in heavy traffic. Other problems, however, are too complex to solve by thought alone.

In some cases, it may be helpful to test a possible solution with a model before trying it in a real situation. Designing vehicles for movement through air or water is an application where a model may be particularly useful. What appears in your head or on paper to be a possible design solution may actually be unsafe or not work as hoped. Models are safer and less expensive than the real thing, so they give you a chance

to test more than one design. Through trial and error — seeing whether small changes can improve the results — you can achieve the best solution to the problem of designing a useful vehicle.

A wind tunnel or a water tank provides endless possibilities for designing and testing models of cars, planes, boats, and other vehicles. If you are interested in doing some serious designing and testing, build a wind tunnel or water tank which is suited to the device you want to design and test. To constuct a wind tunnel, you need a fan to generate wind, a tunnel, and a window through which to view the model.

One common objective in designing a vehicle is to reduce drag (resistance) to a minimum, while still allowing the vehicle to meet certain objectives. These objectives may include optimum fuel efficiency, maximum load, maximum interior space, good driver visibility, a high level of safety, durability, maximum power, maximum speed, minimum cost, and/or beauty, among others.

When water or air breaks up into swirls and eddies of turbulence around a vehicle, drag is present. A convenient way to observe the amount and cause of drag around a model in a wind tunnel is to inject smoke into the tunnel or to dangle yarn from various points on the model. A reduction in turbulence indicates a reduction in drag.

In a water tank, drag can be seen and measured directly. A water tank should be long in comparison with the size of the model to be tested. The time taken by a vehicle to travel the length of the tank is a measure of the drag. Applying the same force to different models allows the different rates of drag to be compared.

Suggestions for Projects with Wind Tunnels and Water Tanks

1. Construct a wind tunnel to test your designs for cars, planes, or other vehicles. You can use the tunnel to work on your own design or hold a competition for the best design. For a competition, agree to a set of rules. For instance, all contestants might be required to build their models out of a certain material (i.e. pine) and within a minimum and maximum range of mass (i.e. 500-600 g). Next, agree to the criteria for judging. For example, a maximum of ten points might be awarded for the least drag, ten points for greatest volume (or usable interior space), and five points for appearance.

2. A wind tunnel is also useful for studying the wind patterns around buildings. By testing models, builders can design and locate buildings in a way that reduces stress on the buildings, as well as unwanted wind patterns at ground level. You might test a model of your school and determine where trees or other wind barriers might be located to reduce turbulent winds on the school grounds. Or you might hold a contest for the design of a group of buildings which would create the most pleasant conditions at ground level.

3. Designs for boats, submersibles, and other water vehicles can be tested in a water tank. Criteria for the best design might be a combination of speed, stability, and maximum cargo-carrying capacity. In this case, the models should be tested both with and without cargo. The sketch on this page shows one way

to test each design with the same pulling force. For a particular model, find out how the speed changes as you increase the pulling force.

If you live near a university with an engineering faculty, find out whether research is done using a wind tunnel or water tank. Describe your project, and ask to see their equipment.

Sources of Information

- faculty of engineering at the local university
- testing facilities (aerospace firms, auto manufacturers, *etc.*)
- the library

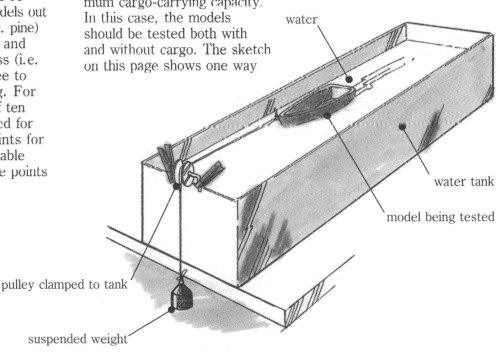

water

water tank

model being tested

pulley clamped to tank

suspended weight

ELECTRO-MAGNETICS

The Daily Chronicle

Georgetown, Thursday, August 15, 1990

Pile-up on T.C.H.

Early this morning a serious accident occurred on the Trans-Canada Highway 5 km east of Georgetown. Six people were hospitalized and are now reported to be in fair condition. Fifteen-year-old Chuck Johnson suffered severe injuries to his right arm . . .

Dale hesitatingly climbed the last few steps to Chuck's hospital room. Last week's visit had been so gloomy. Chuck had been depressed. Up to then Chuck had been concerned about recovering from the horrible accident and happy that he had survived. Now he was thinking about living without his right forearm. "What am I good for? I'm not fit for anything." Dale had tried to cheer him up. But what could he say? There he was standing in front of Chuck — looking fit for anything!

Slowly Dale entered the room. "Hi, Dale," yelled Chuck — and with a grin, "How have you been?" Dale, not with a little surprise, blurted out, "Great. . . You seem to be in good spirits!" And Chuck couldn't hold back the story of the events of the past week.

"You know my Dad works at the university, and he was talking with Bob Scott—he's an electrical engineer doing research on myoelectric prostheses."

"My-o-what?" Dale interrupted. "Say it again."

"MYO-ELECTRIC PROS-THESES," Chuck repeated clearly. " 'PROSTHESIS' just means a substitute part—like an artificial hand. 'MYOELECTRIC' means the substitute part is electrically controlled by signals from your muscles—but back to my story. Dad told Bob Scott about my accident and Bob came to see me. He brought along these photos."

"Look at this one. Sean is working with a drill with his artificial arm. Here he is eating dinner. Look at Adam here. He was fitted with four prostheses not long after he was born. He can colour books and do what you would expect any four-year old to do. He didn't have to train his muscles to provide signals like I'll have to. He just learned to walk and to hold and manipulate things like any other baby does."

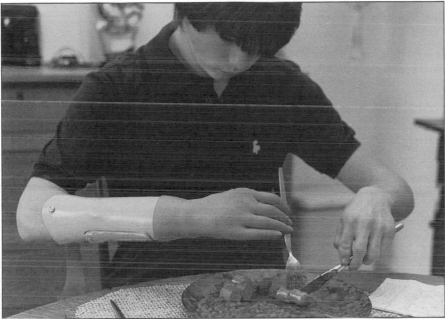

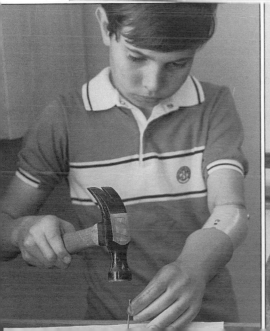

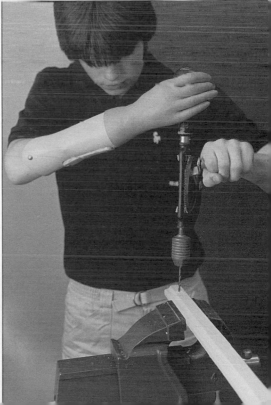

"Chuck, that sure is interesting. It looks as if you can do all kinds of things with artificial limbs."

"Bob told me about Paul, who plays hockey with an attachment that holds a hockey stick. And there's Ed. He can pick up an egg, hold it without dropping it, crack it into the pan, and fry it up! And he makes it all work by thinking — or maybe almost without thinking!"

"Do you think you'll be able to be fitted with a pr-prosthesis?" Dale inquired.

"The doctor says the stump of my arm has healed well and what's left of the muscles in my arm will be able to send good signals to the electrical connections in the artificial arm. Did you know, Dale, that muscles way up here," Chuck said, pointing to the stump, "control the fingers of your hand?"

"No, I guess I didn't," Dale replied.

"You wouldn't believe, Dale, what I have learned in this past week. Bob left me all kinds of things to read."

"It all sounds interesting. Tell me more," encouraged Dale.

"Our muscles and nerves all work electrically. When we want our muscles to do something, an electrical pulse moves down the nerves to the muscles, and the muscles contract or expand, depending on the message being transmitted electrically. Think about it. We can make our muscles contract a little or a lot, fast or slow, hard or weak. Signals from our muscles cause switches to work in the artificial arm, turning a motor on and off, and changing the direction the motor turns. In the arm that was developed at the university, a weak signal from the muscle in the stump will cause the fingers to close and grip an object — gently! But a strong signal will cause the fingers to open."

"You never would think that the electricity in your nerves and muscles would be strong enough to operate a motor," Dale suggested.

"You're right. That little bit of electricity couldn't," Chuck replied, with somewhat the air of an expert! "Artificial fingers require more current than the body's natural ones. It has to be 'amplified' in a circuit that contains a battery which produces a larger current . . . but it is the electricity in the muscles that gets it working. Bob left me these diagrams and I'm trying to figure them out!"

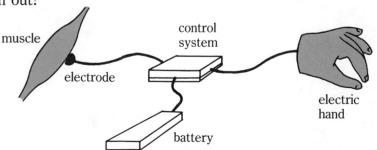

Below-elbow myoelectric prosthesis

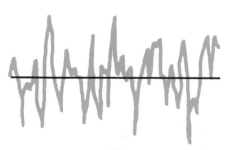

Myoelectric signal seen on a TV-like monitor

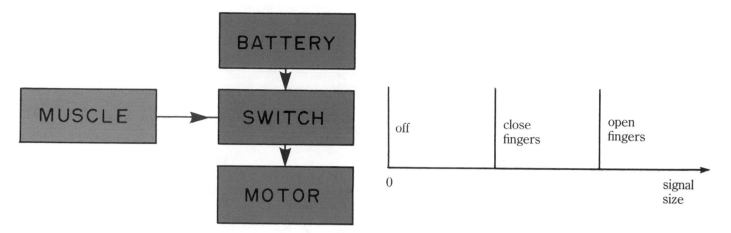

Myoelectric control system   **Myoelectric signal size**

Chuck's story could be repeated many times by hundreds who have received similar hope from the benefits of science and technology. This unit, Electromagnetics, brings together the science and technology of electricity. The "science" part will help you understand the nature of electricity and its behaviour, and suggest how you might use it. Technology comes in when you put electricity to work in practical ways, as in the story you just read.

Think about Chuck's experience again. Consider the following questions:

1. What were some of the changes in Chuck's feelings in the weeks after the accident?

2. What would Chuck have to learn in order to make use of an artificial arm, hand, and fingers?

3. What would Chuck's "myoelectric prosthesis" likely be able to do?

4. What would the electrical currents be able to accomplish?

5. People of many different professions would be needed to develop and to help others use artificial limbs. What would some of these professions be?

6. How would you interpret each of the four diagrams given by Bob Scott to Chuck?

If you were a designer of myoelectric prostheses, you would have to know what electricity is, what good sources of electricity are, how motors operate, how switches can control the size and direction of the motion of motors, and how currents can be measured, decreased, and amplified. You will encounter all of these ideas in this unit. Not only are they necessary for myoelectric prostheses, but also for hundreds of other applications of electricity that you use every day. Think about some of these in the Case Studies that follow.

Making Electricity Work for You: Case Studies

It takes only a little knowledge and skill to make use of many helpful electrical devices. It takes more knowledge to know how they work—and still more to design them. With one or two classmates, discuss, from your joint experience, how electricity works in some of the following situations.

Case Study A

Jenny arrives at the hospital to visit her friend Kim, who is on the fourth floor. Jenny uses the elevator. What information can Jenny get from the elevator lights? What control does Jenny have over the elevator's operation? Are there other controls aside from those which Jenny can affect? For example, are there safety controls to prevent people from walking into an empty shaft? What features of the electrical design are particularly for the passengers' benefit? for their control? for their safety? Sometimes a system provides you with information as it operates. This is called feedback. Can you identify any controls that might be thought of as feedback mechanisms? **Where does the electrical energy used by the elevator come from?** The elevator is a complex electrical system. Although you cannot see the subsystems, you know that they exist because of the functions they perform. Perhaps you could find out more about them by talking to a maintenance technician who is familiar with the elevator's operating parts and subsystems.

Case Study B

"Put the dark wash in the washing machine, Bill!" calls Bill's mother from upstairs. "Watch how you set it—you know how!" Bill has many options in setting the automatic washer. What are some of them? How does he control them? What is the nature of this control? How many different kinds of functions does the machine perform or control? For example, if you only had a small load of laundry to do, could the electrical system control the amount of water needed? Does Bill need to stay beside the washer throughout its cycle? Why or why not? What takes place during the washing cycle? How do you think these events occur? Are there any safety features? feedback mechanisms? **What is the source of electricity for the washer?**

Case Study C

"A plane is travelling at 1000 km/h. Does it break the sound barrier if sound travels at 335 m/s?" Fred looked at the problem, whipped out his calculator, and in a few seconds responded: "Yes, the plane is going faster than the speed of sound. Calculators don't lie!"

Electricity certainly works for you in a calculator. What are some of the functions it performs for you? The calculator is quite complex. However, you do not need to know how it works in order to operate it. How do you control the calculator's various operations? For example, in Fred's problem, what might you do? (By the way, was Fred's response correct — even if calculators don't lie?) **What might be the source of electricity in the calculator?** in the plane?

Case Study D

"I had to walk. My car's in the garage," said Indira to Joyce. "I'm getting the battery charged and the electrical system looked at." What are some of the main functions of the car's electrical system? How does the driver control the operations of the system? Some cars have electrically powered accessories. Can you identify some of them and how they are controlled? Are there any electrical feedback mechanisms that are useful to the driver? What kind of safety features are electrically operated? **What is the car's source of electrical energy?** What energy changes involving electricity take part in the car's operation? What are some devices (energy convertors) which convert electrical energy into other forms of energy?

Case Study E

Write a description of another situation in which electricity does work for you. Name a device, indicate how it is used, identify its operation(s), and describe how you control its operation. How is it powered? What energy changes occur in its operation?

Electricity at Work

CAUTION: Household electricity can be dangerous. Always obey warning signs on appliances: "Caution: Risk of electric shock. Do not open." Read all safety warnings: "Never immerse electric appliances in water." See pages 324, 327-330, and 332 for more safety information.

CAUTION
RISK OF ELECTRIC SHOCK DO NOT OPEN

The familiar situations which you have been analysing in the Case Studies involve complex electrical parts and arrangements. Large quantities of electricity are used in Case Studies A and B. This is true for the operation of most appliances in homes, stores, or industry. A moderate amount is used in Case Study D. Care must be exercised in using these amounts of electricity.

The device used in Case Study C requires only a small amount of electricity. So do most of the Explorations in this unit. They are quite safe to do. Here are four experiments in which electricity works for you. You will notice that it does this by producing different forms of energy. Watch for these different energy forms.

In these experiments the electricity is supplied by dry cells such as those used in flashlights.

Part 1
Let's Have Some Light!

You Will Need

- length of thin copper wire
- flashlight bulb
- dry cell

What To Do

1. Using only these three items, find as many different arrangements as possible which will light the bulb.
2. Sketch each arrangement.

Have you ever looked closely at a flashlight bulb?

insulated part

3. What form of energy does the electricity produce?
4. What are examples of this use of electricity in everyday life?
5. You have constructed an electric circuit. What parts make up this circuit? What would you say an electric circuit is?

Part 2
The Heat Is On

You Will Need

- thin copper wire
- plasticine
- clothespin
- dry cell
- wide rubber band
- steel wool
- aluminum foil
- nichrome wire

What To Do

1. Make a small loop at one end of each of the two lengths of thin copper wire.
2. Bend the wires and support them with plasticine as shown.
3. Attach the ends of the wires to the dry cell, securing them with a wide rubber band.
4. Place a strand of steel wool in the loops. What do you observe? Repeat with a narrow piece of aluminum foil, and then with a length of nichrome wire. Bring your hand close to each but do not touch them. What do you feel?

CAUTION: Do not leave any of the wires in contact with the loops for very long since this will quickly drain the dry cell of its electrical energy.

5. What form of energy does the electricity produce?
6. How do you apply this use of electricity?

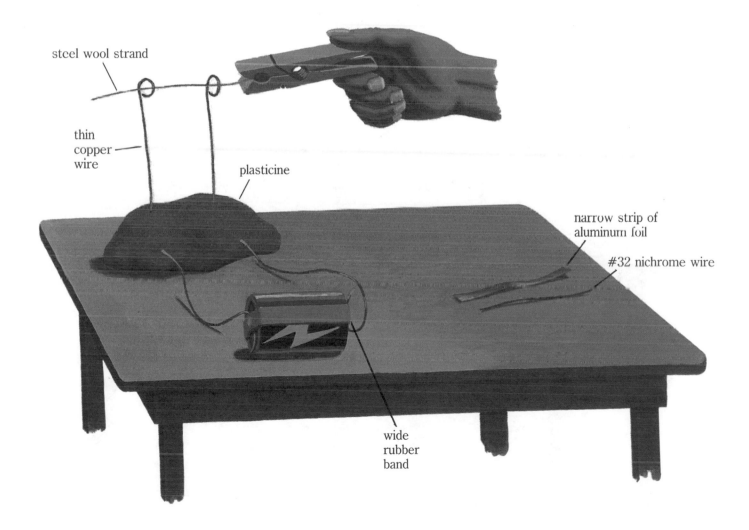

steel wool strand

thin copper wire

plasticine

wide rubber band

narrow strip of aluminum foil

#32 nichrome wire

Part 3
Attractive or Repulsive?

You Will Need

- dry cell
- iron filings
- compass
- thumb tacks
- wood block
- paper clip
- copper wire
- rubber band

What To Do

1. Set up the apparatus as shown. Align the compass needle and place the wire over the compass in a N-S (North-South) direction.

2. Close the electric circuit by pressing down on the contact switch.

3. Replace the compass with a piece of paper with iron filings sprinkled on it. Close the circuit. Press the wire into the filings and then raise the wire. What do you observe?

CAUTION: Do not keep the switch closed for very long.

4. What kind of energy does the electricity produce in this experiment?

5. Can you think of any applications in your daily life that may make use of electricity in this way?

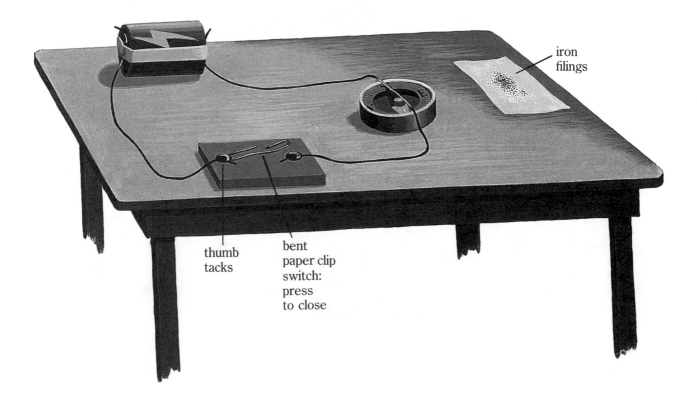

iron filings

thumb tacks

bent paper clip switch: press to close

Part 4
Let's Get Moving

You Will Need

- dry cells
- paper clips
- thin insulated copper wire
- magnet
- support stand
- cork
- tape
- cardboard

What To Do

1. Assemble the circuit as shown in the illustration.

2. Have one person hold a strong magnet near the cork while the other person presses on the contact switch to complete the circuit. Observe what happens. Open the switch. What happens?

3. Turn the magnet around and repeat Step 2. What happens?

4. What kind of energy is being produced by the electricity?

5. Can you suggest practical examples in which energy works for you in this way?

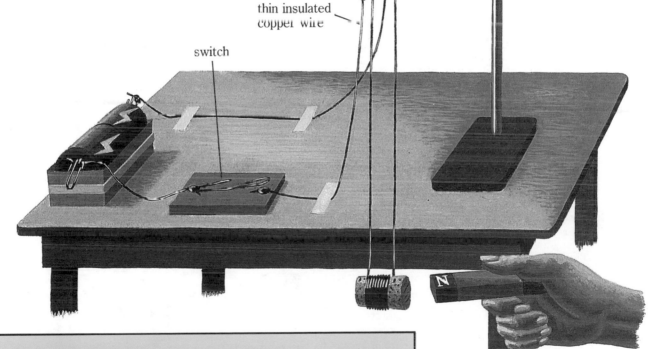

tape

thin insulated copper wire

switch

A Home Project

Make a "dry cell tester". Use one of the arrangements you discovered in Part 1 of Exploration 1. Your task is to devise a bulb holder with wire connected to the holder. Then the other ends can be touched to the dry cell. The brightness of the light bulb will be an indication of the strength of the dry cell.

What Is Electricity?

In Exploration 1 you made electricity work for you by producing other forms of energy. What were they? Later in the unit you will discover that each of these energy forms can in turn produce electricity. Remembering that energy can be transformed from one form to another, would it not appear that electricity itself must be a form of energy just as heat and light are? You may have noticed in the Case Studies that the words electrical energy were used frequently.

Electricity accomplishes these changes in energy when an electric **current** is flowing in a circuit. But what is a current? What is it that flows or moves in the circuit?

Have you ever walked on a carpet with leather-soled shoes and then touched someone? Did you see sparks or feel a shock? If so, you had become electrically charged. Have you ever rubbed an inflated balloon on your clothes and then "stuck" it on the wall? In this case the balloon would have become charged. It is friction which has caused both the balloon and you to possess electrically charged particles. What might these charged particles be? Try this demonstration, in which you will put electric charges on objects and allow them to move along a path.

A "Classical" Current Demonstration

Here is a demonstration similar to one done hundreds of years ago. Follow the steps closely.

1. Rub a plastic strip or plastic ruler vigorously with plastic wrap.

2. Touch the end of a nail on top of a notched coffee cup with the rubbed plastic strip. A wheat puff is suspended near the other end of the nail. What happens?

charged plastic strip

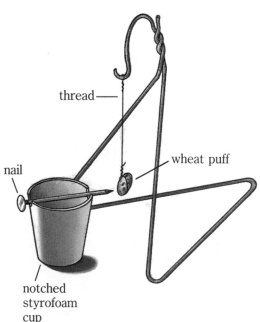

thread

nail

wheat puff

notched styrofoam cup

3. Rub the plastic strip again and bring it close to the end of the nail without quite touching it. Observe the wheat puff.

4. Now rub vigorously a vinyl strip with flannel.

5. Bring the rubbed vinyl strip near the nail and wheat puff that you used in (3). Observe the wheat puff. It is possible to take the charge off the wheat puff. Try it.

How do you explain the events in this classical demonstration?

A Theory of Charged Particles

Scientists believe the following:

1. When one material is rubbed against another, charged particles actually move from one to the other. The accumulated electric charge enables the materials to attract very light or finely divided materials to them.

Where did you observe this happening in the previous demonstration?

2. There are two kinds of charged particles. Scientists identify these as positively charged and negatively charged particles.

Why might you conclude that the charges on the plastic strip and the charges on the vinyl strip are different?

3. Objects charged with the same kind of charge tend to repel one another. Differently charged objects tend to attract one another.

Where did you observe these effects in the demonstration?

4. Charged particles pass through certain materials, called conductors, but cannot pass through other materials, called non-conductors, or insulators. What evidence is there that iron is a conductor of electricity? You might experiment by replacing the nail in the demonstration with a glass rod, a wooden stick, a copper wire or objects made of other materials. Which are conductors? insulators?

The drawings apply the above theory to the classical demonstration you have done. Express in your own words what is taking place in each drawing.

A

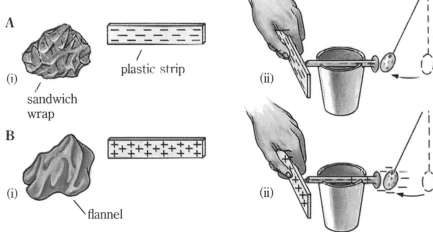

(i)

sandwich wrap

plastic strip

(ii)

B

(i)

flannel

(ii)

(iii)

The theory we have been considering is an interesting one. It helps to explain many of your electrical observations. But do scientists really know what these charged particles are? You can find out by taking an imaginary trip back in time almost 100 years ago and visiting J.J. Thomson in his laboratory, where many important discoveries were made.

A Visit to the Cavendish Laboratory

It is the year 1900 at Cambridge University, England. We can imagine J.J. Thomson talking to a small group of students at the famous Cavendish Laboratory. Listen to what he might be saying:

"Ladies and Gentlemen, we believe that we have discovered the smallest particle of negative electricity. We have obtained a stream of identical negative particles from many metals. In fact we believe that every bit of matter contains these same particles. We call them **electrons***."*

"We believe that most substances are uncharged. Therefore, there must be in all substances charged particles of another type which neutralize the negative charges, producing no overall charge. We have discovered such particles in other experiments. We call them protons. Each proton must have the same amount of charge as each electron but of a different kind."

"In every smallest particle of material there are electrons and protons in equal amount, so that there is no overall charge on the material. Electrons are relatively light and move freely in conductors. Protons, being much heavier, remain fixed in their positions."

J.J. Thomson and his colleagues certainly expanded the theory of charged particles. Did you follow what he was saying to the students? Can you relate it to what an electric current is — such as the current you got when you connected correctly a dry cell, wires, and a flashlight bulb in Exploration 1? Check yourself by doing the next puzzle.

A Current Puzzle

The answers may be found by moving in any horizontal or vertical direction, or both, for a given word. The letters which remain are in the right order to tell you what an electric current is. Copy the table into your notebook, and solve the "current puzzle"!

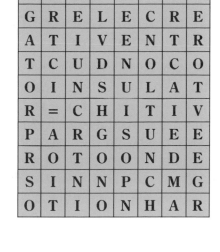

E	N	N	O	R	T	C	U
G	R	E	L	E	C	R	E
A	T	I	V	E	N	T	R
T	C	U	D	N	O	C	O
O	I	N	S	U	L	A	T
R	=	C	H	I	T	I	V
P	A	R	G	S	U	E	E
R	O	T	O	O	N	D	E
S	I	N	N	P	C	M	G
O	T	I	O	N	H	A	R

- A material that allows charges to go through it is a(n) ____?____ .

- A material which does not allow charges to go through it is a(n) ____?____ .

- J.J. Thomson discovered a charged particle that moves readily; it is a(n) ____?____ .

- This type of particle has a(n) ____?____ change.

- The other charged particle in materials, which is more massive and does not move, is the ____?____ .

- It has a(n) ____?____ charge.

- If a material has equal numbers of these two kinds of particles, the material is ____?____ .

Charged or Uncharged?

In terms of the theory of charged particles, what are positively charged, negatively charged, or uncharged objects? What makes them that way? Note that, in the illustrations on page 269, there were no charges shown on the sandwich wrap or the flannel. Should there have been? The illustrations at right give a more complete picture of what happens when a plastic ruler is rubbed with plastic wrap. Count the number of each kind of charge in the before-and-after situations.

(a) Explain the movement of the electrically charged particles.

(b) Now make "before" and "after" drawings for rubbing a vinyl strip with flannel.

(c) The same ball is charged differently in each of the following illustrations. In which figure is the ball slightly negative, strongly negative, uncharged, slightly positive, strongly positive? What remains the same in all diagrams? Why?

before rubbing   plastic ruler

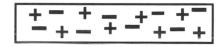

plastic wrap

after rubbing

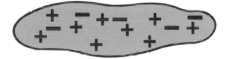
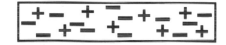

(i) 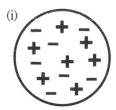 (ii) 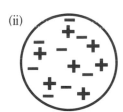 (iii) 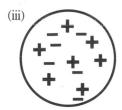 (iv) 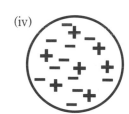 (v)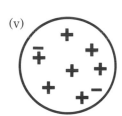

> These diagrams are really unreal! Actually, a ball of iron this size would contain 2 000 000 000 000 000 000 000 000 positive charges and an equal number of negative charges.

Some Current Questions

What causes electrons to move in a conductor to produce a current?

Do you recall charging the wheat puff in the classical demonstration? You brought a plastic ruler which you had rubbed with plastic wrap near the end of a nail. The wheat puff at the other end of the nail moved away. The puff moved because charged particles passed through the nail to the puff, causing it to jump away. The passing of the particles through the nail was a temporary electric current. But how, exactly, did it happen?

First, electrons in the plastic ruler repel (push) electrons in the point of the nail (A) to the right.

Then these electrons repel electrons at B. The electrons at B move to the right, and repel electrons at C . . . and so on all the way through the nail, to the other end (Z).

The electrons at Z are repelled onto the wheat puff. When the puff is negative enough, the repelling force is strong enough to push it away from the nail. The current then stops flowing, since there is nowhere for the electrons to go.

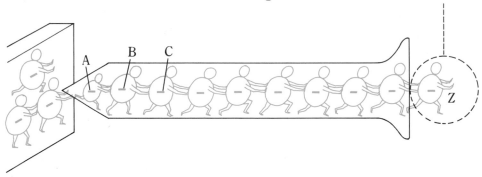

You can see that electrons behave somewhat like falling dominoes. Each electron pushes on the one next to it. If there is a gap in the "chain" of electrons, no electric current can flow.

What causes a continuous flow of current?

You can probably answer this question from what you have read so far! We need two things for a continuous current: first, a continuous supply of charges, and second, a conductor to carry the charges. Isn't that like a water current in our homes? We need a supply of water — the reservoir — and we need a conducting path — the pipes that carry the water.

The conducting path usually includes wire made of a metal such as copper, and at least one device which makes use of the electricity. Trace the conducting path in the diagram, starting at the cell, and coming back to the cell. A complete circuit consists of:

(a) a source of electrical charges
(b) a conducting path
(c) a device to use electrical energy

Match (a), (b), and (c) with the numbered labels in the diagram. What would you add to the circuit so that you could control the continuous flow of charges, that is, to start and stop the flow? What does "to make and break a circuit" mean? What does "to open and close" a circuit mean?

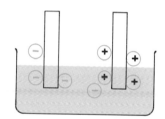

A Continuous Supply

One way to obtain a continuous supply of charges is to use a chemical **cell**. People often call a cell a "battery". However, a battery is actually a group of cells. An example of a real battery, which is made up of several cells, is the battery in a car.

As you have observed, a cell always has a positive and a negative part. These are the electrodes of the cell. They are also conductors. The two electrodes of a cell are made of different materials and extend into a solution of chemicals called an **electrolyte**.

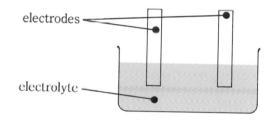

The materials in the cell — the electrodes and electrolyte — interact with one another. The result is that some electrons move from one electrode into the solution while others move from the solution onto the other electrode. The electrode with fewer electrons is therefore positively charged. Why? The electrode with more electrons is negatively charged. Why? This is how a cell is able to produce a supply of electric charges.

How do electrons move through a conducting path such as a wire and bulb? Beginning at the negative electrode of the cell, electrons repel one another throughout the length of the conducting path to the positive electrode. At the same time, the positive electrode of the cell attracts the electrons. Thus, a current flows. As the current flows, the chemicals in the cell keep taking electrons from the positive electrode and giving electrons to the negative electrode. The cell therefore causes a continuous current to flow.

In the dry cell that you used in Exploration 1, the zinc sides and bottom of the cell constitute the negative electrode. The positive electrode is a rod of carbon (graphite) in the centre of the cell which protrudes from the top of the cell. The liquid part of a dry cell (the electrolyte) is in the form of a paste.

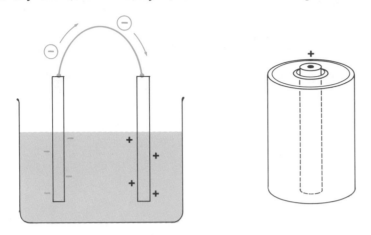

Building a Continuity Tester — A Project

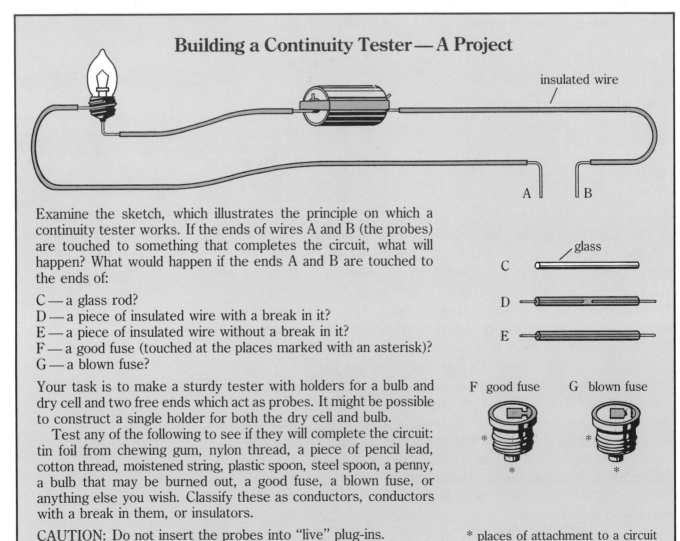

Examine the sketch, which illustrates the principle on which a continuity tester works. If the ends of wires A and B (the probes) are touched to something that completes the circuit, what will happen? What would happen if the ends A and B are touched to the ends of:

C — a glass rod?
D — a piece of insulated wire with a break in it?
E — a piece of insulated wire without a break in it?
F — a good fuse (touched at the places marked with an asterisk)?
G — a blown fuse?

Your task is to make a sturdy tester with holders for a bulb and dry cell and two free ends which act as probes. It might be possible to construct a single holder for both the dry cell and bulb.

Test any of the following to see if they will complete the circuit: tin foil from chewing gum, nylon thread, a piece of pencil lead, cotton thread, moistened string, plastic spoon, steel spoon, a penny, a bulb that may be burned out, a good fuse, a blown fuse, or anything else you wish. Classify these as conductors, conductors with a break in them, or insulators.

CAUTION: Do not insert the probes into "live" plug-ins.

* places of attachment to a circuit

Detecting an Electric Current

Constructing a Current Detector

Your task is to design and construct a durable galvanometer consisting of a small magnetic compass, insulated bell wire, and anything else you need to hold the parts in place.

Hints:

1. Experiment with different numbers of turns.

2. Leave two free ends of the wire to attach to the source of the small current.

3. The galvanometer should be positioned so that the compass needle and the turns of wire are parallel to one another.

4. A small current to test your galvanometer can be obtained from a lemon cell. To make a lemon cell, insert a straightened paper clip and a piece of sanded copper wire deeply into the lemon. The clip and the wire are the electrodes and the juice of the lemon is the electrolyte. You now can hook the free ends of the galvanometer wire to the electrodes.

5. Will your galvanometer be able to give you any information about the size of the current?

What these students seem to be saying is:

"You can't see electricity. But you know it is there by its effects. You can feel the heat produced in an electric stove and you know that an electric current is flowing. Likewise, when you see the faint light given off by a flashlight bulb, you know that an electric current is flowing. In this case, a small amount of current is enough to produce an effect."

Later, you will be making even smaller amounts of electricity. How will you detect them? Look back at Part 3 of Exploration 1 on page 266. What kind of effect did a current of electricity produce in that activity? This effect can be increased many times if you wrap the wire (it must be insulated) around the compass. This is the basis of sensitive current detectors called **galvanometers**.

A Commercial Galvanometer

This galvanometer operates on the principle of Part 4 of Exploration 1, in which you used a current-bearing coil of wire and a magnet. Here the galvanometer has a rotating coil of wire and a horseshoe magnet.

Here is a simplified drawing of a commercial current meter. How does it appear to work? How is it able to measure the amount of current flowing? Keep in mind that the coil of wire itself acts as if it is a magnet with N and S poles. Where might these be located? What is the coiled control spring for?

Inside a Current Meter

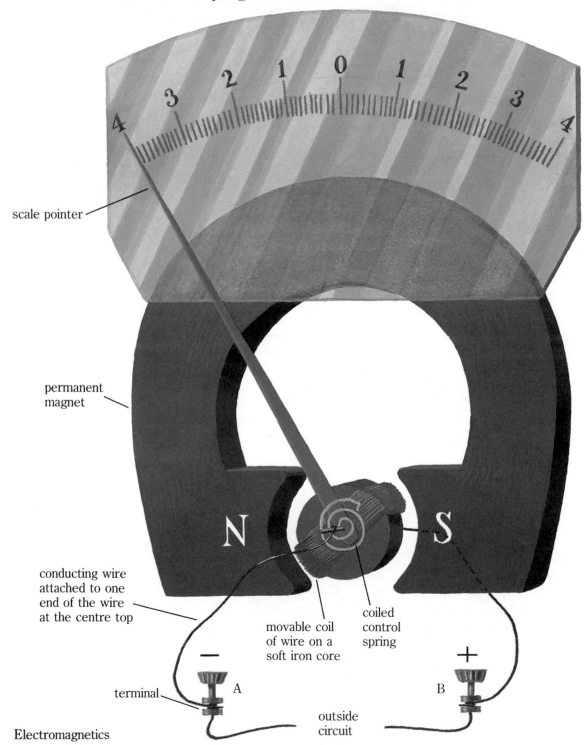

scale pointer

permanent magnet

conducting wire attached to one end of the wire at the centre top

N

S

terminal

A

B

movable coil of wire on a soft iron core

coiled control spring

outside circuit

Sources of Electricity — Chemical Cells

Isn't it surprising how many things operate on cells or batteries? Most cells are chemical cells because they depend on the action of chemical substances to produce electricity. Chemical energy is changed to electrical energy in cells. What other kinds of cells do you know of that produce electricity from another form of energy? What are the advantages of chemical cells? What are their limitations? You have already made a lemon cell. Here you will construct other cells and test your success with your home-made galvanometer.

EXPLORATION 3

Making Chemical Cells

You Will Need

- home-made or commercial galvanometer
- copper wire
- masking tape
- rubber bands
- 2 zinc strips
- 2 copper strips
- blotting paper
- ammonium chloride
- table salt solution
- clothespins

Part 1
Electricity from a Dry Cell

CAUTION: Use goggles and rubber gloves when you work with chemicals.

1. Make a "sandwich" like the one shown.
2. Check the amount of deflection of the needle in the galvanometer. Use your homemade galvanometer or a commercial one.

CAUTION: If you use the latter, break contact if there is full deflection of the needle on the scale.

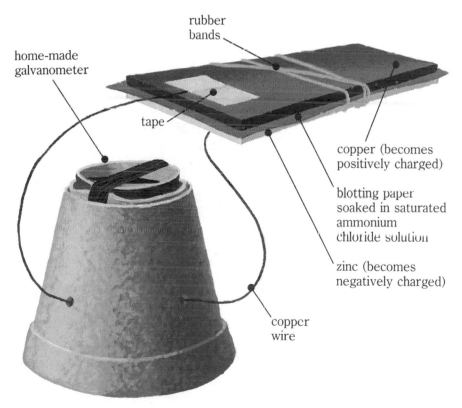

home-made galvanometer

rubber bands

tape

copper (becomes positively charged)

blotting paper soaked in saturated ammonium chloride solution

zinc (becomes negatively charged)

copper wire

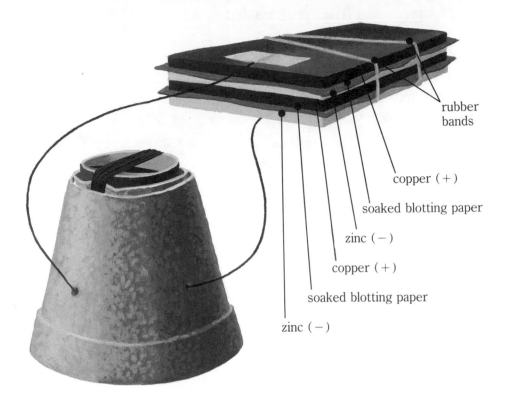

rubber
bands

copper (+)

soaked blotting paper

zinc (−)

copper (+)

soaked blotting paper

zinc (−)

3. Now make a "double sandwich".

4. Compare the amount of deflection shown by the galvanometer with the single and double "sandwiches". The double sandwich is a **battery** consisting of two cells. If you increase the number of cells, you may be able to light a bulb.

5. Check what you know about cells by completing the following statements, which can also serve as the basis for your conclusions to this part of the experiment.

   (a) In a dry cell, chemical energy is changed into ____?____ energy.

   (b) A cell for making a current always consists of two different ____?____ and a ____?____

   (c) A dry cell can be made using the two metals ____?____ and ____?____, and a solution of ____?____ placed on blotting paper.

   (d) Two dry cells produce ____?____ (less current than, the same amount of current as, more current than) one cell.

   (e) When you connect two cells to make a battery, the positive electrode of one cell is connected to the ____?____ electrode of the other cell.

Part 2
Electricity from a
Wet Cell

1. Add enough salt solution to cover one half of the copper and zinc strips.

2. Record the highest reading shown by the galvanometer. What happens to the reading? Observe each electrode carefully. Describe what happens at each electrode.

3. Add more salt solution until it covers the copper and zinc strips.

4. Again record the galvanometer reading.

5. Try other metals and solutions.

6. Before you write your conclusions, check what you may have found out about wet cells.

   (a) A cell converts ___?___ energy into ___?___ energy.

   (b) A wet cell consists of two ___?___ metals and a ___?___ .

   (c) A wet cell may be made using the two metals ___?___ and ___?___ and the chemical ___?___ .

   (d) As more of the metal strips is covered with the solution, the amount of current produced ___?___ (decreases, remains the same, increases).

   (e) As the current continues to flow, ___?___ may be produced around the electrodes.

   (f) During the operation of the cell, the current ___?___ (increases, stays the same, decreases). Try to explain why this happens.

Chemical Cell Technology

You have made some chemical cells. The current produced was very small—enough to be detected by a small galvanometer, but not enough to light a bulb. Chemists and chemical and electrical engineers have developed a great variety of chemical cells and expanded the uses to which they can be put. Chemical cells provide the small amounts of current needed for calculators, radios, flashlights, heart pacemakers, hearing aids, and portable telephones, as well as larger amounts for mobile objects such as cars and spaceships. You will find out about modern chemical cell construction and usage in the next Exploration.

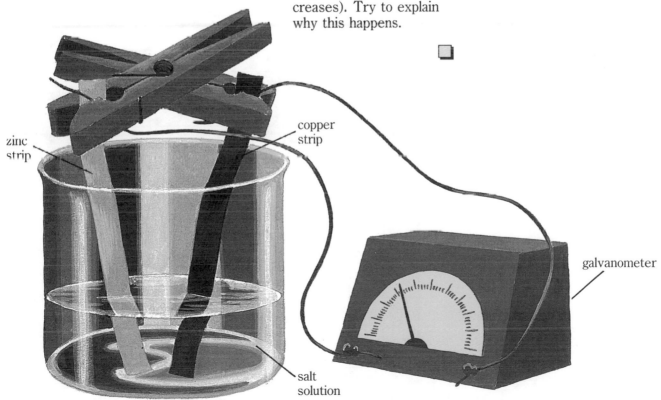

zinc strip

copper strip

salt solution

galvanometer

Electricity From Cells — A Research Project

Much of the research information you need to answer the questions in this Exploration can be obtained from Data Sheets #1 and #2 on the following pages.

Part 1
Dry Cells

(Use Data Sheet #1)

1. What are some of the practical problems associated with the use of simple liquid cells?

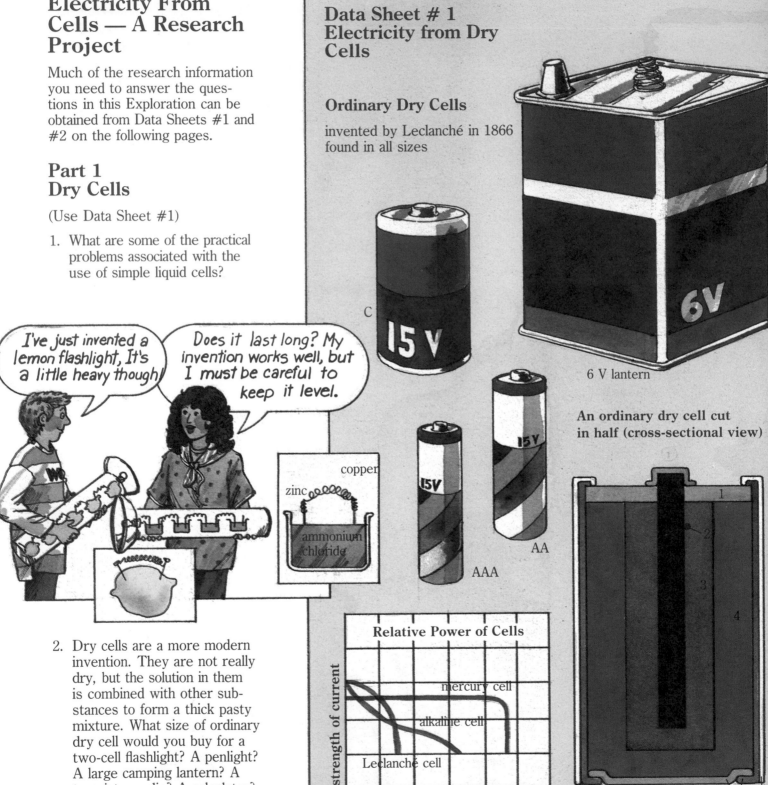

I've just invented a lemon flashlight. It's a little heavy though!

Does it last long? My invention works well, but I must be careful to keep it level.

Data Sheet # 1
Electricity from Dry Cells

Ordinary Dry Cells

invented by Leclanché in 1866
found in all sizes

C

15 V

6 V

6 V lantern

copper

zinc

ammonium chloride

15 V

15 V

AAA

AA

An ordinary dry cell cut in half (cross-sectional view)

1
2
3
4
6   5

Relative Power of Cells

strength of current

mercury cell

alkaline cell

Leclanché cell

number of hours (medium load)

2. Dry cells are a more modern invention. They are not really dry, but the solution in them is combined with other substances to form a thick pasty mixture. What size of ordinary dry cell would you buy for a two-cell flashlight? A penlight? A large camping lantern? A transistor radio? A calculator? Go to a department store or hardware store for ideas.

Alkaline Cell

made in all the sizes of the ordinary dry cell

+ electrode
the sides of the container, combined with an adjacent layer of manganese (IV) oxide

− electrode
the central core of the cell, made of magnesium or zinc; this central core is attached to the bottom of the cell and is surrounded by zinc particles.

electrolyte
potassium hydroxide

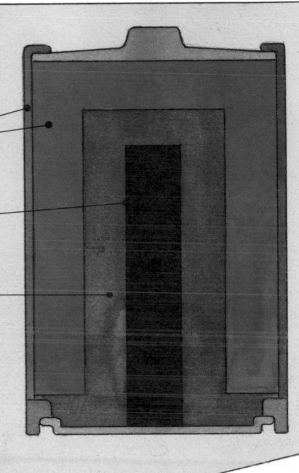

Mercury Cell

a miniature cell
- hearing aids
- light meters (photographic)
- electric watches
- pace makers for the heart

(cross-sectional view)

zinc
(attached to
the top)

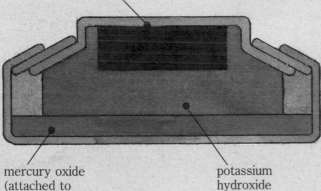

mercury oxide
(attached to
the bottom)

potassium
hydroxide

Lithium solid state cell replaces mercury cells in pace makers

- Invented by Wilson Greatbatch
- Electrodes are lithium and iodine
- Electrolyte made of poly 2-vinyl pyridine (P2VP)
- longer lifetime

3. Use the following description to label the parts of the ordinary dry cell on Data Sheet #1. In your notebook, draw a dry cell similar to this one, replacing the numbered labels with the italicized words from the description. The cell has been cut down the middle to reveal its interior.

Like all chemical cells, the ordinary dry cell has two electrodes or conductors and a solution. The positive electrode has two parts—a *graphite rod* in the centre of the cell and a compressed mixture of *manganese (IV) oxide* and *powdered carbon* surrounding the graphite rod. (Graphite is a form of carbon.) The negative electrode is *zinc*; it actually makes up the sides and bottom of the metal container. The electrolyte is contained in the *ammonium chloride paste* and lies between the two electrodes. The paste consists of ammonium chloride and water mixed with a small amount of starch and wheat flour. At the top of the cell is a waterproof *insulator*. The cell shown here is encased in *cardboard*. The dry cell is the least expensive form of cell; it has a shelf-life of about one year.

4. Did you notice that in the ordinary dry cell the positive electrode is not just a simple metal conductor? Rather, it is made up of a porous rod of graphite (like the lead in a pencil) surrounded by black manganese (IV) oxide and carbon (soot, such as that from an acetylene torch). Look at the other dry cells on the Data Sheets and designate the two electrodes and the electrolyte (solution) for each cell.

5. The dry cell industry has undergone many changes since it began, and continues to change today. Why have changes been needed? What problems have you experienced with the ordinary dry cells you use? How do alkaline and mercury cells meet some of these problems?

6. Sketch and label the three parts of the illustrated dry cells, using chemical shorthand.

7. Research the new zinc/air dry cells which are now available. What are their components? How are these cells used?

Optional Question

8. Here is how an electrochemist would refer to a Leclanché cell, using chemical shorthand.

Zn	NH$_4$Cl	MnO$_2$(C)
(the negative electrode)	(the electrolyte)	(the positive electrode)

Using chemical shorthand and the format for representing cells, describe an alkaline cell, a mercury cell, and a lithium cell.

Data Sheet #2 will give you information about storage cells. One of these, the nickel-cadmium cell, is also a dry cell. You probably know it as a "rechargeable battery".

If you were an electrochemist, your work might be developing new types of dry cells. The cells described on Data Sheet #1 are just a few of the many dry cells being developed and used today. Here is some knowledge you would need as an electrochemist:

• Elements are the simplest substances in nature.

• There are more than 90 naturally occurring elements.

• Elements can combine to form compounds.

• Both elements and compounds are known as "chemicals".

• Batteries (cells) are made of chemicals.

• The electrodes in a cell often consist entirely of metal, but they can be made of non-metals and compounds.

• The electrolyte in a dry cell is a solution of a compound mixed with other chemicals to form a paste or jelly.

This table lists some of the elements you will encounter in your study of cells:

Name	Symbol	Brief Description
zinc	Zn	metal, silver-like colour
mercury	Hg	liquid metal
lead	Pb	soft metal
nickel	Ni	metal
cadmium	Cd	metal
magnesium	Mg	metal
lithium	Li	metal
manganese	Mn	metal
potassium	K	metal
carbon (graphite)	C	a conducting non-metal
oxygen	O	gas
hydrogen	H	gas
chlorine	Cl	gas
iodine	I	solid, non-metal
nitrogen	N	gas
sulphur	S	solid, non-metal

Here are some compounds which are in cells. Can you identify the elements in each of these compounds?

Name	Symbol
lead oxide	PbO_2
mercuric oxide	HgO
manganese oxide (IV)	MnO_2
potassium hydroxide	KOH
ammonium chloride	NH_4Cl
sulphuric acid	H_2SO_4
nickel oxide hydroxide	$NiO(OH)$

Part B
Other Cells

(Use Data Sheet #2)

1. A surge of electric current is needed to start an automobile. It is provided by a group of cells joined together in a battery. Study the drawings on Data Sheet #2 of the original type of lead storage cell and the battery, to discover or infer the answers to these questions:

   (a) What substances make up the two electrodes and the electrolyte in a car battery?

   (b) How many cells are there in a car battery?

   (c) How are these cells connected to one another?

   (d) How do you check the liquid level in the cells? Why is it important to do so?

   (e) Why is a car battery called a "storage" battery?

   (f) Why is such a large battery needed for a car?

   (g) Why are there holes in the battery cap?

   (h) What are some precautions to take when caring for this type of car battery?

   (i) Discover how a garage operator knows when a storage battery needs charging.

2. (a) Find out from a garage operator how automobile batteries have changed over the last ten years. What are the advantages and disadvantages of the new lead storage batteries?

(b) What are "maintenance-free" batteries? Why is a battery spill less likely to occur with them? Why is it not necessary to add water to them? How does the garage operator know when these batteries need to be charged?

3. How is the nickel-cadmium storage cell similar to and different from lead cells? In what way is it superior?

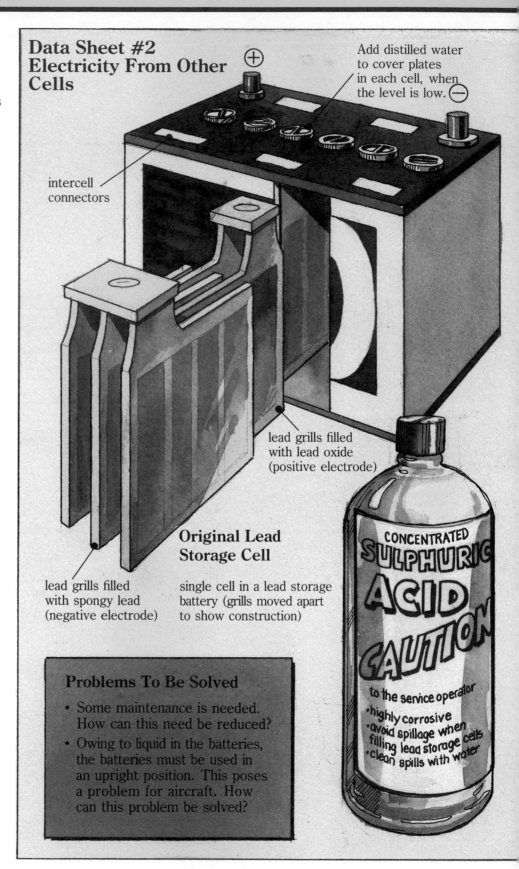

**Data Sheet #2
Electricity From Other Cells**

⊕

Add distilled water to cover plates in each cell, when the level is low. ⊖

intercell connectors

lead grills filled with lead oxide (positive electrode)

Original Lead Storage Cell

lead grills filled with spongy lead (negative electrode)

single cell in a lead storage battery (grills moved apart to show construction)

CONCENTRATED SULPHURIC ACID CAUTION

to the service operator
• highly corrosive
• avoid spillage when filling lead storage cells
• clean spills with water

Problems To Be Solved

• Some maintenance is needed. How can this need be reduced?

• Owing to liquid in the batteries, the batteries must be used in an upright position. This poses a problem for aircraft. How can this problem be solved?

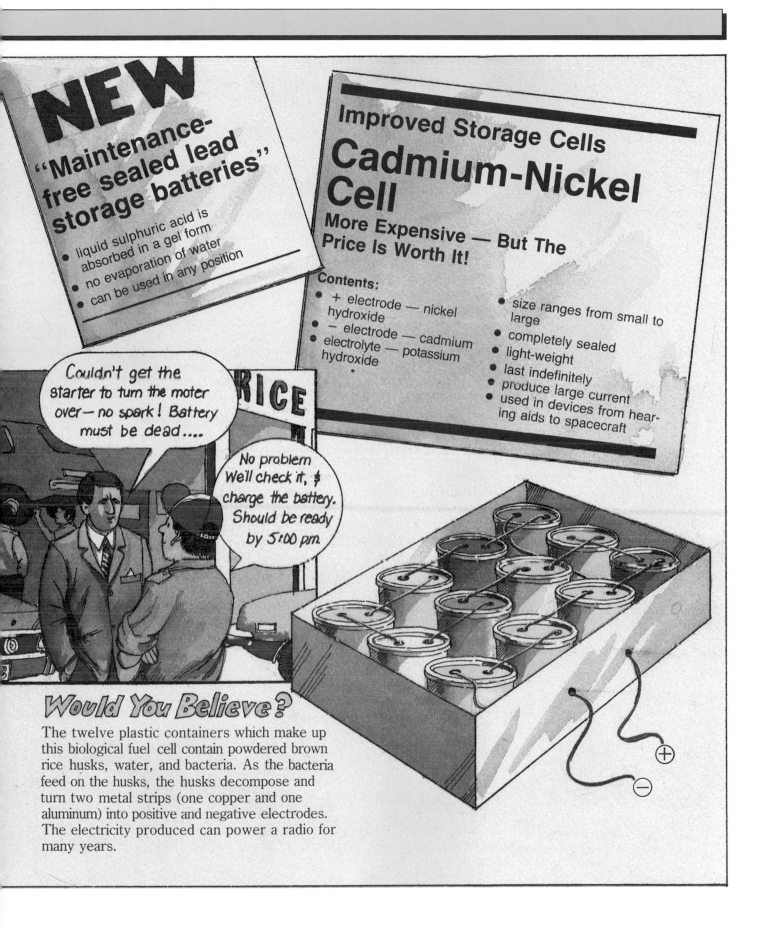

Sources of Electricity—The Electromagnetic Way

You have discovered that magnetic effects can be caused by a current flowing in a wire or coil. Could the reverse be true? Could a magnet produce electrical effects in a wire? Try the next Exploration to find out. There are two parts, an activity that you can do and a completed experiment that you can analyze.

Moving Magnets and Wire Coils

Part 1

You Will Need

- commercial galvanometer
- coil of insulated wire
- strong bar magnet

What To Do

1. Attach a coil of insulated wire to a commercial galvanometer.

2. While watching for effects on the galvanometer, move a bar magnet into a coil, hold it there for a moment, then remove it. Is the galvanometer needle affected?

3. Repeat Step 2 several times, moving the magnet at different speeds. What do you observe? Does moving the magnet into the coil have a different effect on the galvanometer than moving the magnet out of the coil? What might this suggest regarding the direction of current flow in the coil?

4. Disconnect the galvanometer and move the magnet to see whether the magnet itself is affecting the galvanometer.

5. Hook the galvanometer up to the coil again. This time, hold the magnet still, but move the coil over the magnet and back. Observe.

6. Record your observations and any conclusions that you have drawn from them. Do your conclusions suggest answers for these questions?

    (a) How can a magnet produce electricity?

    (b) How is the direction of the current affected by the motion of the magnet?

    (c) How does the speed of the magnet's motion affect the amount of electricity provided?

    (d) What change in energy forms occur in this investigation?

    (e) Can a stationary magnet ever produce electricity?

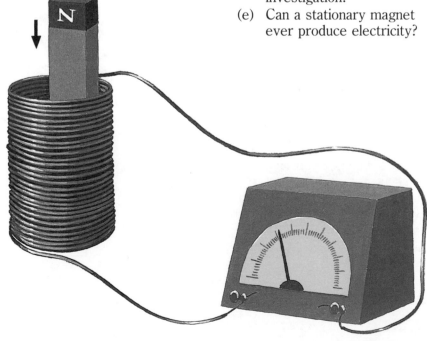

Part 2
Francesca's Experiment

Francesca planned an experiment based on the one she did in Part 1 of this Exploration. She started with a wire coil of thirteen turns. Illustrations (a) to (c) show the average galvanometer readings she recorded. Then she used a coil with twice as many turns.

Illustrations (d) and (e) show her average readings. Francesca tried each part of this experiment three times and obtained similar results each time. What conclusions do you think she drew for each part? Below the illustrations are some hints.

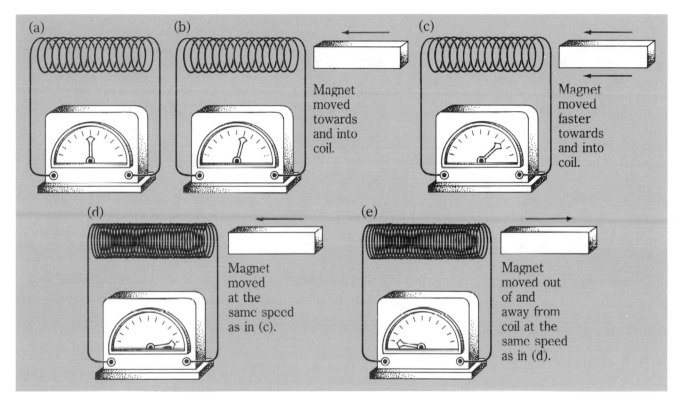

(a)

(b)
Magnet moved towards and into coil.

(c)
Magnet moved faster towards and into coil.

(d)
Magnet moved at the same speed as in (c).

(e)
Magnet moved out of and away from coil at the same speed as in (d).

1. When a magnet moves toward a coil of wire, ___?___ is detected in the wire. It ___?___ its direction when the magnet moves away from the coil.

2. A larger current is produced if ___?___ or if ___?___ .

Suppose Francesca moved the magnet in and out of the coil 15 times per minute. What would happen to the current? How many times per minute would the current go in one direction, then in the opposite direction?

Here is a slightly different experiment that Francesca did. She kept a magnet stationary but moved the wire. What should she conclude from this experiment? What else might she have done in this experiment? What do you predict would be the motion of the needle of the galvanometer if Francesca moved the wire up and down 10 times per minute? What would happen to the current in the wire? How would this current be different from that produced by a dry cell?

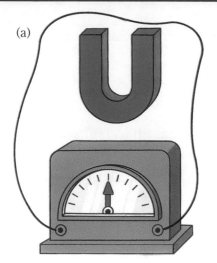

(a)

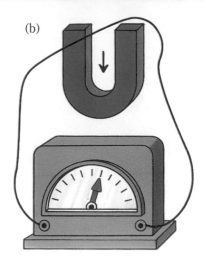

(b)

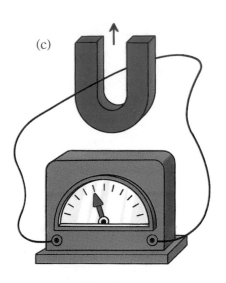

(c)

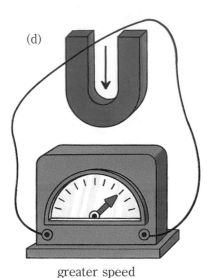

(d)

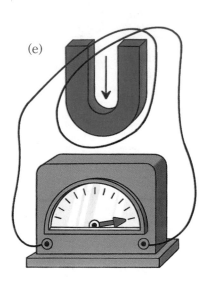

(e)

greater speed

Which of the circuits below, A or B, has direct current? alternating current? Direct current (D.C.) always flows in the same direction. Alternating current (A.C.) continually reverses its direction.

motion of magnet

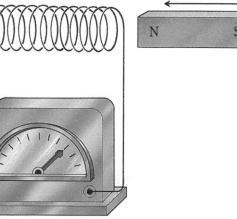

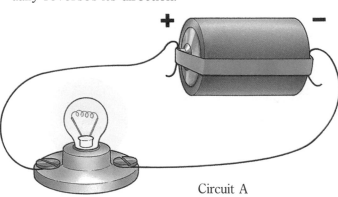

Circuit A

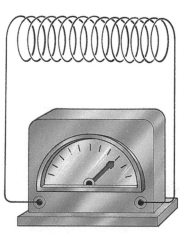

Circuit B

Large Scale Electrical Production: More Technology

Large amounts of electricity are needed in homes and by industries. This energy is produced by an adaptation of the moving magnet-coil arrangement which you have just investigated. In the Exploration you were only able to get small amounts of current by this method. How might you adapt it to produce larger currents?

You will discover ways of producing larger currents by examining the construction and operation of a bicycle dynamo and of the generators used in large power plants.

The Bicycle Dynamo

The bicycle dynamo is a common application of the electromagnetic principle you discovered in Exploration 5. Whenever a magnet moves in the presence of a coil of wire which is part of a circuit, a current of electricity flows in the circuit. Also, if a coil of wire moves near a stationary magnet, the same effect occurs. Rather than a back-and-forth motion, it is easier to use a rotary motion of the magnet or the coil of wire. In the 'exploded' view of the dynamo shown here, look for a magnet that rotates near a coil of wire (B). The dynamo is shown with its parts separated to help you see how it works.

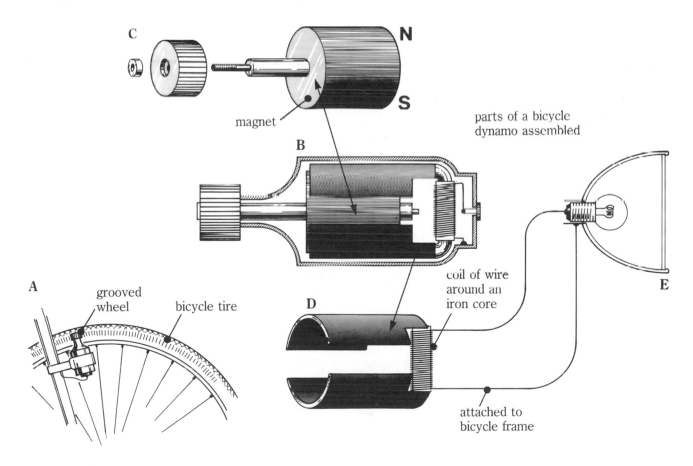

C

N

S

magnet

parts of a bicycle dynamo assembled

B

coil of wire around an iron core

E

A

grooved wheel

bicycle tire

D

attached to bicycle frame

Analyze the dynamo's construction and operation:

1. Locate the magnet in B and C.

2. How does the magnet move? See A, B, and C.

3. Locate the conducting wire that is wound on an iron core attached to a metal casing. The casing helps to transmit the effect of the magnet to the coil, just as if the magnet were actually moving in and out of the coil.

4. Trace the complete electric circuit.

5. Is this an application of the first or second part of Francesca's experiment?

6. The current Francesca got was very small — it could be detected only by a sensitive galvanometer. The current developed in the dynamo is hundreds of times greater — enough to light a bicycle light. What factors in the dynamo design could account for the larger current? Which of Francesca's experiments support your answers?

A Look at Large Generators

Generators like the dynamo use moving magnets to generate electricity in coils of wire. Study the illustration, which shows a large generator. What features of it account for the great amount of electrical energy it can produce? Which parts of Francesca's experiments support your answer?

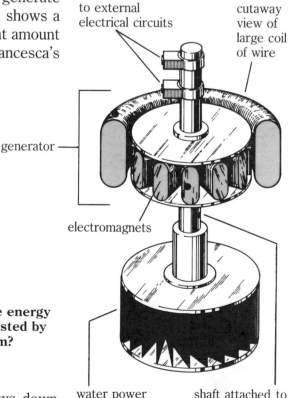

to external electrical circuits

cutaway view of large coil of wire

generator —

electromagnets

water power turns the blades of the turbine

shaft attached to turbine below and magnets above

What is the energy story suggested by this diagram?

Tracing the Flow of Energy

Water in the reservoir has ___?___ energy. As it flows down the runway (sluiceway), this energy changes into ___?___ energy of the moving water. The moving water forces the ___?___ to turn, giving it ___?___ to rotate. The attached ___?___ turn inside a stationary ___?___ in which ___?___ is produced. The resulting energy of the generator operation is ___?___ energy.

Other Generating Stations — A Topic for Research

Trace the path of operations in both the nuclear electric and thermal electric generating stations. Compare them with hydro-electric generators. How are thermal and nuclear electrical generation similar? Research large scale electrical production in your province: what percentage of your electricity is generated by each method? Are there any social or environmental controversies associated with the way electricity is produced in your province?

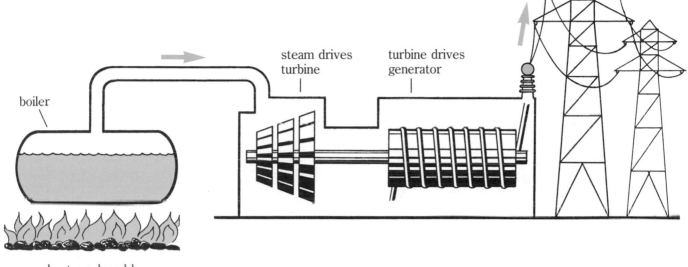

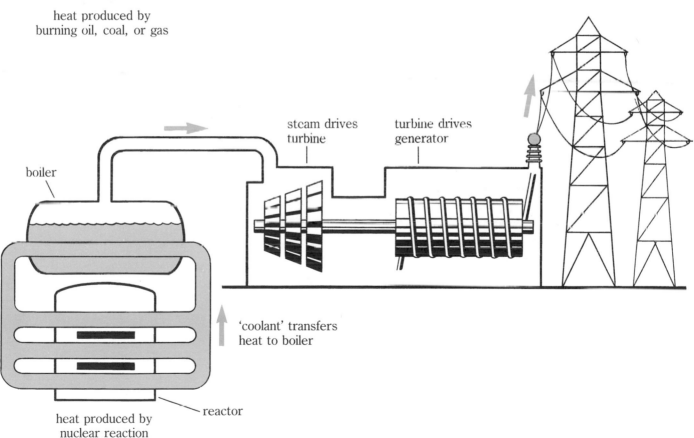

Alternating Currents

In her experiments, Francesca generated an electric current only momentarily. She was able to do this by moving either the magnet or the wire. In the drawing to the right it is the wire that is being moved. The drawing below shows how to convert Francesca's method into a more effective generator that can produce enough electricity to light a bulb. It will also help to explain how alternating current is produced on a large scale.

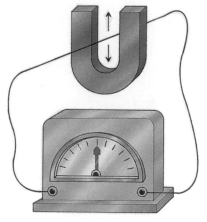

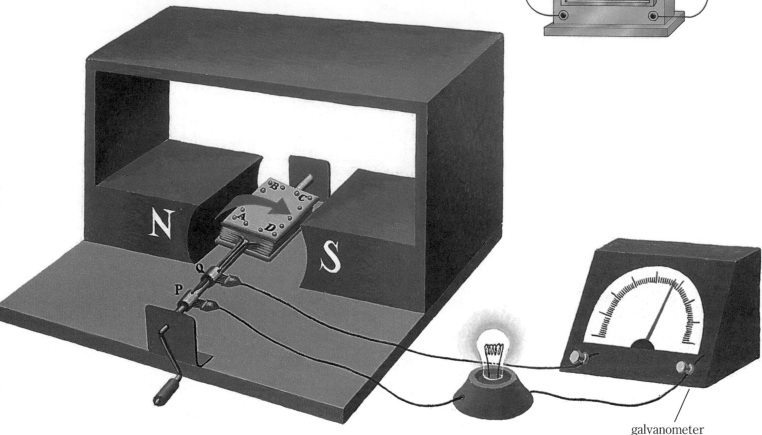

galvanometer

Examine the illustration closely. What is used instead of a single wire? How is the wire moved? How is this motion different from that in Francesca's experiment? What is different in the construction of this generator and the bicycle dynamo?

There are many coils of insulated wire wound around a holder which is attached to the axle. The axle can be turned by a handle so that the coils of wire rotate in the space between the north and south poles of a permanent horseshoe magnet. Attached to the axle, called an **armature**, are two separate metal rings P and Q.

How does this generator produce an A.C. current? Imagine that you could see the first turn of wire of the coil ABCD. The end A is attached to ring Q. The end D then is coiled around the armature many times until it is finally attached to ring P.

Brushes conduct the current developed in the coil to and from the external circuit containing a bulb and a current meter.

1. Trace the path starting at ring Q then to A, B, . . . until you go through the complete circuit and back to Q.

2. Suppose that when the handle of the armature is turned slowly so that section AB of the wire coil moves upwards, the current goes from A to B. Trace the direction of current around the coil to the correct ring and brushes and to the external circuit. Is the current going from left to right or from right to left through the light bulb?

3. After one half-turn of the armature, AB will be moving down. (See the simplified drawing.) In which direction will the current go now? (Remember Francesca's experiment.) Trace the direction of the current once more around the complete circuit. In which direction is the current now moving through the light bulb? Convince yourself that with every half-turn the current through the galvanometer and lamp will reverse its direction.

4. If the armature made sixty full turns in one second, how many times would the current go first in one direction, then in the other direction? Each time the armature turns once, it completes one cycle. In this cycle the current goes in one direction, then reverses direction completely.

The current entering your home makes sixty complete cycles in one second. Have you noticed "60 Hz" (sixty hertz) marked on an appliance? It means that the appliance operates on a current of sixty cycles per second. The hertz is the metric unit for "one cycle per second."

Whether a magnet rotates inside a stationary coil of wire or a coil of wire rotates between the poles of a stationary magnet, an alternating current results. Whether a current is direct or alternating does not affect its use with most thermoelectric devices. Why not?

Direct Currents

On page 273 you were introduced to a chemical cell, its contents, and how it works. Why does the current go in just one direction in a chemical cell? Studying the diagram will help you answer this question.

Direct currents are needed instead of alternating current for many circuits, for example, those in automobiles. Silver or copper plating also requires a direct current, and so do battery chargers.

Since A.C. current is so readily available, is it possible to change A.C. into D.C. for those circuits requiring D.C.? Is it possible to get rid of the current going in the reverse direction? The following Exploration suggests one way.

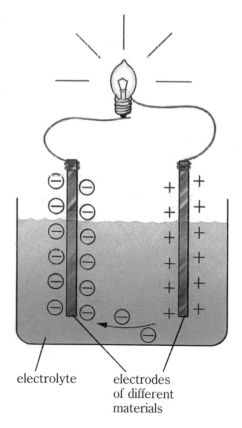

electrolyte

electrodes of different materials

Diodes

You Will Need

- dry cell in holder
- diode (IN400Z)
- bulb and holder
- connecting wire
- 2 alligator clamps

What To Do

1. Assemble the circuit shown (1). Does the bulb light?

2. Turn the battery around to make the current go in the opposite direction (2). What do you observe?

3. The diode is like a valve. Observe the drawing which shows a funnel through which water can flow in one direction but whose flow in the other direction is blocked by a ball valve. Do you see why?

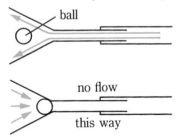

Diodes are also valves that allow one-way travel of electrons. The next section introduces circuit symbols, which scientists use for drawing circuits. The symbol for a diode looks something like a funnel. Its shape will help you to remember the direction of electron flow through a diode. When you draw a diode symbol, think of its funnel shape, and the funnel, ball and water analogy will show you the direction of flow of electrons.

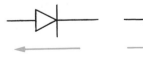

Electrons can flow this way through the diode funnel.

Electrons cannot flow this way through the diode.

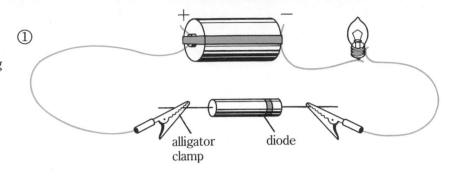

① alligator clamp   diode

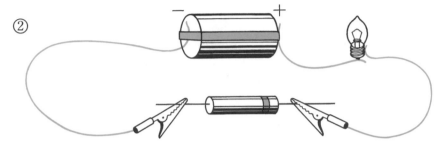

②

4. (a) Will the bulb light in any of the following circuits?

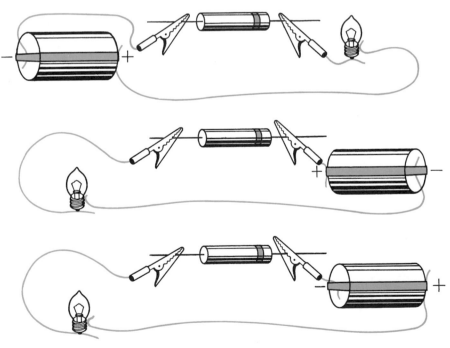

(b) What effect will a diode have on alternating current? Suppose an alternating current is passed through an appropriate size of diode. What do you think happens to the current that flows through the diode? Why? This is an important use of a diode.

CAUTION: Never connect a diode to a dry cell without a light bulb in the same circuit.

More About Circuits and Currents

Circuit Components

In many of the circuits that follow you will be using bulbs, cells, and switches. If you have not already designed bulb and cell holders, switches, and connecting clamps, it would be good to do so now. All of these are available commercially but you may wish to create your own.

The illustrations show some designs of circuit components which were made by students.

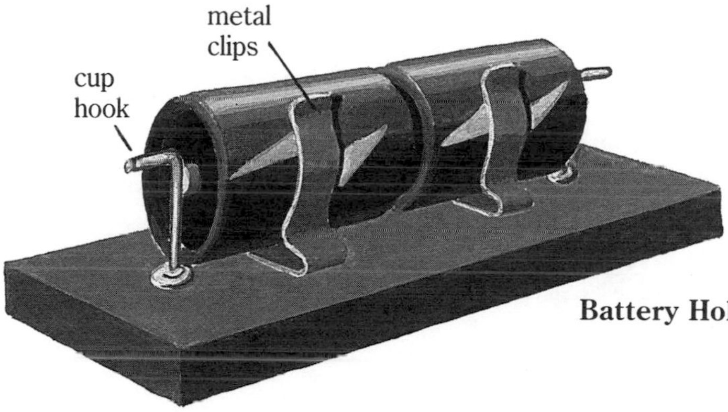

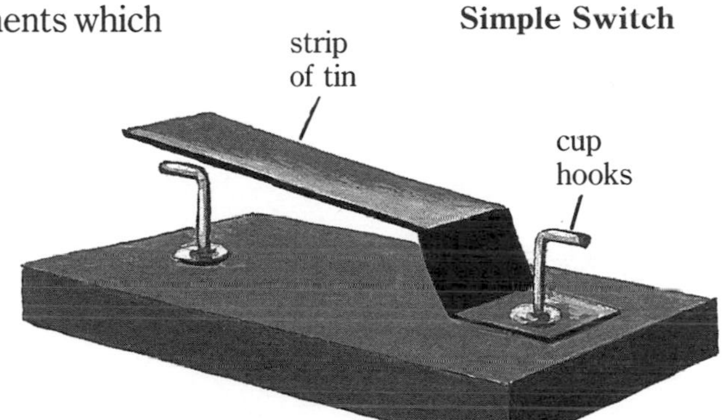

Simple Switch

strip of tin

cup hooks

cup hook

metal clips

Battery Holder

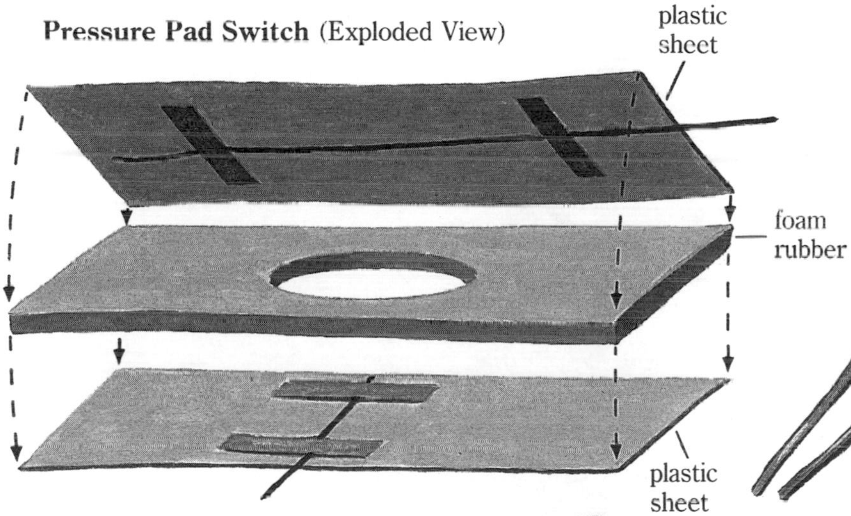

Pressure Pad Switch (Exploded View)

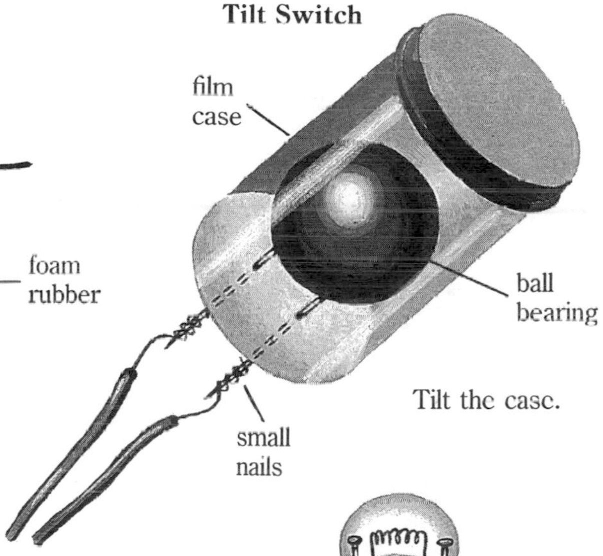

plastic sheet

foam rubber

plastic sheet

Tilt Switch

film case

ball bearing

Tilt the case.

small nails

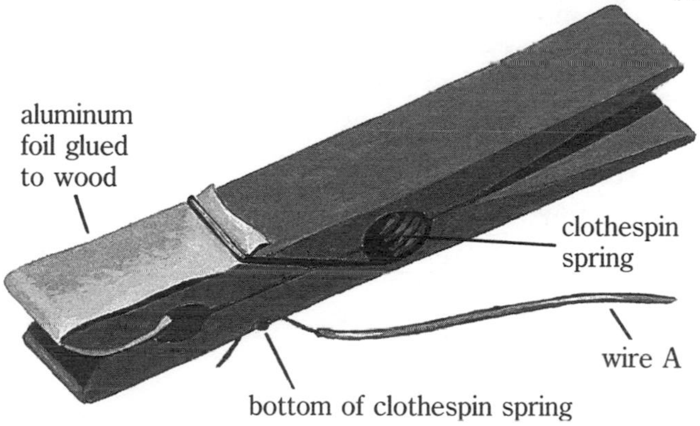

aluminum foil glued to wood

Alligator Clamp

clothespin spring

wire A

bottom of clothespin spring

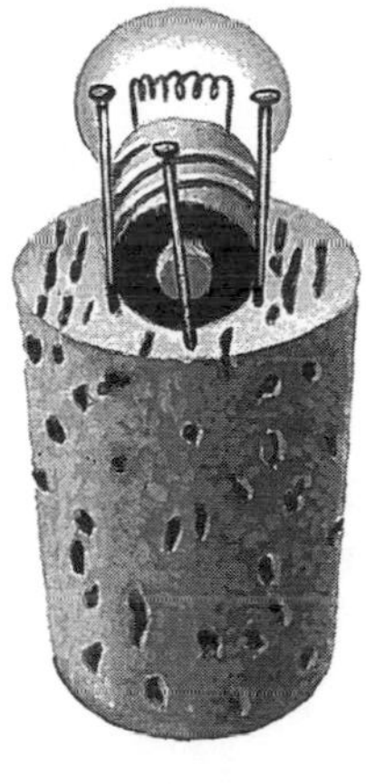

Simple Bulb Holder

Circuit Symbols

People depend on symbols and signs instead of words in many situations. Scientists, engineers, and electricians use symbols in circuit diagrams when designing and maintaining electric circuits. Familiarize yourself with the following circuit symbols.

| | = cell (The long line represents the positive end.)

|∎|∎|∎ = battery of three cells

——— = conducting wire

= lamp

= coil of wire

= switch

= galvanometer

Examine how they are used to represent this circuit.

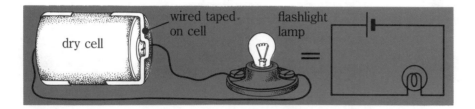

How would you draw a circuit symbol diagram for the circuit below?

Try drawing circuit diagrams for each of the circuits in Explorations 1 and 3.

An Incredible Trip

We normally observe on a large scale. However, it can be interesting to view objects on the microscopic scale. But what would it be like to see and experience on the scale of an electron? If you were an electron, could you describe a trip through the circuits you have just drawn? Write about one circuit that interests you and incorporate what you know about electrons, charges, and circuits in your description.

A Conduction Problem to Investigate

The Problem: Do all wires conduct an electric current equally well? Here are some questions to investigate as you seek an answer to this problem.

A. Does the kind of metal affect the production of current?
B. What is the effect of different thicknesses of wire?
C. Does the length of wire influence the current?
D. What happens if a wire resists the flow of current?

You Will Need

- thin copper wire
- thin nichrome wire
- thick nichrome wire
- wooden dowel
- dry cells
- flashlight lamp
- newspaper
- cardboard container
- aluminum foil
- paper clips
- rubber bands

Part 1
Investigating Questions A and B

1. Prepare equal lengths of the three wires which you will test.

2. Set up the circuit as shown in the illustration, using one of the three wires. Observe the brightness of the light.

3. Do the same for each of the other wires. Observe the lamp in each case.

Conclusions

(a) Is it easier for a current to flow through thin nichrome wire or thin copper wire?

(b) Is it easier for a current to pass through thin nichrome wire or thick nichrome wire?

(c) How might you explain your observations?

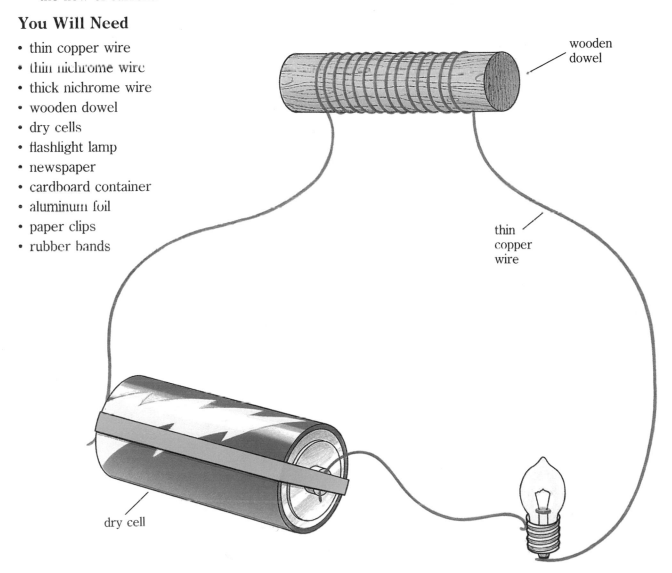

wooden dowel

thin copper wire

dry cell

Part 2
Investigating Question C

Vary the length of the thin nichrome wire in the circuit by placing the contact wires at different points along the wire. Observe the lamp.

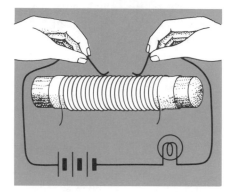

Conclusions

(d) Is it easier for a current to pass through a long or short piece of nichrome wire?

(e) How might you explain this observation?

Do your answers for (d) and (e) match the information below?

Interpreting Parts 1 and 2

Some wires do not allow electric charges to move through them as readily as others. In other words, these wires offer more resistance to the flow of the charges. Which offers more resistance: nichrome or copper wire? Thin or thick nichrome wire? Long or short nichrome wire?

Resistance can be compared to friction. In what ways do you think they are similar?

Friction

Flick a coin with your finger. It moves a little, slows down, and stops. What causes this slowing down? As the coin slows down and stops, where does the kinetic energy of the moving coin go? Here's how you can find out. Produce a large amount of friction by placing your finger firmly on the coin and rubbing it back and forth a dozen times on a table top. Now touch the coin to your lips. What kind of energy was produced?

Kinetic Energy → Heat Energy

Resistance

Resistance is like friction. Electrons flow because they receive electrical energy from a cell. As the electrons flow through a piece of nichrome wire, the wire resists the flow of the electrons— in much the same way that the nails resist the rolling marbles in the illustration.

If the nails were a little closer together, what effect would they have on the rolling ball? Would this situation represent a wire with more, or less, resistance?

What form of energy do you predict will be produced from the electrical (kinetic) energy of the electrons as they are slowed down?

You will check your prediction in Part 3.

Part 3
Investigating Question D

Connect the circuit as shown. Note that no lamp is included. Wrap the wire with newspaper, then watch it for one minute. Now disconnect the circuit and unwrap the newspaper. Touch the wire carefully.

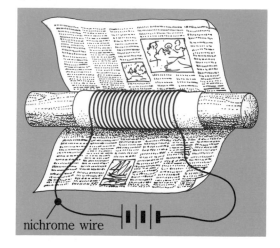

nichrome wire

Conclusions

(f) When a wire resists the flow of current, what happens?

(g) What energy change is taking place in the nichrome wire?

Any conductor that offers considerable resistance is called a resistor and is represented by the symbol ⎓⎔⎓ . Using circuit symbols, draw a circuit containing two dry cells, a coil of nichrome wire, a switch, and a bulb.

Applications of Resistance

What could you use resistors for? You have found that they produce heat and inferred that they slow down the flow of current. Each of these characteristics is useful.

1. *Heating Devices*. Nichrome wire has a large resistance. It is used to produce heat in many household appliances such as irons and toasters. Appliances which produce heat when an electric current flows through them are called **thermoelectric** devices. Why is this a good name for them?

    Make an on-site survey of the thermoelectric devices used in your home or school or in a workplace; write a list of them. Also include the rate at which they consume electrical energy and produce heat energy. How do you do this? Look at an information plate, or engravings on the appliance, for the number of **watts**. One watt means that 1 joule of energy is produced or used in one second. So a 1000 watt electric kettle uses 1000 J in 1 s. How much energy would it take to boil a kettle of water?

2. *Reducing Current Flow*. In Part 2 of Exploration 7, you were using the nichrome wire as a variable resistor (or *rheostat*). Why is this called a variable resistor? What might be a use for it? Such resistors are in common use; the volume control of a radio is one example. Look at the picture of one kind of commercial rheostat used for currents. Do you see how the resistance is varied?

The bottom of an electric kettle—a thermoelectric device

Rheostat

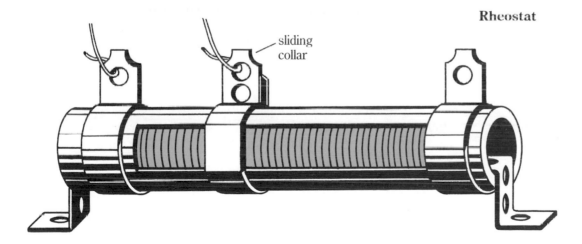

sliding collar

A Project

Here is a practical project. Convert the arrangement used in Part 2 of Exploration 7 into a durable rheostat. What might you use it for?

Making Circuits Work for You

How have you made use of electric circuits in the last twenty-four hours? How have they worked for you? Constructing simple circuits to perform functions is the challenge of the next Exploration.

Constructing Circuits

You Will Need

- sandpaper
- 6 copper wires (each 10 cm long)
- masking tape
- 3 cells
- 3 flashlight bulbs in holders
- 2 contact switches

Part 1
Exploring

You can devise any circuits you wish. Use some or all of the equipment listed above to construct your circuits. Make any arrangements desired. If you want to use more than one dry cell and do not have a holder, you can use masking tape to hold them together. If the bulbs light up, you have complete circuits. After constructing your circuits, draw them using circuit symbols. Suppose that a certain number of electrons flow out of the cell(s) in a given time. Describe the path(s) taken by these electrons.

CAUTION: Dry cells quickly drain if left in a closed circuit without sufficient resistance (for example, a bulb). If a switch is placed in the circuit and kept open until you check the circuit's operation, you will conserve the dry cells.

Part 2
Solving Circuit Problems

The following are a series of circuit problems. What arrangement of circuit components would you make to accomplish the functions described in each problem?

First make a circuit diagram of your proposed solution. Then construct the circuit:

1. A circuit that will light two bulbs, A and B, at the same time when the switch is closed. If A is unscrewed, B also goes out; and vice versa. This type of circuit is known as a **series** circuit.

2. A circuit that will light two bulbs, A and B, at the same time when the switch is closed. If A is unscrewed, B stays lit; and vice versa. This is known as a **parallel circuit**.

3. A circuit which contains three bulbs, A, B, and C. If A is unscrewed, then B and C go out. If B is unscrewed, A and C stay lit. If C is unscrewed, A and B stay lit.

4. A circuit with two bulbs and two switches, P and Q. When P and Q are closed, both bulbs come on. If either switch is opened, no bulbs light.

5. A circuit that contains two switches and two bulbs. If both switches are open, no light shines. If either one of the switches is closed, both bulbs light.

6. Analyze your findings.
   (a) Where have you used series circuits before in this unit?
   (b) Is there any parallel circuitry in the room where you are now? How could you find out?
   CAUTION: Don't expose high-voltage wiring.
   (c) Circuit 5 contains both series and parallel arrangements. Identify them.
   (d) Identify the type(s) of arrangement(s) in circuit 4.

Part 3
Current Questions to Investigate

Fact: The brightness of the light bulb is a measure of the amount of current flowing.

You Will Need

- light bulbs
- switches
- batteries
- copper wire

What To Do

Construct each of the circuits shown in the table, and record the results in your notebook in a similar table. Make certain that switches are included in the circuits you construct.

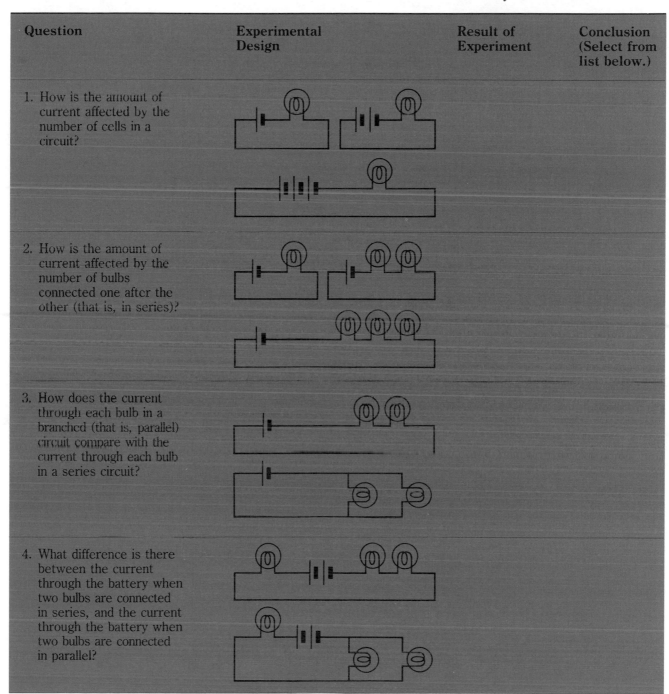

Question	Experimental Design	Result of Experiment	Conclusion (Select from list below.)
1. How is the amount of current affected by the number of cells in a circuit?			
2. How is the amount of current affected by the number of bulbs connected one after the other (that is, in series)?			
3. How does the current through each bulb in a branched (that is, parallel) circuit compare with the current through each bulb in a series circuit?			
4. What difference is there between the current through the battery when two bulbs are connected in series, and the current through the battery when two bulbs are connected in parallel?			

Below are a number of statements with options. Each statement, with the correct option, is a valid conclusion for one of the four experiments you just did. Choose appropriate conclusions for each experiment.

(a) Connecting bulbs one after another in a circuit (decreases, increases) the amount of current flowing in the circuit.

(b) If the number of cells are increased in the circuit, the amount of current is (decreased, increased).

(c) If more bulbs are connected in series in a circuit, the resistance of a circuit is (decreased, increased).

(d) If two lamps are placed in a branched circuit rather than in an unbranched circuit, the current through the battery is (decreased, increased).

(e) Arranging lamps in parallel rather in series (decreases, increases) the current through each lamp.

(f) The resistance of a circuit is decreased when the bulbs are placed in (series, parallel).

(g) The resistance of a circuit is (more, less) with three bulbs in series than with two bulbs in parallel connected to a third in series.

How Bright Are You? — A Quiz

How well can you apply what you discovered in Exploration 8? In the circuits shown on the next page, choose the correct brightness (S for standard brightness; L for less than standard; M for more than standard) for each of the twenty numbered bulbs. All bulbs are identical in their construction.

First note the three illustrated degrees of brightness L, S, and M. The standard brightness, S, to which L and M are compared, is the brightness of a single bulb connected to a single dry cell.

Indicate your choices in a table similar to this one. Be prepared to defend your choices. Number 1 is done for you.

This bulb gives standard brightness

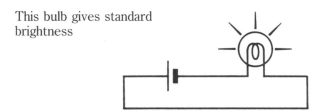

less than standard (L)

more than standard (M)

Situation	L, S, or M
1	S
2	
3	
etc.	

Scorecard

Over 15   You dazzle me!

10–15   You are bright!

Under 10   You need enlightenment!

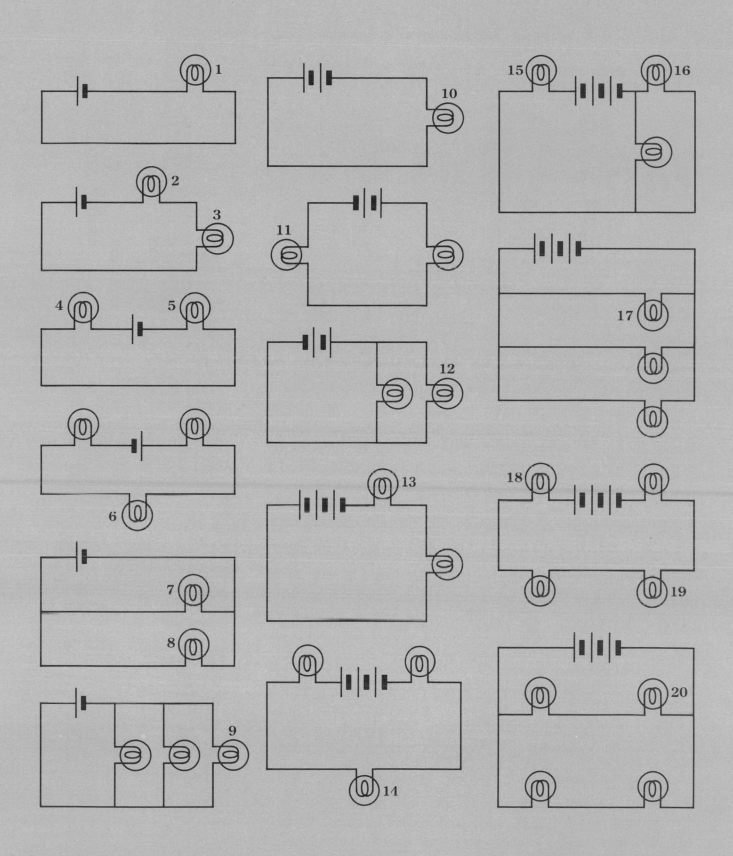

Controlling the Current

". . CKHB is on the air . . . Jim Murphy bringing you the 7 A.M. Morning Show. . . . Get a cup of coffee! Sit . . . or lie down and relax! First the news-tick tick tick tick-STRONG WINDS AND FLOODS threaten . . ."

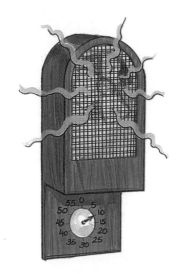

With this sound Nick awoke with a start, looked at the time on the radio clock that had just come on, turned it down, and jumped out of bed . . . In the bathroom he turned on the fan timer switch for 10 min . . . Now at breakfast, he pushed down the bread in the toaster. In a few minutes golden brown toast popped up . . . Knowing he would be getting home late that night, Nick set the oven to come on at 7:00 P.M. to cook the casserole for one hour. Already late, Nick jumped into his car, backed out of the driveway to the sound of the beeper telling him to buckle up . . . When Nick returned that night, his apartment was already lit. The sensor light in the hallway had come on, and shining brightly in the front room was the burglar safety light . . . and best of all there was a delectable smell in the air. He dimmed the kitchen lights and sat down to a relaxing meal.

Automation! More and more people depend on various types of circuits, switches, and controls to make life easier and more convenient. Although you may not know how they work, you are well able to make use of them.

(a) How many automatic devices are mentioned in this story?
(b) Which of these devices have switches which just turn electricity on or off?
(c) What are some of the kinds of control that affect what is being accomplished by the appliances and electrical devices?
(d) Which of these switches or controls operate by mechanical means? by response to light? by some other means?

Simple Current Controls

Here are two circuits which control the operation of a light bulb. Which contains just an on/off control? What does the other control do? How?

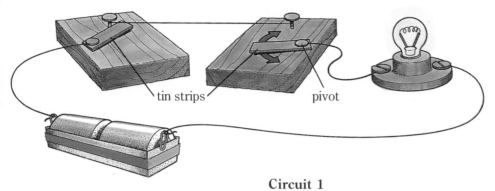

Circuit 1

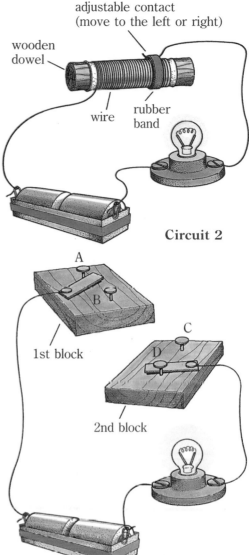

Circuit 2

Anne's conversion of Circuit 1

Draw a circuit diagram for each circuit.

Anne converted the switch in Circuit 1 into another kind of switch by adding more nails to the wooden blocks as shown in the diagram.

The metal strips on each wooden block can pivot easily between the two nails A and B, and between C and D. She then connected wires between the two blocks so that the following things happen:

1. When the strip in the first block moved from A to B, the light came on.

2. Then she moved the strip on the second block from D to C and the light went out.

3. Next she moved the first strip from B to A; the light came on.

4. Finally she moved the second strip from C to D; the light went out.

Where did Anne connect the two wires between the two blocks? Where have you seen switches which operate in a similar way to those Anne constructed?

Circuit 2 causes a variation in the amount of electrical energy supplied to the light bulb. Circuit 2 has an application in the common dimmer switch, which you can buy to replace the normal flip switch controlling ceiling lights in a room.

Can you imagine what the inside of a dimmer switch looks like? As you turn the knob counter-clockwise the lights in the circuit become dimmer. Sketch what you think might be inside the "black box" which causes it to perform its function.

A Design Challenge

Use the lead in a pencil to construct a dimmer switch for a flashlight bulb powered by a dry cell.

CAUTION: Be sure that the power is off before installing a dimmer switch.

A Switch in Time!

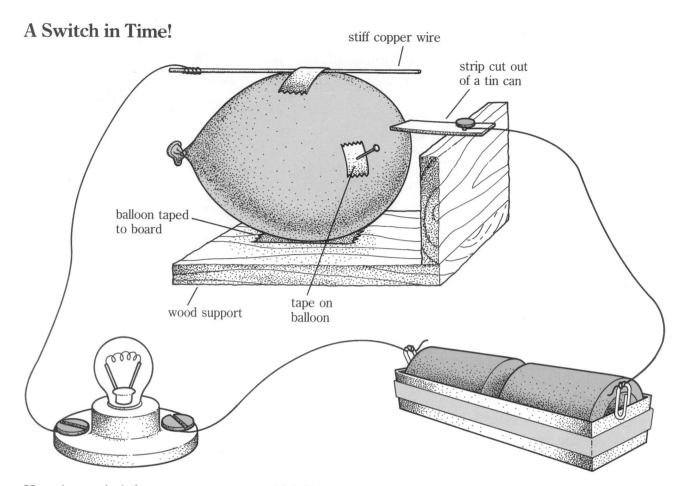

stiff copper wire

strip cut out
of a tin can

balloon taped
to board

wood support

tape on
balloon

Here is a switch for you to construct which illustrates the principle of time delay. To operate it, puncture the tape on the end of the balloon with a small sharp pin. This allows the air to escape slowly from the balloon.

1. How does this switch operate?

2. How long was the delay from the puncturing of the balloon to the lighting of the bulb?

3. What is one disadvantage of this switch?

4. Can you think of switches in your home that have a time delay?

5. Timer switches can turn a circuit on immediately, or after a time delay, and then turn the circuit off after another delay. Can you identify some uses for timer switches?

For example, here is a common type of clock mechanism timer switch. It could be used to operate a fan for a given period of time. For how many minutes is the timer switch set? In which direction is the switch moving? Can you think of how the circuit might be broken when zero is reached?

What are some common applications of "timed" switches? You will find some in Nick's story. How many of these seem to operate on a mechanical clock mechanism?

You remember that Nick awoke to the morning broadcast on the radio. Some radio alarm clocks have a motor mechanism to turn the electrical circuit containing the radio on and off. Study the drawing of the mechanism. Explain how it works.

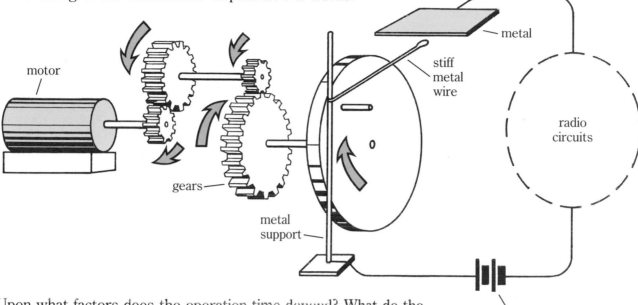

Upon what factors does the operation time depend? What do the gears do?

A Heat Switch

In the pictured circuit the bimetallic strip is the switch. The term bimetallic means that there are two metals that are bonded together. Note what happens when a bimetallic strip is heated. Why does this occur? How does this characteristic break or close a circuit? What type of energy is operating this switch?

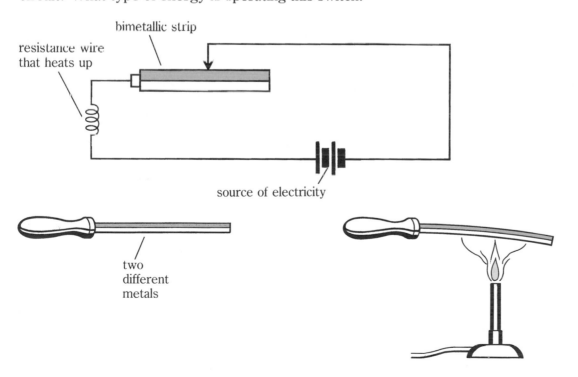

Sometimes, as in thermostats, bimetallic strips are in the form of spring-like coils. Heat causes them to tighten up. Study the circuit containing Switch A. How does the bimetallic strip break the circuit? How would the circuit be closed again? Where might this method of control be used?

One application of the bimetallic strip is in thermostats or temperature controls. Here is a sketch of a thermostat which controls the operation of a furnace. Study it closely. How does this switch work? Can you visualize the whole electric circuit and the conducting path through the thermostat?

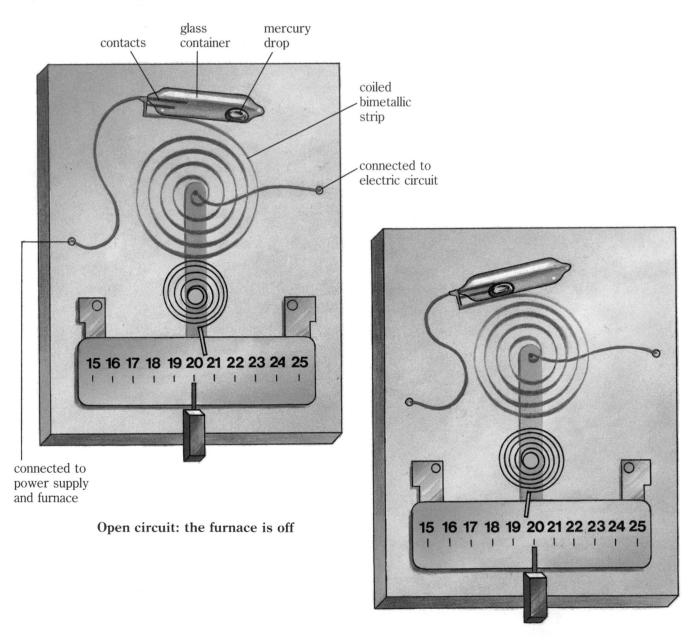

contacts glass container mercury drop

coiled bimetallic strip

connected to electric circuit

connected to power supply and furnace

Open circuit: the furnace is off

Closed circuit: the furnace is on

A Magnetic Switch

Observe the two illustrations of the magnetic switch. How does it operate? What must be a characteristic of the metals making contact in the switch if the switch is to open when the magnet is moved away? Could just any metal be used, for example, copper? (Try bringing a magnet close to copper wire.) What kind of energy operates this switch? Why would this magnetic switch be appropriate for poor environmental situations such as water, mud, or snow? If you were to buy this switch commercially, you would ask for a Reed switch.

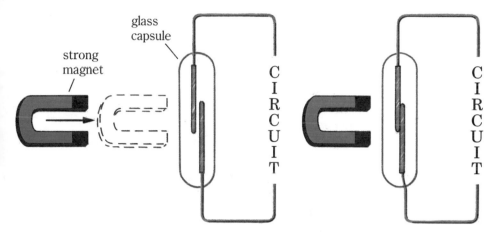

A Lever Switch

The switch shown is an example of a commercially available lever type of switch. Note in the illustration that if the lever is pushed upwards lightly, Circuit 1 is broken and Circuit 2 is closed. Picture the arrangement inside the switch. Draw it. Invent a situation where a lever switch might be of value.

If you visit an electrical shop, you will find many other kinds of switches, components, and circuit controls.

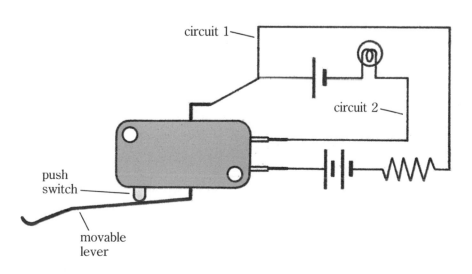

Switched On!

Apply the experience you have gained thus far to design and construct one or two of the following circuits. Follow these steps:

1. Brainstorm possible solutions with one or two classmates.
2. Choose the best solution.
3. Draw your design.
4. Assemble the materials and construct a model of it.
5. Suggest and try possible improvements.
6. Decide a good application for the circuit.

Problems

(a) Construct a circuit with two lamps and two switches. Each switch operates one lamp only.

(b) Construct a circuit with two lamps and three switches. One switch turns on both lamps; the other switches can turn the lamps off one at a time.

(c) Construct a circuit with a lamp, a switch, and a brightness control.

(d) Construct a model circuit of a doorbell operated by two different push buttons.

(e) Construct a circuit with a time switch other than the balloon one.

(f) Construct a circuit containing a simple switch that could be operated by a magnet.

(g) Construct a circuit that is closed when a given temperature is reached.

Electromagnets

Electromagnets are current magnets. You have already made a kind of electromagnet when you made a galvanometer. The current-bearing coil of wire acted like a magnet and affected the magnetic compass needle. Look at the circuit in the accompanying diagram. This arrangement of a spike and a coil of wire is called an electromagnet.

Electromagnets enable electricity to work for us in many more new ways. An electromagnet consists of a core of soft iron or soft steel, surrounded by a coil of insulated wire. (Why must the wire be insulated?) When the current flows through the wire, the core quickly becomes a temporary magnet. Note that there is a switch in the circuit to allow the circuit to be disconnected easily. Why should the switch not be closed for too long?

Working with an Electromagnet

You Will Need

- paper clips
- washers
- thin insulated copper wire
- battery
- iron spike
- switch

What To Do

Choose two or three classmates to work with you. Your task will be to make a functioning electromagnet, then to discover how its strength can be increased.

Making an Electromagnet

Use the materials illustrated to make an electromagnet that will support a paper clip from which some washers are hanging. Identify the parts of the circuit and trace the path of the current. The circuit consists of a dry cell, copper-conducting wire, and a switch. Note that the spike, paper clip, and washers are not part of the circuit. How many washers can your first design hold?

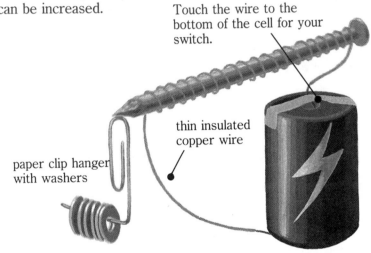

Touch the wire to the bottom of the cell for your switch.

thin insulated copper wire

paper clip hanger with washers

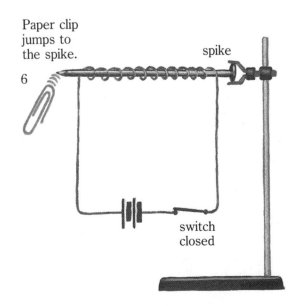

Paper clip jumps to the spike.

spike

switch closed

Increasing the Electromagnet's Strength

How can you make your electromagnet hold more washers? Before you do an experiment to increase the strength of the electromagnet, you must design the experiment. Take time to discuss the following:

• apparatus
• factors or variables that might be altered
• ways to measure the magnet's strength
• safety precautions
• recording results

Present an outline of your design for approval. Then assemble the necessary apparatus, do the experiment, record the results, and draw conclusions based on your results.

A huge lifting electromagnet. How does it release its load? In the metal recycling industry, electromagnets are used to sort out the iron from scrap piles.

Puzzling Circuits

Often, when you buy a model airplane or a bicycle repair manual, you spend time puzzling over the diagrams. The diagrams show how something operates, or how parts should be assembled. The following are five diagrams of circuits containing electromagnets. In groups of three or four, determine how any two of the circuits work. A few hints are provided in some of the drawings.

A good plan is to begin with the source of the electricity, then follow the path of the complete circuit back to its source. For example, in the doorbell circuit, when the "bell push" is pushed down, the circuit is complete. Electrons flow along this path: battery, wire, contact screw, springy metal strip of the armature, wire, coil, and back to the battery. Then retrace the path and think about what is happening in each part of the circuit, especially the electromagnet.

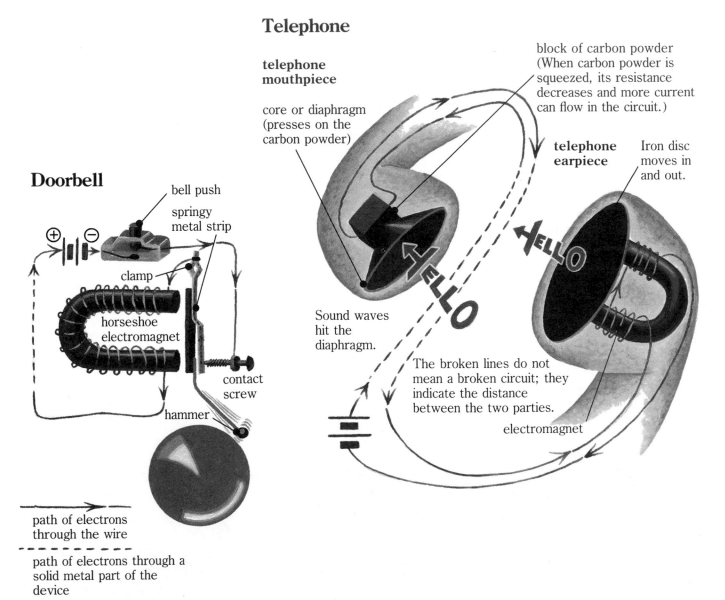

Telephone

telephone mouthpiece

core or diaphragm (presses on the carbon powder)

block of carbon powder (When carbon powder is squeezed, its resistance decreases and more current can flow in the circuit.)

telephone earpiece

Iron disc moves in and out.

Sound waves hit the diaphragm.

The broken lines do not mean a broken circuit; they indicate the distance between the two parties.

electromagnet

Doorbell

bell push

springy metal strip

clamp

horseshoe electromagnet

contact screw

hammer

path of electrons through the wire

path of electrons through a solid metal part of the device

Electric Buzzer

Why not try to make this device?

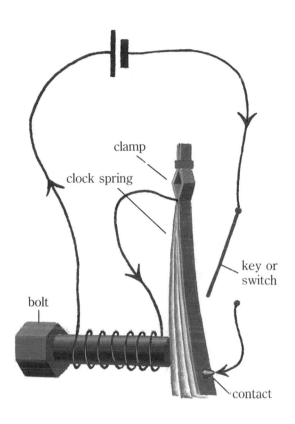

clamp

clock spring

key or switch

bolt

contact

Burglar Alarm

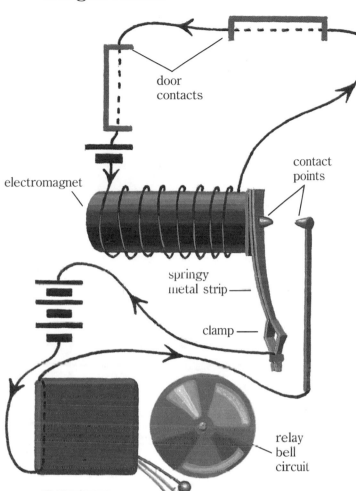

door contacts

electromagnet

contact points

springy metal strip

clamp

relay bell circuit

Car Starter

An electromagnet may be used to cause a small current in one complete circuit to initiate a large current in a second circuit. This is an example of a relay. In a car, for instance, a small current in the key switch circuit switches on a large current in the starter motor circuit.

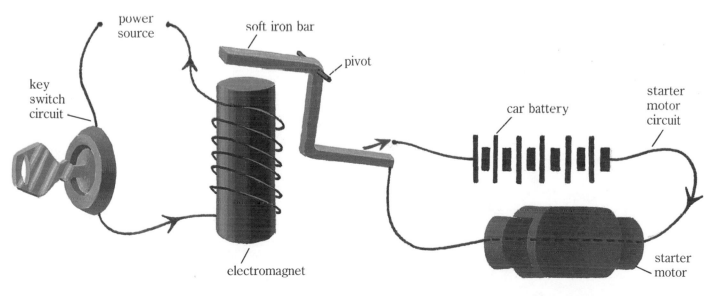

power source

soft iron bar

pivot

key switch circuit

car battery

starter motor circuit

electromagnet

starter motor

Constructing Model Relays

Part 1
Using an Electromagnetic Switch

Construct the following circuits controlled by a commercial electromagnetic switch.

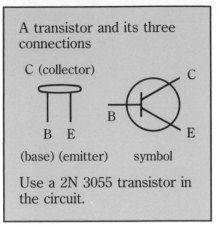

A transistor and its three connections

C (collector)

B E
(base) (emitter)   symbol

Use a 2N 3055 transistor in the circuit.

circuit B

circuit A

4.5 V

1.5 V

Where do you think such an arrangement might be useful?

Part 2
Using a Transistor

Note how similar the following circuit is to the one above. How is it different? Construct this relay.

CAUTION: A transistor needs a resistor (such as the bulb) in the circuit to keep the current through the transistor small.

Transistors are called semiconductors. In some situations they conduct electricity and in others they do not. Note that when Circuit A is open no current flows in circuit B. No bulbs light. Apparently the transistor blocks the flow. However, whenever Circuit A is closed, current flows in Circuit B. The transistor no longer blocks the flow of current, and the bulbs light up.

If you are interested in electronics, do a little research into transistors, their strange behaviour, and their widespread use in radios, television, computers and space technology. At the same time you will find out about integrated circuits.

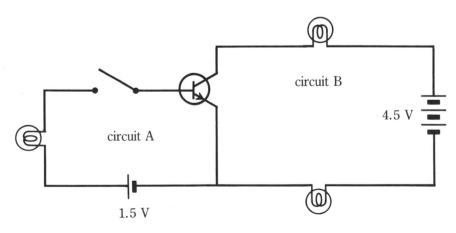

circuit B

circuit A

4.5 V

1.5 V

Moving Coils — Revolutionary!

One of the most common applications of electromagnets is the motor. Can you imagine life without its use? The invention of motors was revolutionary in more than one way!

The next time you look at a small motor, such as the one in a washing machine or furnace, look at the metal tag attached to it. You may see information similar to that shown here. Some of these word and symbols may be unfamiliar to you. What do you think "Rev." means? (Some tags use "RPM" instead.)

"Rev: 1500" means that the motor makes 1500 revolutions per minute. A revolution is one complete turn about a central axis.

What part does an electromagnet play in a motor? What part of a motor revolves? To find out, try this demonstration: assemble this device and close the circuit. What happens?

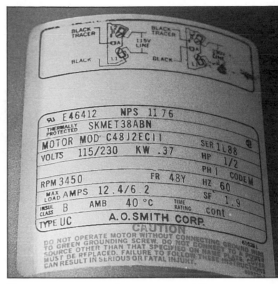

How many complete turns will this motor make in a minute?

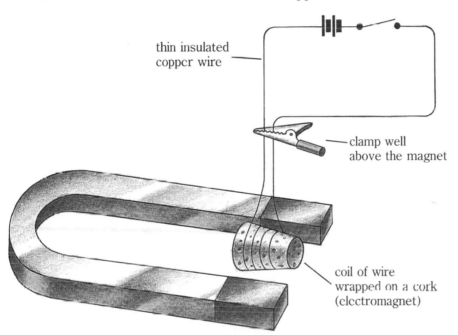

thin insulated copper wire

clamp well above the magnet

coil of wire wrapped on a cork (electromagnet)

The coil of wire acts like a magnet. When a current flows, the coil has North and South poles. If, as in the illustration, you grasp the coil with your left hand so that your fingers go in the direction of the flow of electrons, the position of your thumb gives you the North pole. Locate the N and S poles of the coil. What will be the interaction between the N pole of the magnet and the N pole of the coil? between the S pole of the magnet and the N pole of the coil? What other interactions are there? Convince yourself that the coil will rotate in the presence of the horseshoe magnet when a current is flowing. Will it turn clockwise or counter-clockwise? Can the coil make a complete turn? If you reverse the coil's connections with the battery after it has turned halfway, what would happen? What is it that causes a continuous rotary motion in a motor? Constructing a motor will help you see the importance of coil connections with the wires of the circuit.

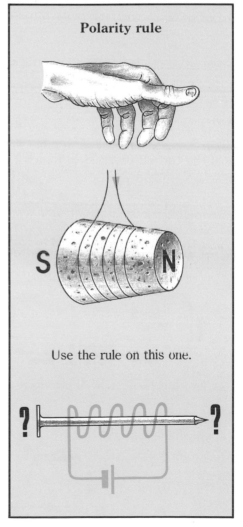

Polarity rule

Use the rule on this one.

A Model Motor

Before building this motor, read the labels and comments in each step.

1

channels for wire cut in the cork

2 pins pushed into the end of a cork

short knitting needle pushed through the middle of a cork

30 turns of thin insulated copper wire wound around the cork, starting at one pin and finishing at the other (Scrape insulation off wire at the point of contact with the pins.)

2

Plasticine to raise the magnets

ends of wire just touching the pins

N

S

tack to hold wire in such a way that the end just touches the pin

3 V or 4.5 V (2 or 3 dry cells)

3

Do you see how the direction of the current reverses in the coil?

C
D
B
A

direction of flow of electrons

Why must the circuit reverse to keep the armature going?

B
A
C
D

4

Cork has rotated one half turn.

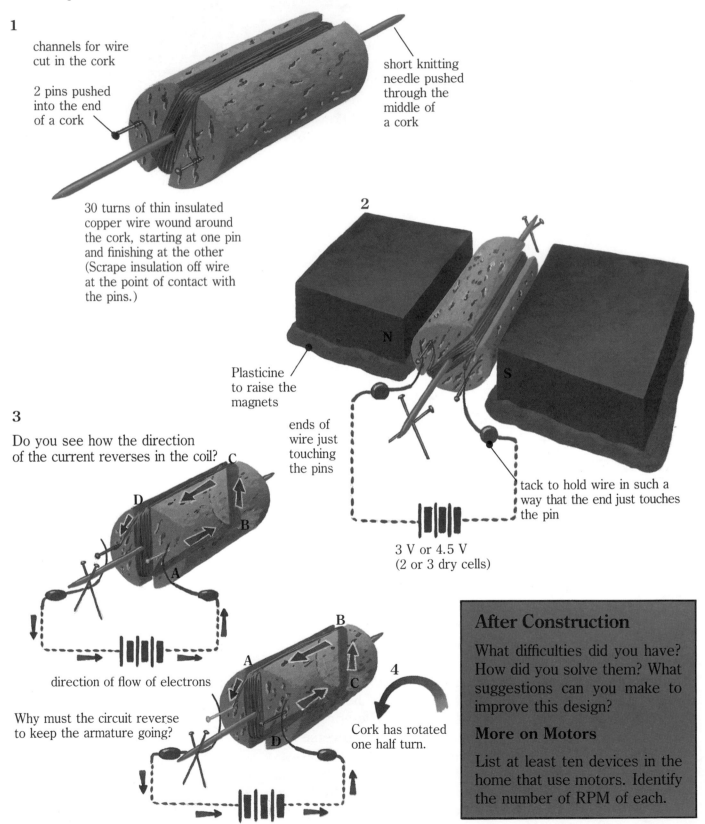

After Construction

What difficulties did you have? How did you solve them? What suggestions can you make to improve this design?

More on Motors

List at least ten devices in the home that use motors. Identify the number of RPM of each.

Specialized Production Technology

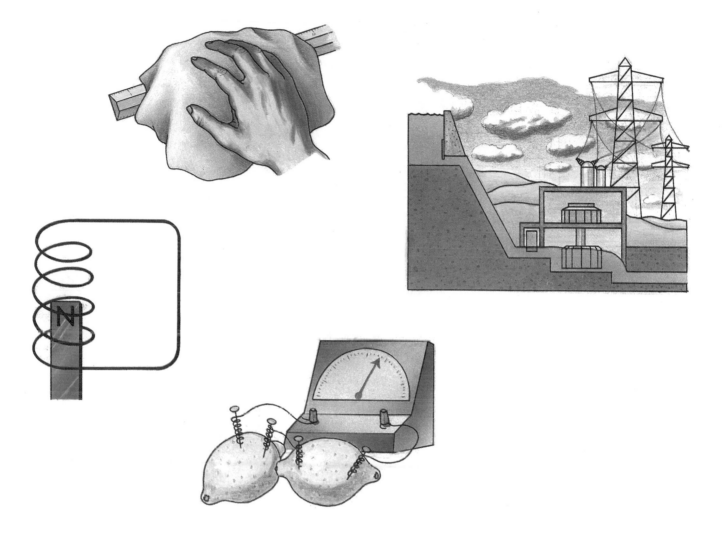

You have produced electricity on a small scale from (1) kinetic energy alone, (2) chemical energy, and (3) a combination of kinetic energy and magnetic energy. Can you match each of these ways with one of the sketches?

You have also investigated applications of (2) and (3): chemical cell technology and the production of electricity by generators powered by moving water, coal, oil, and nuclear reactions. In the following section you will discover that electricity can also be produced from light energy, heat energy, and from mechanical (pressure) energy. Sunlight is an excellent source of energy in space and in remote areas where other sources of power are not readily available.

Production of electrical energy by heat energy and mechanical pressure is quite specialized; that is, these methods generate only small amounts of electricity that is used to operate special devices. The following Exploration will introduce you to these less conventional means of producing electricity and their value to you.

Research Projects

Project 1
Solar Cells

Electricity from solar cells is something you may be familiar with. Try some experiments with a solar cell using different levels of light at various distances from the solar cells — and check on the amount of electricity that is produced in each case.

Solar generation of electrical energy for large scale production is being studied. One of the problems is the space required for the numerous huge panel collectors. Could this be solved by individual power generation? Have you seen solar panel installations on the roofs of houses? Find out about solar cells incorporated into roof shingles. Why is solar power a good source of energy in space? Research solar energy production.

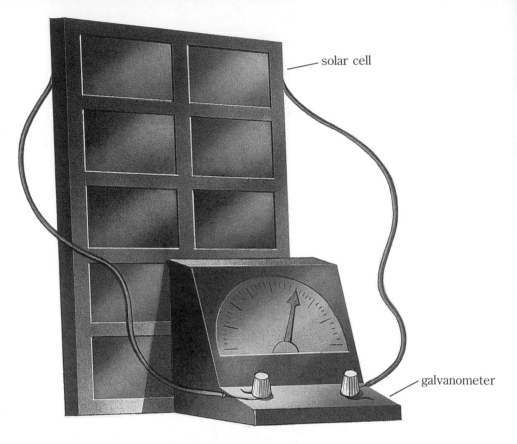

solar cell

galvanometer

Project 2
Thermocouples

A thermocouple consists of wires of two different metals joined well at a junction. Heat is applied at the junction and electricity is produced. Make a thermocouple and detect the electricity produced with a galvanometer as various sources of dry heat are applied to the junction.

Thermocouples have had a limited use as a source of electrical energy. Why do you think this is so? Only recently have engineers developed systems to use them for electrical production in space. However, they are used commonly to measure temperature by the amount of electricity developed in them. Thermocouples are used to measure high temperatures in industrial furnaces. They are also used as part of electrical control systems to maintain set temperature values. How might they do this? Research their use in the oil-refining industry. Find out what metals are best used for various temperature measurements.

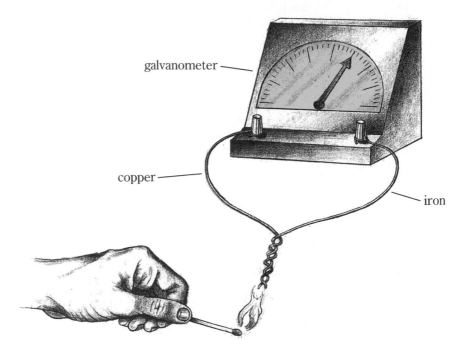

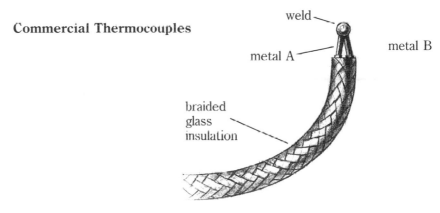

Commercial Thermocouples

Project 3
Piezoelectricity

Mechanical pressure on crystals such as quartz can produce electricity. You may have not realized that the crystal in the arm of a turntable of your record player is generating electricity as the needle rides the grooves of the record, which push up on the crystal. Pressure production of electricity is called the piezoelectric effect. It is used in lighters such as those on gas barbecues. Microphones generally operate on the piezoelectric principle. Find out how each of these applications work.

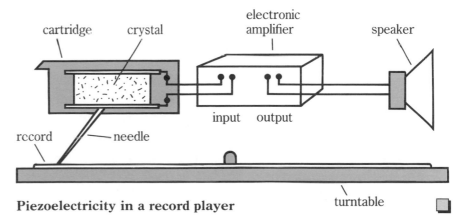

Piezoelectricity in a record player

How Much Electricity?

You know from an earlier section that most appliances have information tags. You have already learned what the terms "Rev.", "Cycles", and "Hz" on these plates indicate. But, what is the meaning of other words or numbers found on the plates such as amperes and volts? To understand these you need to know about another quantity called coulombs. Comparing the flow of electric charges in a circuit with the flow of water in a water system will make the meaning of amperes, volts, and coulombs and other quantities clearer. Read A Water Circuit and An Electric Circuit. As you do, compare these two circuits by making entries similar to the ones below.

	A Water Circuit	An Electric Circuit
A. what flows	water	electrons
B. measurement of quantity	litres	coulombs
C. rate of flow	?	?
D. measurement of potential energy per quantity	?	?
E. rate of energy change	?	?

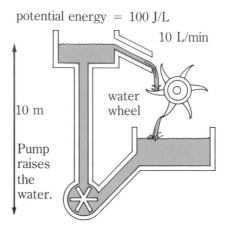

potential energy = 100 J/L

10 L/min

10 m

water wheel

Pump raises the water.

A Water Circuit

1. We may measure the *quantity* of water in a circuit in *litres*; for example, suppose the upper container in this water system contains 50 L of water.

2. The *rate* at which water flows may be measured in *litres per minute*. This would be a measure of the water *current*.

3. The pump raises the water to a certain height, giving it potential energy. Potential energy is measured in *joules*. You know that the work to raise 1 L (1 kg mass or about 10 N weight) of water to a height of 10 m requires about 100 J. Therefore, the potential energy given to 1 L of water is 100 J. The potential energy of 50 L of water raised to this height is $100 \times 50 = 5000$ J.

4. If the pump raises the water 20 m instead of 10 m, the water will gain more potential energy. As the water flows downward from the greater height, it flows faster. Greater potential energy therefore gives a greater rate of flow of current.

5. As the water flows downwards, its potential energy changes into other forms of energy. When one joule of potential energy changes into kinetic energy in one second, the rate of energy change equals one **watt**.

    1 J/s = 1 W

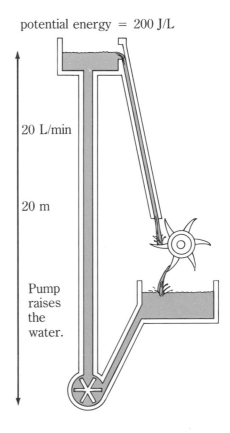

potential energy = 200 J/L

20 L/min

20 m

Pump raises the water.

An Electric Circuit

1. Since the charge on a single electron is extremely small, the *quantity* of charge in an electric circuit is measured, not in electron charges, but in units called **coulombs**. One coulomb (C) is the charge on 6.24 billion billion (6.24×10^{18}) electrons.

2. The *rate* at which electric charges flow is the current. It is measured in *coulombs per second*, more commonly known as **amperes** (A). One ampere equals one coulomb per second.

   1 A = 1 C/s.

3. A cell gives electrical potential energy to the electric charge flowing through it — just as the pump does to the water. Potential energy per charge (called potential) is measured in joules per coulomb, or **volts**. A volt (V) is defined as one joule per coulomb. A 1.5 V cell gives 1.5 J of potential energy to every coulomb of charge going through it. A 110 V electrical source gives 110 J of energy to 1 C of charge.

4. A 3 V source gives more potential energy to the flowing charges than a 1.5 V source. This in effect means that there are more electrons being crowded on the negative electrode due to the chemical action. Therefore, there is a greater force of repulsion tending to move electrons flowing in the circuit. For this reason it is common to refer to the voltage of a cell as "electrical pressure" driving the electrons. The higher the voltage, the greater the pressure.

5. The energy converter in a circuit, for example, a light bulb, converts energy at a certain rate. For example, a 40 W light bulb changes 40 J of electrical energy into heat and light energy every second. A 40 W light bulb uses 40 J of electrical energy per second. One watt of electrical energy is defined as one joule per second.

   1 W = 1 J/s

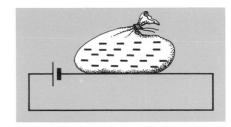

One coulomb of charge is like a bag of 6.24 billion billion electrons.

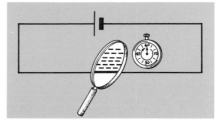

Electrons with 10 C of charge passing a point in 1 s = 10 A of current.

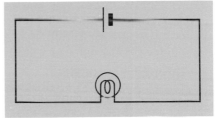

1.5 J of electrical potential energy given to 1 C of charge by the cell

Figuring It All Out

Volts, amperes, joules, watts! These units can be confusing. A little practical use of them will give them more meaning. Here is a self-help practice for you to try. How many answers can you get without looking? Cover up the right hand margin.

Situation A

First read the definition of ampere from #2 of An Electric Circuit.
   When you plug in this toaster, the electrical source supplies 5 A to the toaster. It takes 3 min (180 s) to toast the bread.

10 C/s = 10 A   1.5 J/C = 1.5 V

1. When 1 A of current flows, then in 1 s _____?_____ C of charge flows from the cell.

2. When 5 A of current flows, then in 1 s _____?_____ C of charge flow in the circuit.

3. In 3 min (180 s) _____?_____ C of charge flow.

4. To obtain the number of coulombs, you multiply the number of _____?_____ by the number of _____?_____ .

5. Suppose the same source supplied 0.5 A to a light bulb for 1 h. How much charge would flow through the bulb?

Now read the definition of **volt** from #3 of An Electric Circuit.

6. A 1 V electrical source supplies _____?_____ of electrical potential energy to 1 C of charge.

7. A 110 V electrical source supplies _____?_____ to 1 C of charge passing into the circuit.

8. A 110 V source supplies _____?_____ J of energy to 900 C (see Question 3 above) flowing through the toaster.

9. To obtain the number of joules of energy, you multiply the number of _____?_____ by the number of coulombs; that is,

    joules = _____?_____ × _____?_____

10. Now combine the two statements in Questions 4 and 9:

    coulombs = amperes × seconds
    joules = volts × coulomb
    therefore,
    joules = volts × _____?_____ × _____?_____

1. 1

2. 5

3. 900

4. amperes
   seconds

5. 1800 C

6. 1 J

7. 110 J

8. 99 000

9. volts
   volts
   coulombs

Situation B

First, read the definition of **watt** from #5 of An Electric Circuit. Electric appliances are rated in watts, according to the rate of which they use electrical energy. (This is also called the **power** of the appliance.)

11. A 1 W appliance uses _____?_____ J of electrical energy every second.

10. amperes
    seconds

12. The 800 W iron shown here uses ___?___ J of electrical energy every second.

13. If the iron is used for 15 min, it uses ___?___ J of electrical energy.

14. To obtain the number of joules of energy used, you multiply the number of watts by the number of ___?___, that is, J = ___?___ × ___?___ .

15. A 500 W hair dryer produces ___?___ J of heat energy in 20 min.

11. 1

12. 800

13. 720 000

14. seconds
watts
seconds

Situation C

You noticed in Situation B that, by multiplying power in watts by time in seconds, you get electrical energy consumed in joules. Utility companies use a more convenient unit to measure the electrical energy consumed by the householder. It is obtained by multiplying power in kilowatts (kW) by time in hours (h) which gives the unit kilowatt-hour (kWh).

Imagine that you have left a 2000 W electrical heater on for five hours.

16. 1 kW = 1000 W. The power of the heater is ___?___ kW.

17. The energy used by the heater is obtained by multiplying power in kilowatts by the time in hours. Energy consumed is ___?___ kWh.

18. The heater was used for ___?___ s.

19. Energy used by the heater in joules is obtained by multiplying ___?___ by seconds. The heater uses ___?___ J of electrical energy.

20. 10 kWh is the same amount of energy as ___?___ J. (See Questions 13 and 16.)

21. Therefore, 1 kWh = ___?___ J.

Do you see why the kilowatt hour is a more useful unit for large amounts of electrical consumption?

15. 600 000

16. 2

17. 10

18. 18 000

19. watts
36 000 000

20. 36 000 000

21. 3 600 000
Hopefully,
yes!

A Problem to Ponder

Most appliances have marked on them their power measured in watts and the voltage of the electrical source on which they operate. The current they use is not marked on them. By working with the two ways of calculating joules of energy in Questions 10 and 14, show that amperes = watts/volts. According to the tag, what current in amperes would flow through this appliance?

KPI-TIRHAFIIAI
TINKE FUWERS E

**4000W
220V**

Volts, Amperes, and the Human Body

You are not concerned about electric shock when you use dry cells. Why not? It is not that dry cells cannot produce enough current to be harmful. The resistance of the skin is very great and this prevents a dangerous current from flowing through it. What happens if the resistance is decreased? Look at the graph to the left. What happens when the skin gets wet? What implications does this have for working with electricity? How high should the bar for the resistance of dry skin be, if the bar for wet skin resistance is 5 cm high?

Now look at the second graph to see what size of currents are safe for the body to receive. Are you surprised at the small current that our bodies are able to receive internally without causing havoc? The resistance of our skin is very important considering the current flowing even in ordinary light bulbs.

What about voltage? The voltage of a dry cell is 1.5 V, that of a car battery is 12 V, that of the electrical source in homes in Canada is 110 V for most circuits, and of clothes dryers and stoves 220 V. What is safe? Generally any voltage above 30 V is dangerous. Remember that voltage is a measure of available electrical energy and can also be thought of as the pressure forcing the current in a circuit. Higher voltages can force enough current through the skin to cause shock or more serious damage. What kind of procedures and protection would you suggest for people who have to work with high voltage circuits?

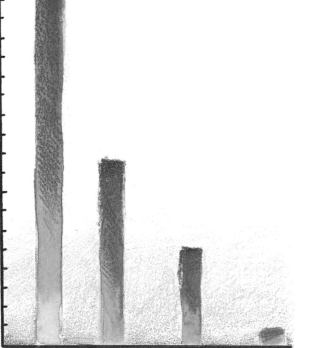

dry skin resistance | wet skin resistance | internal resistance hand to foot | internal resistance ear to ear

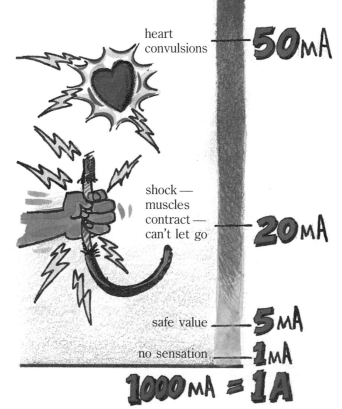

household current in a 100 W bulb

1A

heart convulsions — **50**mA

shock — muscles contract — can't let go — **20**mA

safe value — **5**mA

no sensation — **1**mA

1000mA = **1A**

How Much Does It Cost?

Saturday finally arrives! Miyako enjoys the luxury of getting up at 9:30 a.m. Her day proceeds as follows:

- She takes a bath, which causes the hot water heater to come on for 30 min.
- She washes her hair and dries it with the hair dryer for 10 min.

- She makes herself toast and tea, using the toaster and electric kettle for 10 min each.
- She goes out to a school function for the remainder of the day.
- She returns home in the evening and watches television for 1.5 h.
- She goes to her bedroom at 10:30 p.m., turns on her radio, the 60 W ceiling light, and the 40 W reading light.

- She turns off her ceiling light after 1 h, jumps into bed, and reads, falling asleep with the light and radio on.

It is now Sunday. A sleepy Miyako drags herself to breakfast with her family at 8:30 a.m. The conversation goes something like this . . .

Dad's Instruction	Miyako's Reply	Calculations
1. First you look at your appliance for the number of watts.	(Looking at the reading lamp) Here it is . . .	40 W
2. This measures the rate at which the appliance uses electrical energy. It is called the "power" of the appliance.	Oh . . .	
3. Then you count the number of hours you use it in a month.	A little over 3 h each day . . . in a month, that's about . . .	100 h
4. You multiply the number of watts by the number of hours to get the total energy used.	watts × hours . . . 40 × 100	4000 Wh
5. Energy is generally measured in kilowatt hours. Divide watt hours by 1000 to get the number of kilowatt hours.	4000 Wh divided by 1000 equals . . .	4 kWh
6. Electricity costs us about six cents for every kilowatt hour.	So in one month, my reading lamp costs . . .	24 cents

Miyako decided to calculate what the electricity she used on Saturday had cost her, so she looked at the information tags on each appliance, then did some calculations.

What was the total cost of the electricity Miyako used on Saturday? Which cost more to use for 1.5 h, the radio or the television? Why?

Appliance	Watts	Volts
hot-water heater	2000	220
hair dryer	750	110
toaster	840	110
electric kettle	1500	110
television	120	110
radio	12	110
ceiling light	60	110
reading light	40	110

What cost-saving suggestions are depicted here?

From the information provided in the table, calculate the current which flows in each of the appliances Miyako used.

Do your own cost estimate for a period of twenty-four hours of consumption of electricity. You may need to check the information tags on the appliances you use to be certain of their power.

You might also do a survey of electrical energy use for one day for your home, school or some business. Others might keep track of information for you during the day. Enter the information in a table similar to the following one. Note the kind of information you could gather.

Appliance	No.	Volts	Watts	Amperes	Hours	Seconds	Joules	kWh
light bulbs	4	110	60	0.55	3.0	10 800	648 000	0.18
toaster	1	110	700	0.64	0.5	1 800	1 260 000	0.35
motor on furnace etc.								

Electrical Safety

When it blows,
No current flows.
So be sure to use
In each circuit a ___?___ .

A Mini-Experiment

On page 298, you were asked to touch a nichrome wire when a small current was going through it. It was hot! The greater the current that flowed, the hotter the wire was. Copper wire used in electrical wiring throughout the home can also get hot when too much current flows through it, causing a fire hazard. What solution could you devise to stop the current from flowing before the wire gets so hot that it starts a fire?

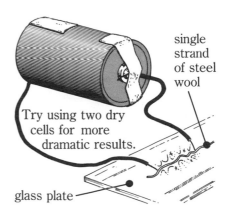

Try using two dry cells for more dramatic results.

single strand of steel wool

glass plate

You Will Need

- strong dry cells
- tape
- steel wool
- glass plate
- copper wire
- household fuse
- automobile fuse

What To Do

1. Hold the free ends of the wires in your hands and touch them together for just a few seconds. Do the wires get hot?

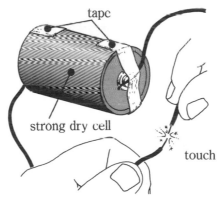

tape

strong dry cell

touch

2. Now touch the free ends to the ends of a single strand of steel wool lying on a glass plate. Did the steel wool "flash"? Actually, it melted very quickly and broke the circuit, so no current would flow. The steel wool acted as a **fuse**. One meaning of "fuse" is "to melt". A fuse is an automatic switch which interrupts the flow of current before any damage from heat results.

3. Study the structure of the house fuse. How does it resemble a light bulb?

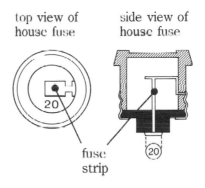

top view of house fuse

side view of house fuse

fuse strip

4. Locate the ribbon-like metal in the fuse. This is the part that melts. Can you infer where the ends of the ribbon are attached?

5. Locate the ribbon of metal in an automobile fuse.

6. Locate the numbers on the fuses. The numbers refer to the maximum number of amperes of current the fuses will allow in a circuit before they blow or melt.

A circuit with a 20 A fuse is made of thicker copper wire than a circuit with a 15 A fuse. The thicker the copper wire, the less resistance it has to the current, and the more current it can carry before becoming too hot. What is the danger of replacing a blown 15 A fuse with a 20 A fuse?

Overloading a Circuit

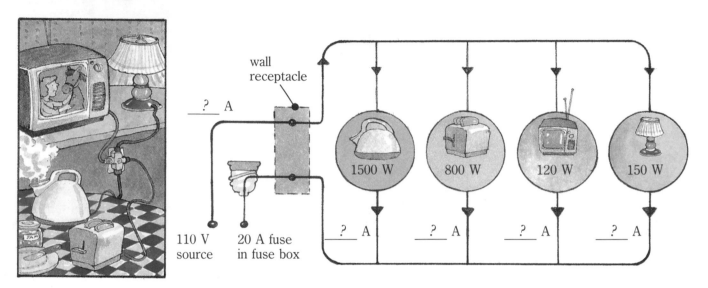

Is there anything wrong in this picture? Has Bart overloaded the circuit? How can you find out? Inserting a four-way plug into the electrical outlet makes a four-branched circuit. You can find the current in each branch by dividing the number of watts by the number of volts of the source of electricity. This is usually 110 V for a house circuit.

According to the diagram, how much current goes through the kettle? toaster? television? lamp? What is the total current? Is it too much for the connecting wires? Will the fuse melt, breaking the circuit?

For the next two circuits, check the current needed by each appliance in each branch. Is either circuit A or B overloaded?

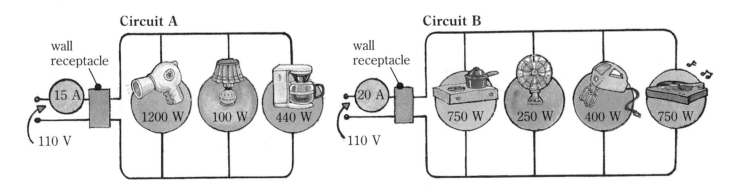

A Traffic Short Circuit

This section is an analogy intended to help you understand the section which follows. Don't "short circuit" any part of this reading, even if you feel some "resistance"! As you read, answer the questions.

The people of A often travelled to B. Before 1990 they had to go through Newtown to get to B. During rush hours, traffic was slow. At what speed did the traffic move?

After 1990, all through-traffic used a bypass to travel from A to B. How fast did the traffic move? The bypass provided a "short circuit" for the traffic, so it did not get held up by Newtown. Now there were two roads for traffic. Which road had the least resistance? Which permitted traffic to travel faster?

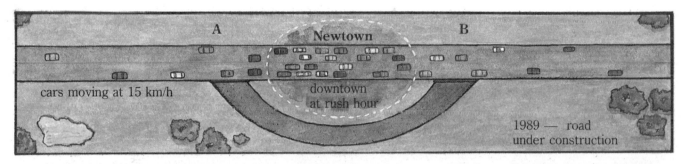

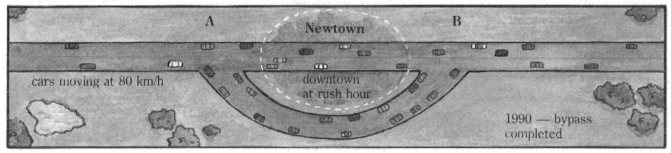

An Electric Short Circuit

Now study the two diagrams shown here. Then answer the questions, on the basis of the analogy you have just read and the diagrams.

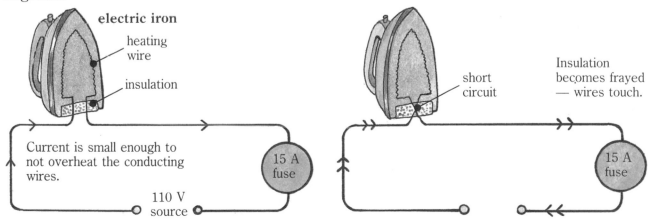

1. What slows down the electric charges, so that the current remains small?

2. In the short circuit drawing, trace the two possible paths for the current.

3. Which path has the least resistance?

4. Can the current bypass the resistance of the iron?

5. If the resistance of the short-circuited path is much lower than the original, will the electrical source provide a smaller, the same, or a larger current?

6. What change in the connecting wire occurs as the size of current changes?

7. What happens in the circuit to prevent overheating which results from a rapid surge of current?

Were you able to answer all these questions? If so, you analyzed how a short circuit may create a fire hazard against which a fuse is a safeguard.

To check your answers, read the following explanation. Each sentence is lettered and you can match these letters against the question numbers.

(a) The resistance wire in the iron minimizes the size of the current from the electrical source. (b) If a short circuit occurs in the iron, the current can go either through the resistance wire or through the new short-circuited path of much less resistance. (c) Most of the current will go by this latter path. (d) Because this path has such a low resistance, more current will flow from the electrical sources through the household wiring and the wall receptacle to the iron. (e) Actually, there will be momentarily a large surge of current when the short circuit occurs. (f) This surge of current would heat the household wire to a dangerously hot temperature if it continued for any length of time. (g) Fortunately, before this happens, the ribbon in the fuse (which is part of the household wiring circuit) melts, the circuit breaks, and the current ceases to flow."

In summary, a fuse acts as a safety device in two ways. It can protect wires from overheating caused by (1) the overloading of an electric receptacle with too many appliances or (2) a short circuit resulting from the wearing away of insulation around the conducting wires. Often, instead of fuses, circuit breakers that can be reset provide protection.

Circuit Breakers

Newer homes and larger buildings generally use circuit breakers rather than fuses to protect against overloads and short circuits. Like fuses, circuit breakers are rated to respond when a certain size of current flows.

Study the illustrations to see how circuit breakers are made. Also determine how they work by comparing the two diagrams. These questions may help:

(a) What would cause the bimetallic strip to bend?

(b) What does the spring attached to the trip lever do?

Circuit breakers are more expensive to install than fuses but they have several distinct advantages. What do you think these may be?

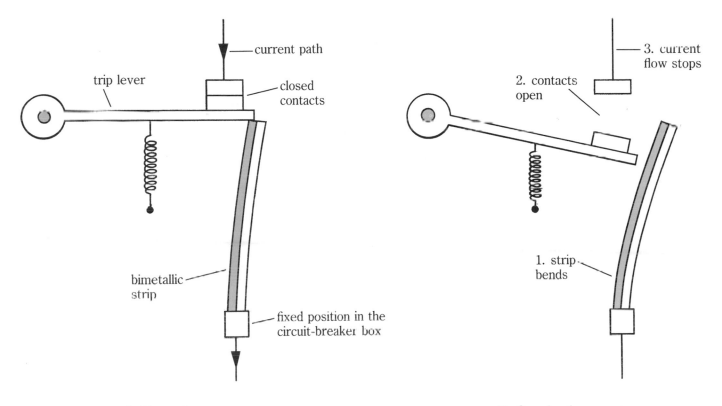

A. Normal current

B. Overload current

The ON/OFF switch has three positions. When the circuit breaks, it goes to a tripped position. To reset the breaker, it is first moved all the way to the OFF position and then back to the ON position.

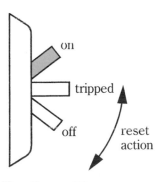

Handle positions

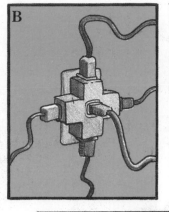

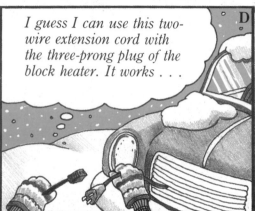

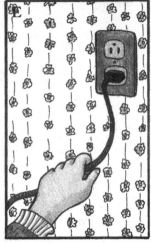

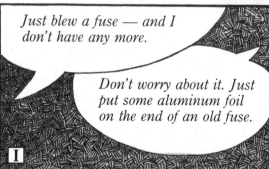

A Quiz and Quest

First, find what's wrong with each situation illustrated. Now imagine that, as Safety Engineer for the Electric Power Company, you must prepare a leaflet for householders on "Safety in Using Electricity". Form a task force and design the leaflet.

Brain Teasers

1. Explanations, please!

   (a) A negatively charged plastic ruler is brought in turn near three light, metal-covered spheres suspended by nylon threads. It repels A and attracts B and C. A attracts B and C attracts B. What are the charges on each of the spheres?

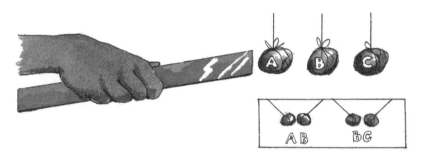

   (b) What is happening in this sequence? (**Hint:** Study the whole sequence of steps, then reason out your explanation, working back from (iii), (iv), and (v).)

2. Electrifying News

Dangerous *Nic Rome* was captured by Detectives Ronald and Rhoda *Franklin*. They work for the *A.C.D.C.* (After Criminals Detective Company). Nic Rome has been charged with the *conduction* of an *attractive* 18-year-old *coil*, Millie *Volt* and with the theft of valuable *joules*.

This is *watt* appears to have happened. The criminal avoided a *battery* of police by escaping on his *kinetic cycle*. Spotting him from a *parallel* road, the detectives *proton* their hats and jumped into their *motor* car. In an instant the *thermocouple* were in hot pursuit. They forced Nic Rome off the road, causing him to crash into a *coulomb* of *poles*. Nic grabbed his *carbon rod* weapon and swung it with vicious *energy* to *ampere* his arrest. The detectives warded off this *series resistance* and subdued the *potential* killer.

Nic Rome is now in *solar*tary confinement in the local *cell*. His trial will be held in the *current* court session presided over by the *circuit* judge. The community is relieved at the capture of the crime *generator*. As a result, they have agreed to *elect Ron* and Rhoda Detectives of the Year.

What a shocking misuse of words! Help straighten out the reporter by using this Glossary of Electrical and Magnetic Words. Select from the report the appropriate italicized word or name that fits each description of the glossary.

Glossary of Electrical and Magnetic Words

(a) On Units

1. Unit of electric charge
2. Unit of current; or, one coulomb per second
3. Unit of energy
4. Electrical energy given to one coulomb; or, one joule per coulomb
5. One joule of energy used in one second

(b) On Energy and Energy Converters

6. Type of energy possessed by an object raised to a height
7. Energy of moving objects
8. Device which converts electrical energy into mechanical energy
9. Device in which electrical energy is produced by chemical action
10. Device in which a current is produced by a magnet revolving near a coil of wire
11. Group of electrical cells
12. Sensitive device for measuring temperature

(c) On Scientists

13. He performed the famous "kite-and-key" experiment in electricity.

(d) On Circuits

14. Motion of electric charges in metals
15. Path through which electrons flow
16. Type of friction met by electric charges moving in a conductor
17. Type of circuit in which appliances are connected one after the other
18. Type of circuit with branches
19. Part of an electromagnet
20. A current which moves in one direction then in the opposite direction
21. A current which moves in one direction only
22. Rate of flow of electric charges in a conductor
23. Wire with high resistance to the flow of current
24. One reversal of current

(e) **On Charges and Cells**

25. Smallest particle of negative electricity

26. Small particles of positive electricity

27. Metals in a cell

28. Part of the positive electrode of a dry cell

29. Condition of an object which has more electrons than protons

30. Given to electrons by a cell

31. Type of cell used for obtaining electrical energy from light energy

(f) **On Magnets**

32. Type of force between N and S poles of a magnet

33. Parts of a magnet where the strength is greatest

3. A Poem to Complete

Ode to Units!

If units must be taught
Then let us start with watt.

A one watt light will, by our rule,
In __?__ second use the energy of __?__ joule,

One ampere you may check
Is the same as one __?__ in one sec.

One __?__ of energy you know well
Is given to one __?__ by a one volt cell.

Let's review the units just once more,
To make your knowledge more secure.

A 25 W bulb will, by our rule,
In 6 s use energy of __?__ joules.

Two amperes you may check
Are equal to __?__ C in 4 sec.

__?__ joules of energy (you know well)
Are given to 4 C by a two volt cell.

4. How Much or How Long?

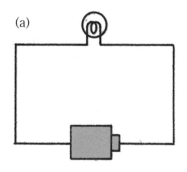

(a)

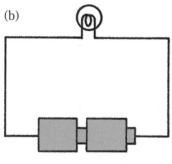

(b)

dry cells in series

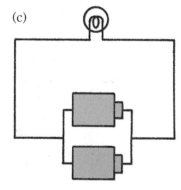

(c)

dry cells in parallel

Predict the brightness of the bulb in (b) and (c). You have seen (b) before but perhaps (c) is new to you. Of course, two cells have the same energy output no matter how they are hooked up. The question is: do the two cells give a large amount of energy for a short time or a smaller amount of energy for a longer time?

5. Mr. Cassidy, the science teacher, asked his students to draw a circuit containing two switches (S_1 and S_2), two light bulbs (L_1 and L_2), and one dry cell. He asked them to arrange the circuit in the following ways:

(a) If only switch S_2 is closed, L_1 will light.

(b) If only switch S_2 is closed, nothing happens.

(c) If switches S_1 and S_2 are closed, both lamps will light.

Now, using your notebook, take the role of Mr. Cassidy, and mark your students' work. Allow 5 marks for a correct arrangement. You can give part-marks for circuits which are partly correct.

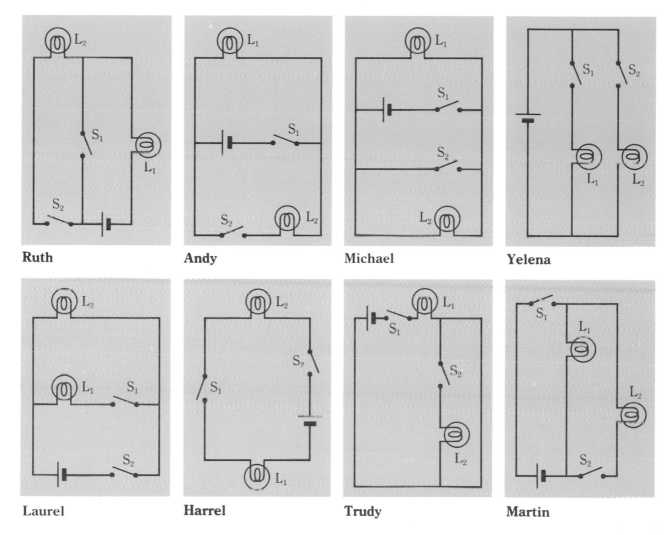

Ruth   Andy   Michael   Yelena

Laurel   Harrel   Trudy   Martin

6. How many 100 W bulbs can you hook up in piggy-back fashion to blow out a 15 A fuse? (Don't try it!)

7. How much energy can you get for $1.00? How long can you operate a 1500 W electric kettle? A 100 W light bulb? A 12 W television? A 250 W lawnmower?

8. Win, Lose, or Draw!

If you can complete these drawings, you will likely win! At least you will have circuits under good control.

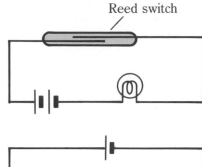

(a) Draw in something which will light the bulb.

(b) Add something to the circuit to keep the cell from being drained of its electrical energy.

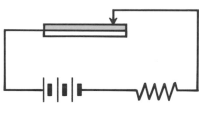

(c) Redraw the circuit, putting in what is necessary to turn each light on and off independently.

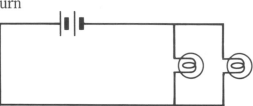

(d) Add something to the diagram which will turn the current through the resistor off.

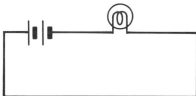

(e) Redraw the circuit, putting in what is necessary to turn the light on by switches located in two different places.

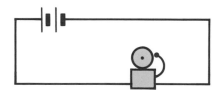

(f) Add something to the circuit to cause the bell to ring after 2 min.

(h) Redraw adding a switch that will turn all of the bulbs on and off. Add another switch that will turn B off when the first switch is closed. Then redraw the circuit so that each bulb can be controlled by its own switch.

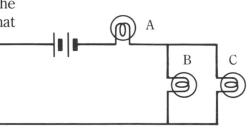

(g) Redraw the circuit, putting in a drawing of something which will control the brightness of the light.

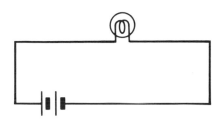

(i) Draw two switches that will operate the circuit so that, if the bulb is lit when one switch is closed, the other switch will be able to open the circuit — and vice versa.

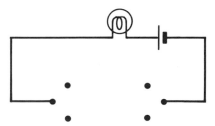

(j) Here a complete drawing is given to you. Redraw the circuit with the movable double throw switch moved from contacts A and B to contacts C and D. Then suggest a function for this switch.

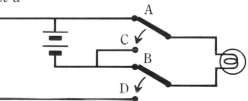

9. Authors Needed

You have been chosen to write and edit the "How It Works" section of a science magazine for people aged 10 to 13. You have a two-page spread for each article. Here are some topics:

"How a flashlight works"

"How a bicycle dynamo works"

"How a telephone works"

"How a generator works"

"How an electric bell works"

"How a two-way switch operates"

"How a fuse works"

"How a light bulb works"

"How a motor works"

Choose one topic. Write in a clear style, explaining any difficult terms you use. Design an attractive layout which incorporates photos, drawings, and cartoons. When you are finished, share your article with others who have chosen other topics. Evaluate and constructively criticize each other's work. Revise your article where necessary, then give it to a younger person to read. How will you test whether you are a successful author?

10. How do you like Terry's Mousetrap? How does it work?

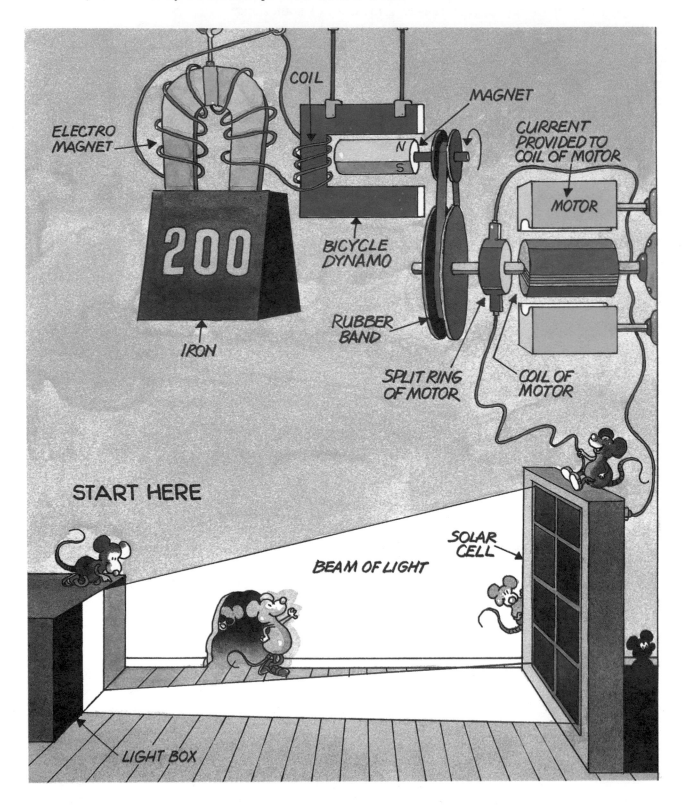

Now it's your turn to invent something! How about a super arrangement to wake you up in the morning? Perhaps your mother could press a button and . . .

11. Many apartment buildings have outside doors which can be opened by pressing a button in the apartment. How does this circuit work?

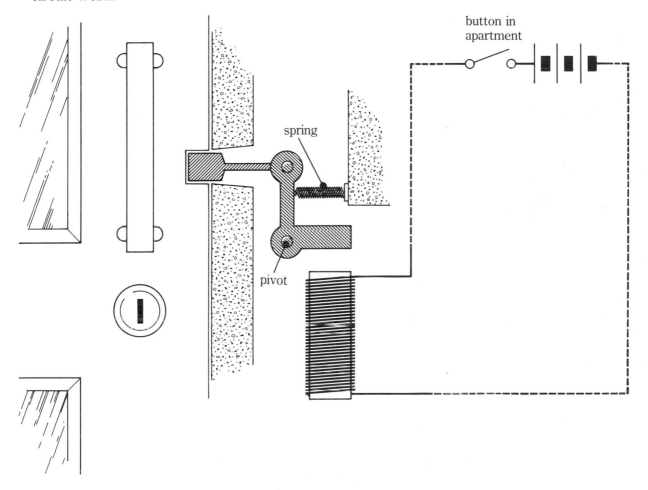

12. You have just been appointed chemist with Power Plus Corp. Your first assignment is to test the effectiveness of different materials which constitute a wet cell (see page 279). Outline your plans and procedures. You might collect the necessary materials, perform the procedures, and evaluate the results.

Electronics

Electronics Engineering Technology

Suzanne Beck-Mitchell is an electronics engineering technologist. She qualified for her profession by completing a two-year program of post-secondary studies. Suzanne now teaches technology at an institute of technology.

Q: Prior to your present job as a teacher, what did you do?

Suzanne: My last job was at an engineering firm where we made new electrical products. I usually worked with an engineer who did most of the designing while I did the testing. Together we worked to make a marketable product.

Q: Why did you become a technologist?

Suzanne: When I was a child, I did not take apart clock radios or anything like that, but I liked math and physics. Engineering technology was a practical choice, something that would make a living for me — and it has, very well.

Q: What do you find most interesting and most frustrating about your job?

Suzanne: The most stimulating aspect is designing something, putting it together and finding it works the way you expected. The most frustrating thing is when it does not work.

Q: What high school subjects are most important for those interested in becoming technologists?

Suzanne: Math and physics. It is necessary to understand basic math so you can make your way through circuits. You must also understand fundamental physics, so you can understand the principles behind electronic devices.

Q: What skills and abilities are most important in engineering technology?

Suzanne: I think you need an ability to work with your hands, patience, an attention to detail, and an ability to communicate with the engineers with whom you work.

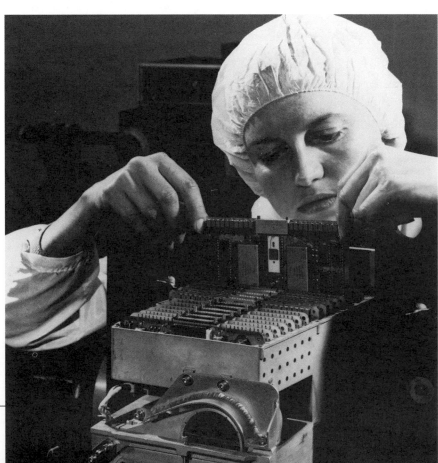

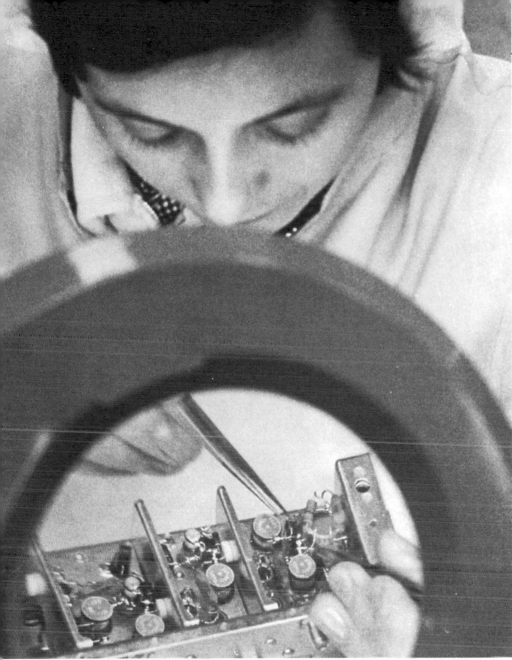

A worker assembles tiny electronic components for use in a telecommunications system.

Electronics Engineering

Lynn Bowser is an electrical engineer whose specialty is electronics. Her enjoyment of math, physics, and chemistry courses in high school was a factor in her decision to enter the engineering program at university. Lynn graduated with a Bachelor of Engineering degree. It qualified her to work as an electrical engineer with a telephone company. She has found this work challenging and worthwhile.

Q: What aspect of your work do you find most stimulating?

Lynn: Making something work is exciting. It is satisfying when we design something in the office, it is built by the craftsmen, and it goes into the field and works exactly the way the customer wants.

Q: You must have had some unusual experiences working for a telephone company.

Lynn: Yes. For example, once there was no dial tone from a local that was about 100 m down in a salt mine. The equipment on the surface was working fine; the connections were all showing continuity. So we went down into the mine to check out the telephone set. The phone worked all right, so we were able to conclude that the problem was in the line. We then fixed the problem. I particularly enjoyed this experience because I had a chance to get my hands on the equipment. Normally, I do most of my troubleshooting in an office. I design solutions to problems that originate in the field.

Q: What subject areas in school are most important to engineering?

Lynn: Students should take science courses, especially physics, chemistry, and math. It is unfortunate that many students avoid science and math courses when they go to high school. Later they find they have not taken the right courses to do the things they want to do. Students should not limit their options.

Q: What are some important concepts in the field of electrical engineering?

Lynn: The formula E = IR, which students encounter in high school, summarizes most of them. E is the voltage, I is the current, and R is the resistance. Things get a little more complicated, though, and a little more fun, when there are capacitors and inductors in a circuit.

Q: To qualify as an engineer, you must have a Bachelor of Engineering degree. What would you say is the greatest value of a university education to your work?

Lynn: In my job it is necessary to study constantly and learn new things. A university degree not only means that you have gained some fundamental knowledge in a given field; it also proves that you can learn.

Q: Besides the ability to learn, what other skills are important for a person who would like to become an engineer?

Lynn: The ability to communicate accurately and clearly is very important. Leadership ability is also helpful. This means being able to give a clear explanation of a proposal, both its good points and its bad points, so that others can decide whether it is the right solution.

A technician does a final check on a telephone switching system before it is in operation.

344

A technician checks the photographic mask of an electronic printed circuit board made by a Canadian telecommunications company.

Some Project Ideas

You can construct models which involve different electronic devices. Many people make models from kits purchased at electronics supply stores. You can also do so by referring to a circuit design or written instructions, as long as you have access to the electronic parts required. Ask your teacher or school librarian for reference material on electronics projects. Suzanne Beck-Mitchell suggests these devices for projects:

1. a photo-cell circuit, which detects the presence of light

2. a digital counter, whose design uses the binary number system

3. a digital combinational circuit; this device uses relatively inexpensive integrated circuits which perform logic functions, demonstrating how the functions AND, OR, and INVERT relate to the concepts of union and intersection in mathematics.

Before commencing any of these projects, you should consult an expert for an explanation of the device you have chosen. For instance, electronics engineers work for telephone companies, electronics firms, and university electrical engineering departments, among other places. You could also get help from high school and vocational school electronics teachers, physics teachers, and math teachers (especially concerning Boolean algebra, which is used in the design of computer circuits).

Electrical Engineering

Fred Gallagher is an electrical engineer with a power corporation. He manages the distribution planning department. Fred's qualifications include a university degree in electrical engineering, and many years of utility distribution experience.

Q: What do you like most about your work?

Fred: I like to see a project go from planning to completion. It gives me a lot of satisfaction.

Q: Do you experience any frustration in your job?

Fred: Yes. The amount of paper that seems to circulate across people's desks is particularly frustrating. We are experiencing a paper revolution of sorts. One of the most difficult things is to be able to absorb the important information that comes forth, get rid of what is useless, and circulate what is pertinent.

Q: What major problems face the power industry at this time?

Fred: One thing that is very important, which I do not think is being properly addressed, is the issue of nuclear power. I do not think that the average person understands the options we have available for energy — the comparative costs and risks. I think this is a very important issue of our day.

Q: Besides basic math and physics, what skills and abilities should be developed for engineering work?

Fred: I think young people should work to develop their communication skills: writing and speaking. Often, engineers are not trained to communicate well. You must know how to write properly, when you are faced with writing about a particular subject. When you are asked to present a paper at a meeting, you must be able to speak in public, to present your facts clearly and concisely, and to debate and defend your arguments.

Some Project Ideas

1. Develop a plan to reduce the electric power consumption in your household. First record the length of time that various electrical appliances and lights run, over several days. Then calculate power consumption (the product of the number of watts and time) for each device. Find out the cost of a kilowatt hour of electric power from the power company which supplies your home.

   How much money can be saved by running appliances and lights in your home for the minimum time necessary?

2. Organize a debate on the merits of different sources of electric energy. Prepare for the debate by researching the availability, costs, advantages, and disadvantages of various energy sources (hydroelectricity, nuclear power, coal, oil, wind, solar, geothermal, etc.). Contact your local power utility and ask to speak to an engineer or engineering technologist about your project. You can also obtain assistance from physics teachers and professors.

Communications Technology

Canada is a world leader in the development and use of communications technology. And no wonder — its population centres are scattered across a vast territory. Canada's very existence as a country depends on efficient communications.

To find out more about communications technology, try one of the projects suggested below. The first set of projects is technological, the second is historical, and the final set deals with societal problems related to the introduction of new technology.

Projects in the Technology of Communication

Today's revolution in communications is based on electronics. If you enjoy working with electronic devices, you could assemble a working model of a telegraph, telephone, or radio for a project. Ready-to-assemble kits can be obtained at hobby shops or electronics stores. With help from an electronics specialist, you might also be able to design and build your own radio or telephone. Parts can be purchased at an electronics store, or taken from discarded electronic equipment. Be prepared to explain how your device works.

If you are able to obtain old radios or telephones, you can create an exhibit illustrating how the radio or telephone has changed. By removing the cabinets or casings of these devices, you can demonstrate how electronic technology

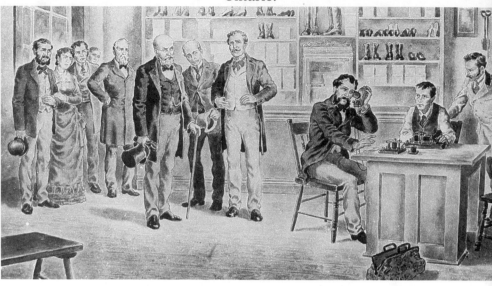

Alexander Graham Bell makes the first long-distance phone call on August 10, 1876, from Paris, Ontario, to Brantford, Ontario.

has evolved. In particular, you can demonstrate how changes in technology have made it possible to reduce the size and cost of electronic devices.

Another idea for a project is to find out and demonstrate how computers, fibre optics, satellites, lasers, or other devices are used in communications. Try to get assistance from someone who works with the particular device that interests you.

Projects in the History of Communications Technology

The era of modern communication began with the telegraph (1837), the telephone (1876), and the wireless telegraph (1895). Two of these devices, the telephone and the wireless telegraph, were developed partly in Canada. In 1876, *Alexander Graham Bell* made the world's first long distance telephone call between

Brantford and Paris, Ontario. In December 1901, the Italian physicist Guglielmo Marconi received the first transatlantic wireless telegraph message in St. John's, Newfoundland.

Several Canadian inventors, including *Reginald Fessenden* and *Edward Rogers*, contributed to the development of radio communication. A report or poster display on the life and work of one of these inventors would inform others about significant work done in Canada.

Canadians have continued to be at the forefront of development in communications technology, with advances in satellite broadcasting and other areas. To find out what Canadians have done and are doing in this field, refer to the *Canadian Encyclopedia*. Follow this up by seeking more information. See Sources of Information at the end of this section.

An artist's conception of the Anik C communications satellite. The satellite was placed in orbit in 1982 by the Space Shuttle *Columbia*.

Societal Concerns Related to Communications Technology

New technology can create problems as well as benefits. There are many societal concerns related to communications technology. First, much of the new technology provides better information, but at a greater cost. If the user pays the full cost, those with lower incomes may become more disadvantaged than at present.

Second, cable television and direct broadcast satellites have expanded the choice of American television programs available in Canada. One result could be fewer opportunities for Canadian artistic and cultural expression.

Third, office automation has caused an increase in the efficiency of processing information. This benefit to the business can be a source of distress to the employees, who must learn the new skills involved in the new technology. In certain businesses, office automation can lead to the displacement of employees.

These are just a few of the issues raised by advances in communications. Select one and research it carefully. You will need to become well-informed about the technology behind the issue as well. Present your research and conclusions in the form of a report; include recommendations for dealing with the issue.

Sources of Information

- Department of Communications, Ottawa
- the telephone company
- departments of physics or electrical engineering at universities
- the library

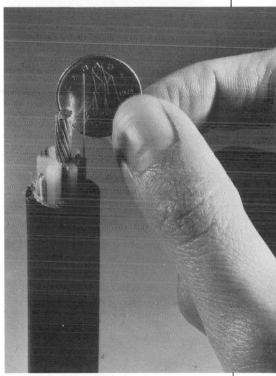

Fibre optic technology has revolutionized telecommunications. The tiny strand at the right of the picture can handle 600 telephone calls simultaneously.

ENVIRONMENTAL QUALITY

The Environment

This unit is about the environment; its components, its interactions, and the signals that indicate that all is well — or not well — with the environment. It is also about making decisions, whether they are personal decisions that may in some way affect the environment or collective decisions that may have an even larger impact — either positive or negative. As well, you will be asked to examine issues from the perspective of others who may have differing interests and opinions. Maybe your views and those of others will be enriched or changed through your exploration.

Let's start by examining one of the ideas in the paragraph above. Our lives involve making many kinds of decisions. What decisions have you made in the past that may have had some effect on the environment? Perhaps you chose to ride your bicycle to a destination rather than riding in a car. What effects might this decision have had on the environment? Make a list of decisions that you have made and try to decide what positive and negative effects each one may have had. Keep this list in mind as you examine the next section, which further examines your ideas about the environment.

A Picture Study

Today everyone seems to be discussing the environment. What do you know about the environment? What is the environment? What is meant by "environmental quality"? In groups, use the pictures which follow to formulate your viewpoint. The following questions may help you to focus on the task. Prepare responses to share with your classmates.

1. What is the environment?

2. What impact do humans have on the environment?

3. Is human impact *always* harmful to the environment?

4. Are there ways to minimize negative human impact on the environment?

Here is a further challenge for your group. Come up with statements that convey your understanding of the idea of environment. Share your statements with other groups. Afterwards, look at the statement about the environment at the end of this unit in Brain Teaser 1. Compare your statement with it.

Putting It All Together

The following diagram is one view of the environment. Examine it carefully.

1. What do each of the circles represent?

2. Each circle overlaps the other three. What do the overlapping areas represent?

3. Are living things found in all parts of the atmosphere? the hydrosphere? the lithosphere? What do these terms mean?

4. What is your understanding of the meaning of the term "biosphere"?

5. Where on the diagram would you expect to find the greatest diversity of living things? Why?

6. Are human beings a part of the environment? Where would humans fit on the diagram?

7. Reread the statement that you made about the environment. Do your statement and the diagram say the same thing?

8. From the picture study suggest specific examples of how changes in the quality of air, water, and soil have direct effects on living things.

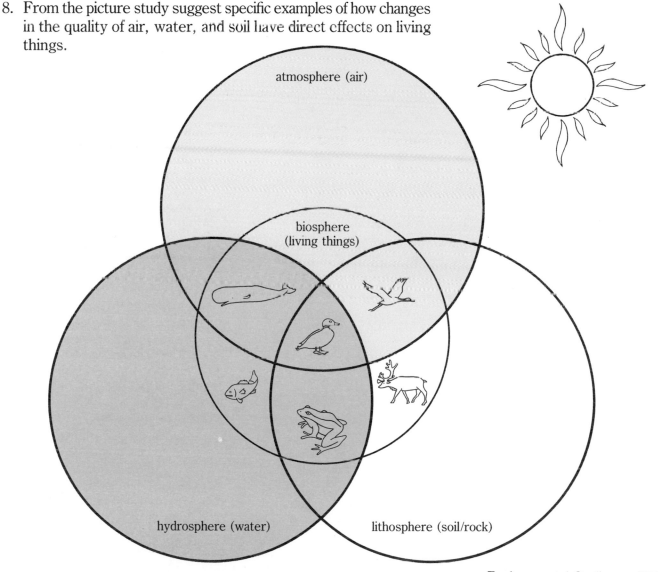

Changes in The Environment

When living things, including humans, interact with their environment, they often bring about changes. Such changes may be intentional, or planned. What are some examples of intentional changes in the previous section A Picture Study?

Sometimes human actions have brought about changes that were unintentional. What examples can you find of unintentional changes in the picture study? For example, do you think that farmers intend to increase soil erosion when they plow their fields?

And, of course, there are changes going on in the environment that have nothing to do with human action. Such changes are natural: plants are part of the process of soil formation; moving water and wind are agents of weathering and erosion; living things are part of the balance that maintains the proportion of oxygen and carbon dioxide in the atmosphere. Does the picture study suggest other examples of natural interaction and changes?

In Exploration 1, you will be exploring a familiar environment and observing changes that result from human and natural actions.

Observing Changes

Form groups and take a mini-field trip into the environment outside your school building. In a short time find examples of changes in this environment that are:

- caused by humans and are intentional changes
- caused by humans and are unintentional changes
- not caused by humans and are examples of natural changes

Try to find examples of changes that affect the atmosphere, soil, water, and living things. Afterwards:

1. Decide which of the changes have had a negative impact on the quality of the environment and which ones have had a positive impact.

2. List the changes that may have had a negative impact but are important for meeting a human need. For example, some people say that automobiles produce a negative impact, but would you want to do without this means of transportation altogether?

3. Sometimes people may change the environment in some way but are not able to foresee the effects of that change. For example, in creating a park for human enjoyment, certain plants may lose their habitat or, in creating a path down an embankment, erosion of soil may increase.

   (a) What examples of changes did you see on your walk where the effects were unforeseen at the time?

   (b) Suggest other changes with which you are familiar that had unforeseen results.

Environment Is . . .

Share your views of the environment through a poster session. You may focus on one particular environment, such as the school, the backyard, the pond, or you may look at the wider environment. Your presentation might be written from the environmental viewpoint of an animal or plant that lives or used to live in the area. Your poster may include pictures, drawings, poems, and stories.

Headlines

Issues

One way of finding out about current environmental issues is by reading and listening to the news. What are the issues of today? Are the issues you read about in the daily paper:

- local issues — caused by and can be solved by people in your community?

- regional issues — caused by and can be solved by the larger community, such as your province?

- global issues — caused by and can be solved by the whole world community?

You will investigate these questions in the next Exploration.

Environmental Issues

Working with a classmate, classify the headlines from a number of newspapers across Canada as *local*, *regional*, or *global issues*.

Thinning may be a natural phenomenon

The thinning of the ozone layer may be due to natural events and not to pollutants added to the atmosphere, a local scientist says. In a paper delivered to a symposium on the environment . . .

Two years needed for mills to eliminate dioxins — industry

Vancouver (CP) — The pulp-and-paper industry needs two more years to stop its mills from contaminating paper products and the environment with dioxins, an industry spokesman said Wednesday.

A federal Health Department study released this week said traces of dioxins and furans are seeping into milk from paper milk cartons.

Golf tees made from peat moss

An Alberta man has invented a biodegradable golf tee made from peat moss.

Watts up?

Electric-powered car research charges rapidly ahead

In July, 32 universities from across North America will show off the latest in solar-powered vehicles as university teams race 3000 km from Florida to Detroit.

Metal pollution is spreading over Earth

Metal pollution must now be considered a global problem, not just a regional issue, Canadian and Norwegian scientists warn. Almost every industry around the world produces metal-containing pollution. Thousands of tonnes of the metal are released into all parts of the environment — air, soil, and water.

Tree makes its own insecticides

For hundreds of years, the people of Southeast Asia have valued the neem tree for its many medicinal and insecticidal properties. Spreading neem leaves over newly harvested crops (rice, sorghum, millet) protects them from insect infestation.

Now the ozone layer is in trouble in the Arctic as well

Canadian scientists studying the ozone layer in the Arctic are beginning to understand the complex chemical events that lead to the breakdown of the ozone. This new understanding has led to the realization that the ozone layer is breaking down faster than was originally predicted.

Acid runoff: more trouble for our lakes

After years of dealing with acid rain, Canada's mining industry is now facing a multi-billion dollar clean up of acid runoff. And, for a change, the industry is taking a leading role in addressing the problem instead of waiting for government coercion.

Headline Analysis

1. Which headlines were difficult to classify according to these criteria?

2. Which ones were optimistic in their outlook?

3. Which headlines suggest that differing views are held regarding the issue?

4. Make a list of all terms — "pollutants" and other words — whose meaning you are unsure of. Check the definitions using libraries, books, and resource people. Report any information that you discover.

Headline Hunter

Explore the newspapers and magazines in your home and help develop an "Environmental Bulletin Board" in the classroom. Perhaps you can group the articles according to the three criteria. Be sure to include the "good news" as well as the "not-so-good news". For each article, include a brief analysis. Your analysis could include the information shown here.

Subject title: _____

Source: _____
(name of publication, date, page)

Name: _____

Definitions: (words whose meanings you are unsure of)

Summary: (a brief description of what the article is about; include in your summary whether the issue is a local, regional, or global one)

A Symposium on the Environment

"There will be a gathering of scientists, politicians, representatives from industry, environmentalists, and interested citizens to present papers on the state of the environment."

Presentations are invited on all topics:

- problems — local, regional, and global
- solutions
- efforts made by individuals, industries, and governments to maintain a clean environment

The presentation can include background information and recommendations for action, where appropriate, based on the research done. Some of your information should come from something that you have done yourself and not from written material.

Method of Presentation

This will be a poster session. Each presenter can use one full sheet of bristol board, plus a written submission. The poster may exhibit writing, diagrams, pictures, and graphs.

This is a preliminary call for presentations from all interested parties. The symposium will be held four weeks from today.

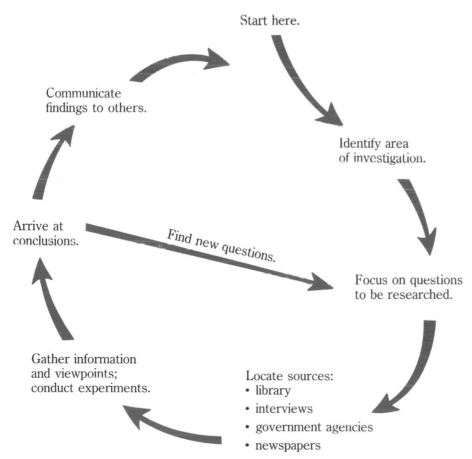

Start here.

Communicate findings to others.

Identify area of investigation.

Arrive at conclusions.

Find new questions.

Focus on questions to be researched.

Gather information and viewpoints; conduct experiments.

Locate sources:
- library
- interviews
- government agencies
- newspapers

You as Part of the Symposium

This is your challenge — to simulate the symposium and give a poster session on some aspect of the environment. You can play the role of a scientist, a politician, a representative of industry, an environmentalist, or yourself as an interested citizen. Part of the project must be done through non-book sources. This component could be:

- an interview (that is, if you are playing the role of a scientist, you can interview a scientist)
- a collection (for example, a collection of pond plants if you are studying a pond)
- a poll or survey
- photographs that you took
- experiments that you conducted

Here are the steps you may go through as you get ready for your symposium presentation:

1. identifying and stating the area of investigation
2. determining the kinds of information needed and possible sources
3. deciding on the non-book component of your project
4. gathering the information, conducting a survey, doing an interview
5. arriving at conclusions and recommendations
6. communicating your project through a poster session

Good luck on your presentation at the symposium.

Listening In

Let's listen in as members of Paul's class discuss their plans. In each case, what are they doing for the non-book component of their project? Perhaps in a few days, after you have had a chance to think about your topic, your class can share ideas on this aspect of individual projects as well.

Jill: I decided to do my project on what is happening to the ozone layer high up in the atmosphere. I will play the role of a scientist. I want to find the answer to two questions. What may be causing a problem? What can individuals do to help solve the problem? I used the periodical index in our library to find information to answer the first question. A scientist at the university suggested a number of ways that I can be part of the solution.

Paul: I am doing my project on how this city treats its wastes. In particular, I want to find out what steps are involved and how "clean" the water is after treatment. Most of the information for my project is coming from non-book sources. As an interested citizen, I visited our sewage treatment plant and interviewed the guide who showed me around.

Sara: I read in the paper that the peregrine falcon is making a comeback after nearly becoming extinct. I will answer three questions in my project: What habitat does the falcon need? Why is it endangered? Why is it making a comeback? Since I live in an area where the falcon is normally found, I am taking pictures of its habitat and of what is happening to it. I found some valuable information on efforts to save the peregrine falcon in the magazine *International Wildlife*.

Another Way of Sharing Your Findings

Upon completion of the projects, share the findings of your symposium with family and friends through a newsletter. The newsletter could be called *Environmental News*. Each reporter would submit an article based on the research done for the poster session.

Symposium Ideas

"What will my topic be?" Decision making is a difficult part of any project! Your area of research may focus on an aspect of air, soil, or water quality. In the following sections you will be investigating these in more detail. Your project may focus on an intentional or unintentional change in the environment caused by human action. The environmental change may be positive or negative. A list of symposium ideas follows — but you may have a better one.

1. Visit a local business such as a dry-cleaning establishment. What chemicals do they use that have an impact on the environment? What guidelines or regulations are they following to minimize their impact on the environment?

2. Interview someone from Environment Canada, a local university, or your provincial Department of the Environment who is involved in testing and maintaining the quality of the environment. But first, decide what you wish to find out and what questions you wish to ask. What is their job? What tests do they conduct? How does the public learn about their discoveries? Are their discoveries published in newspapers and journals?

3. In agriculture, chemicals are used for a variety of purposes: fertilizers, pesticides, and insecticides to grow crops; gasoline and oil to run machinery. Choose one such chemical and do an impact study on it. Why is it used? What is the potential for negative impact? How can this potential be minimized?

4. Do research on an animal or plant that is on the endangered species list. Why is it endangered? What can be done about it? One magazine you may find useful is *International Wildlife*.

5. Do a litter study in your neighbourhood or in the school area. You could map the area and, by using codes, indicate the type and quantity of litter. You could also use a questionnaire to find out more about people's attitudes regarding litter.

6. If you live near a wetland, such as a marsh, pond, or slough, determine its value to farmers and hunters through interviews. Perhaps the farmer views the wetland more as a headache because it reduces the amount of land that can be cultivated. You could also investigate the kinds of animals that make the wetland their home or make a display of plant life that is unique to the wetland.

7. Do a project on forest management. What are the different ways of harvesting the forest? How are forests replanted? Is it being done? Will our forests run out?

8. In many parts of the country there is a debate on whether to develop an area or to leave it in its natural state. This debate is being waged around such issues as developing housing subdivisions on farm land, ski slopes in park areas, and logging in wilderness areas. As your project, develop a case for **both** sides of the debate and present your conclusions.

9. Read your local papers for items that are of concern in your area. The newspaper article could be the start of an interesting study.

10. An interesting project might be to study the effects of acid deposition on your area. Find out more about acid rain and its effect on your area. You could develop a poster that contrasts the causes, effects, and solutions to the problem of acid deposition in two parts of the country: eastern Canada and western Canada. A good place to start is with your regional office of Environment Canada.

11. Perhaps you live near a mine where a natural resource is being extracted from the earth. Your project could include a study of the importance of the mine to the community, the changes in environmental quality that occurred as a result of the mine, and what the managers of the mine are doing to cause as little change as possible.

12. You might like to do a historical study on how your community has grown over the years. Did the growth result in loss of agricultural land? You could use maps to compare the size of the community at various times in its history.

13. Find out where your drinking water comes from and how it is treated. What happens to your waste water after you use it? Do a project on how waste water is treated in your community.

Water Quality

Water, Water Everywhere

Water is an essential requirement of all life on earth. It is the life-blood of the environment.

The earth has a lot of water — 1 385 000 000 km³! Of this, 37 300 000 km³ are fresh water. Canada is rich in water resources. We have 20% (or 7 000 000 km³) of the world's fresh water. However, 11% of this fresh water is frozen in glaciers. But that still leaves a lot of fresh water, enough, in fact, to flood the entire country to a depth of 2 m!

Look at the map of Canada. On what three oceans does Canada border? Global issues such as the quality of ocean water, health of fish stocks, and the well-being of ocean animals are a vital concern.

Observe the very large lakes on the map of Canada. What are their names? They are the world's largest freshwater lakes, covering an area of 246 050 km². More than 350 chemical compounds have been found in this freshwater ecosystem. The presence of these chemicals is a regional, as well as a national concern. When you realize that the average Canadian uses 250 L of water daily, we can be grateful for the amount of water we have. But the quality of this water is a real concern to all of us as individuals.

As you can see, a study of water quality could be a *global,*

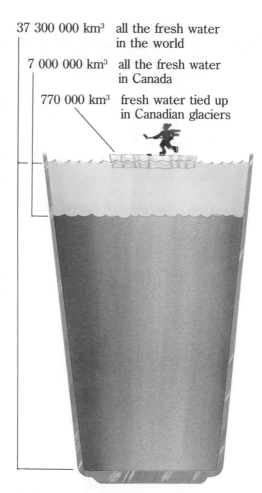

37 300 000 km³	all the fresh water in the world
7 000 000 km³	all the fresh water in Canada
770 000 km³	fresh water tied up in Canadian glaciers

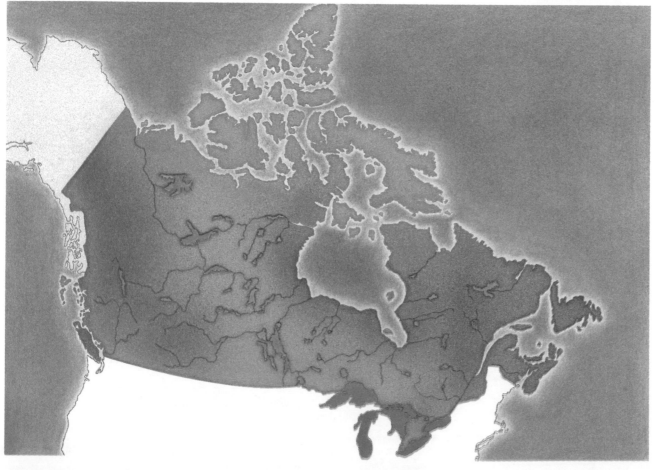

regional, or *local* issue. How would you classify each of these concerns?

- concern with the quality of safe drinking water
- concern regarding the quality of water in lakes and streams and the health of the plants and animals living there
- concern about the health of the oceans and the animals living there
- concern over the quality of the water that falls on a region as rain and snow; acid precipitation is considered by many people to be Canada's most serious environmental problem

In the next few sections we will investigate water quality as a local issue.

Thinking About Water

In the previous section, a number of facts about water quality were given. What else do you know about water quality? In groups of three or four, share as many facts and ideas about water as you can. Here are a number of questions that may help you get started.

- Is tap water pure?
- Where would you find the purest water?
- Is water that is suitable for swimming also suitable for drinking?
- If you consider pond water unsuitable for drinking, does that mean it is polluted?
- How many differences can you suggest between drinking water and stream water?
- What are the ideal characteristics of drinking water?
- What questions regarding water would you like answers to? In your group, suggest two.

Share your responses with the rest of the class. The following sections may help expand your answers to these questions.

The Crowchilds' Pond — A Case Study

Susan and Rick Crowchild have dug a pond in a low area of their property. It had a gravel bottom and was fed by natural springs. The water looked pure and clear. They thought that the pond would be just right for a few trout for their own use. What are some characteristics of the pond water that might be important to the trout? Would this pond be suitable?

Trout's Needs	Pond Water Characteristics
pH 6.7 to pH 8.6	pH 7.2
dissolved oxygen — over 10 mg/L (milligrams per litre)	dissolved oxygen — 11.7 mg/L (milligrams per litre)
temperature — 17°C and below	temperature — 2°C to 18°C
turbidity — Water needs to be clear and free of silt or colouration — trout are visual feeders and need to see their food.	turbidity — Water is clear.
biochemical oxygen demand (B.O.D.) — less than 5 ppm (parts per million)	biochemical oxygen demand (B.O.D.) — less than 5 ppm (parts per million)

The table introduces a number of measurements and terms relating to water quality characteristics: pH, parts per million, biochemical oxygen demand, and turbidity. What do these terms mean? In the following sections you will answer this and other questions — starting with "What is pH and what is its effect on living things?"

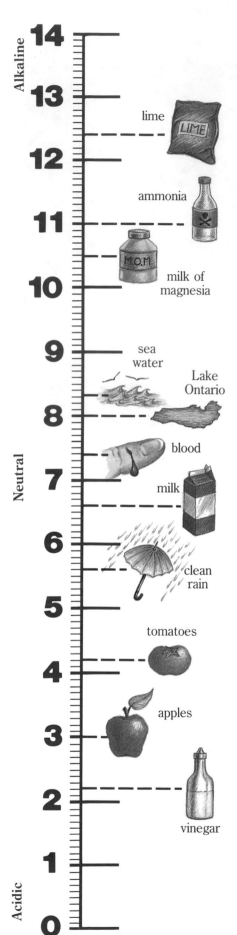

The pH Scale

Reviewing pH

Review the following information on pH by answering the questions below. After this review you will investigate the effects of pH on living things.

The acid or base content of a substance is measured on a pH scale of 0 to 14. Any substance that has a pH value below 7 is acidic: the lower the number, the greater the acid concentration. A pH value above 7 indicates the presence of a base rather than an acid. Bases are also known as *alkalis*. Alkaline substances can counteract acids; that is, they lower the acid content of a substance. The scale will tell you something about the acid or base content of many foods.

Check the table for yourself.

1. Is ordinary rainwater acidic?

2. Which has a higher acid concentration, an apple or a tomato?

3. Have you heard of people taking milk of magnesia for an acid stomach? Why would they do this?

4. Home owners often put lime on their lawns in spring. Why?

5. The pH scale is an unusual one. When the pH drops by one point, the acid content increases by 10 times. When the pH drops by two points, the acid content increases by 100 times. What would be the increase in acid content if the pH dropped by three points?

6. (a) In some areas rain may have a pH as low as 3 or even 2. What materials have a comparable acidity?

   (b) Would the Crowchilds' trout be affected if acid lowered the pH of the pond water?

   (c) What can be done about bodies of water that have a lowered pH? The next section offers one solution.

Simulating an Acid Lake

Acid rain or snow may be a greater problem in one part of the country than in another. Winds carry the pollutants that are responsible for acid precipitation into eastern Canada. This is not as large a problem in western Canada. As well, soil in much of western Canada is a bit alkaline and tends to neutralize any acid. In other parts of Canada, home owners, gardeners, and farmers add lime to the soil. This substance also counteracts (neutralizes) the acid in the soil. Another such substance is limestone. Countries such as Sweden have experimented with improving the quality of acid rivers and lakes by lining the water beds with limestone. This procedure is expensive and there are questions about how long the beneficial effects last. You can demonstrate the neutralizing effect of limestone on acid in the following way.

You Will Need

- vinegar
- watch glass
- pH paper
- limestone chips or chalk

What To Do

1. Add a few millilitres of vinegar to a watch glass. Determine its pH by dipping a small piece of pH test paper into the solution. Compare the colour of the pH paper to the colour chart on the container of pH paper.
2. Add a few chips of limestone or a piece of chalk to the vinegar. After a few minutes find the pH of the vinegar again. Explain your observations.

A Case Study — The History of a Lake

How can scientists study the effects of pH changes on living things? One way is to observe changes that are already occurring. Scientists with Environment Canada studied the problem in another way. They artificially increased the acidity of a lake and studied its effects. As you read about Lake 223, find out what happens:
(a) to the trout as the pH is progressively lowered
(b) to the fathead minnow and white sucker
(c) to the plants

1976: pH 6.8

1977: pH 6.1

- increase in bacterial activity
- increase in invertebrate aquatic animals, small animals which are food for larval fish, insects and large crustaceans

Lake 223

- increase of green algae
- decrease of brown algae, which is normally dominant
- increase of insects

1978: pH 5.8
- disappearance of one type of copepod, a crustacean species
- reproductive failure of the fathead minnow
- increase in deaths of lake trout embryos
- decrease in slimy sculpin

1979: pH 5.6
- increased plant production in depths of lake
- development of mats of algae along shoreline
- disappearance of opossum shrimp, a major food source for lake trout

- decrease in hardness of crayfish exoskeleton
- severe decline in fathead minnow
- decrease in white sucker abundance
- decrease in lake trout abundance

1980: pH 5.4
- disappearance of another copepod
- infestation of parasites in crayfish
- decreased reproduction and abundance of crayfish
- increase of pearl dace, a small minnow
- reproductive failure of lake trout

1981: pH 5.1
- reproductive failure of white sucker

At present, Lake 223 is being maintained at pH 5.1 to study further developments. Although the experiment is an artificial manipulation and does not occur in nature, it provides very valuable guidance. It helps us to understand the process which might be expected to happen in thousands of lakes now becoming acidified.

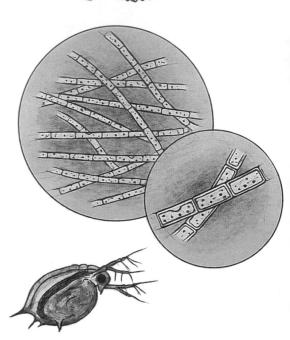

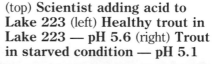

(top) **Scientist adding acid to Lake 223** (left) **Healthy trout in Lake 223 — pH 5.6** (right) **Trout in starved condition — pH 5.1**

Questions

1. "Often a small change in environmental quality can have a large effect on living things in that environment." Can this statement be supported by evidence from this reading?

2. Of what value are studies like this one?

3. Do some organisms benefit from a pH change while others are adversely affected? Give an example.

4. Was this a reliable experiment? How can you be sure the changes would not have occurred anyway?

Devising an Experiment

You have just read about how Canadian scientists artificially reduced the pH of a lake to study the effects of pH changes on living things. Now it's your turn. Your task is to devise an experiment to find answers to one or both of the following questions.

Defining the Problem

1. What is the effect of a lowered pH on growing plants?

2. Are all plants affected in the same way by a lowered pH?

Making a Plan

In groups, devise a plan of action. In your plan, include:

- a hypothesis — the expected outcome as a result of changing the pH

- a list of variables that must be controlled so that the results of the experiment are reliable

- a description of the experiment; this description should include the type of plants to be investigated and other materials needed

- the ways observations and data are recorded and communicated

Here are some ideas that others have suggested.

"Planting fast-growing seeds like radishes will speed up the experiment."

"We can plant flower seeds such as marigolds as well."

"An egg carton makes a good planter. We can treat the seeds planted in each compartment differently."

"Acid rain can be simulated by using different concentrations of vinegar in water. We can use pH paper to obtain the pH we want."

"We need a control so that we know how the plant should look when watered with ordinary water."

"Our write-up could look the same as the report on Lake 223."

Carrying Out and Evaluating the Plan

It is now time to try your experiment. This can be done in class or at home. Perhaps each member of the group can have certain responsibilities. Report your findings in a similar way to the report on Lake 223. After completing the experiment, describe any changes you would make to improve the experiment.

The Pond Ecosystem

What's in the Water?

Even pure water contains much dissolved and suspended matter — often in minute quantities. The Crowchilds' pond contained over 10 mg/L of dissolved oxygen. Often this is recorded as 10 parts per million (or 10 ppm). This was suitable for the needs of the trout.

1. What does "parts per million" mean?

2. What factors affect the solubility of gases such as oxygen in water?

3. What other dissolved gases beside oxygen are important to living things?

4. What happens to the concentration of dissolved oxygen as a result of the presence of living things in the pond?

5. How can the concentration of dissolved oxygen become too low for living things?

6. What is the biochemical oxygen demand (B.O.D.) and what does it tell us?

These are the questions that you will be investigating in the following sections.

What's a Part Per Million?

The terms "parts per million (ppm)", "parts per billion (ppb)", and "parts per trillion (ppt)" are used to describe extremely small concentrations. Earlier you saw that trout require water with a dissolved oxygen concentration of at least 10 mg/L. This is the same as saying 10 ppm.

Just a few years ago parts per million was the usual range for recording such concentrations. Now technology allows us to measure concentrations in water, air, soil, fish, breast milk, or gulls' eggs in amounts as small as parts per trillion. But the fact that contaminants can be detected does not necessarily mean that their presence is harmful to human health.

Explore the meaning of these very small concentrations in the following Exploration.

Exploring Parts Per Million

Part 1
Making a Solution

You Will Need

- four 1.5 or 2 L plastic containers
- one 100 mL graduated cylinder
- four plastic spoons
- 1 g of salt

What To Do

Make a salt solution that has a concentration of 1000 mg/L (1000 ppm). Do this by dissolving 1 g (1000 mg) of table salt into 1 L of water. You can do this in a clean ice-cream container. Stir using a clean plastic spoon, since you are going to taste the solution afterwards.

It is easy to see why the concentration of your salt solution is 1000 mg/L, since you added 1000 mg of salt to 1 L of water. But why can the concentration of salt in the solution also be expressed as 1000 ppm? Here are the mathematics.

concentration of salt solution
= 1 g of salt per 1 L of water
= 1 g salt per 1000 mL of water
= 1 g salt per 1000 g of water
= 1000 mg of salt
   per 1 000 000 mg of water

Note that the mass of salt is 1 g (1000 mg), and the mass of the water is 1000 g (1 000 000 mg). Now do you see why 1000 mg/L is the same as 1000 ppm?

Part 2
Making a Smaller Concentration

Now form weaker, or more dilute, solutions with the following concentrations.

(a) 100 ppm (100 mg/L)
(b) 10 ppm (10 mg/L)
(c) 1 ppm (1 mg/L)

Here is how to do part (a). *You* figure out how to do parts (b) and (c).

To make a solution with a concentration of 100 ppm from one that has a concentration of 1000 ppm, take any volume of your original solution and dilute it by a factor of 10. In other words, you could take 10 mL of your salt solution and add water until the new volume is 100 mL.

Prepare all of the solutions. Can you taste the presence of the salt in a solution of 1000 ppm? 100 ppm? 10 ppm? 1 ppm?

Part 3
Making Comparisons

These concentrations are small. Perhaps the following table will help you to visualize just how small they are! Some values are missing. Copy the table and fill in the missing parts.

1 part per million (ppm)	1 part per billion (ppb)	1 part per trillion (ppt)
$1 in $1 000 000	$1 in $1 000 000 000	$1 in $1 000 000 000 000
1 s in 11.6 days	1 s in (?) years	1 s in 32 000 years
1 bad apple in (?) barrels	1 bad apple in 2 000 000 barrels	1 bad apple in (?) barrels
1 mg oxygen in 1 L of water	1 mg oxygen in 1000 L of water	1 mg oxygen in (?) L of water

The Pond Over Time

Earlier you saw that trout require an oxygen level of 10 ppm. Where does the dissolved oxygen come from? What factors affect the amount of oxygen dissolved in water? Will the amount of dissolved oxygen in a pond change over time? Why? The following tasks will help you to answer these questions.

Task 1: The Solubility of Oxygen in Water

The solubility of oxygen in water is given in this table. The table assumes that air contains 21% oxygen.

Temperature (°C)	Oxygen solubility (ppm)
0	14.6
5	12.7
10	11.3
15	10.1
20	9.1
25	8.3
30	7.5

(a) Graph this data. Place *temperature* on the horizontal axis and *solubility* on the vertical axis.

(b) Draw conclusions from the graph which describe the solubility of oxygen in water.

(c) Does the temperature of the Crowchilds' pond ever rise high enough so that the dissolved oxygen in the pond becomes a problem for the trout?

(d) Do you think that all gases behave similarly to oxygen when dissolved in water? For example, does carbon dioxide follow this rule? Examine the data in the table which follows. The table assumes that air contains 0.03% carbon dioxide.

Temperature (°C)	Carbon dioxide solubility (ppm)
0	1.00
5	0.83
10	0.70
15	0.59
20	0.51
25	0.43
30	0.38

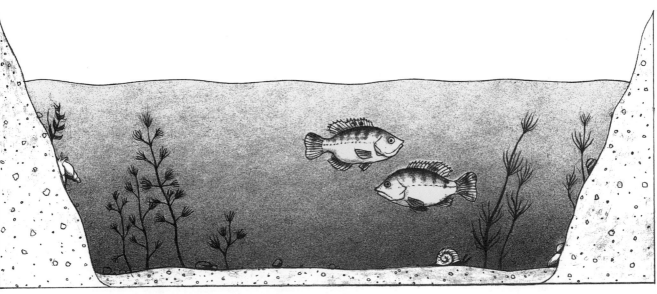

Task 2: The Effect of Living Things on Dissolved Oxygen and Carbon Dioxide

(a) Living things in the pond affect the dissolved oxygen and carbon dioxide concentrations. When Susan and Rick introduced trout into their pond, the levels of dissolved oxygen decreased and the levels of dissolved carbon dioxide increased. Use the diagram on the opposite page to explain what caused this change.

(b) After some time, plants became a part of the pond ecosystem. These included leafy plants and algae. Microscopic analysis of the water indicated an abundance of diatoms. All are *producers* — that is, during the process of photosynthesis, they use energy from the Sun to produce food. In this process, carbon dioxide is taken in by the plant and oxygen is released. Why would the carbon dioxide and oxygen concentrations in the pond water be affected?

(c) Now examine the following, slightly more complex drawing of a pond showing parts of its larger environment. The arrows illustrate the movement of carbon throughout the environment. This is often called the **carbon cycle**. Make a list of anything the cycle seems to be "saying". Discuss how the animals and the plants meet each other's needs.

The Carbon Cycle

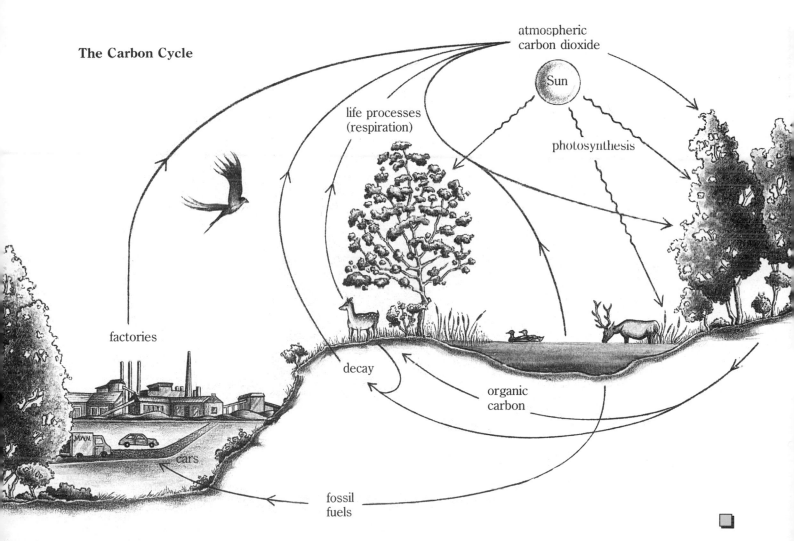

Italy's beaches closed because of algal bloom

Many tourists are thinking twice about vacationing on the Adriatic this summer. The waters are covered by a mat of slimy algae. The nutrient rich water has produced a burst of algal growth called an algal bloom. Local residents who depend on fishing for their livelihood are also affected as more fish turn up dead on the beaches. Many of them have been criss-crossing the water in their boats in an attempt to supply air to oxygen starved fish. Scientists are calling this an ecological disaster . . .

Algae growing in a freshwater pond: how could this affect the concentration of dissolved oxygen?

Biochemical Oxygen Demand (B.O.D.)

The fish mentioned in this newspaper article died of suffocation. How is it that an over-abundance of algae, which are plants, resulted in a depletion of the dissolved oxygen? Plants produce oxygen during photosynthesis. The answer lies in the organisms that use oxygen.

What are some of the animals in a pond, beside trout? Look back at the description of Lake 223 on page 369. The names of at least six other animals present in the lake were mentioned. All of these require oxygen for survival, as do all other animals. They breathe oxygen *dissolved* in the pond or lake water.

You may know of other organisms which are present in ponds. They are called decomposers. What are they? If you think that they are bacteria, yeasts, and moulds that decay organic matter, you are right. Organic matter is the waste of plants and animals and the dead plants and animals themselves. Decomposers aid in the decomposition of this organic matter. Decomposers also require oxygen. They put a *demand* on the dissolved oxygen in the water. They use up oxygen while returning carbon dioxide to the water. If there were too many decomposers in the water, what might happen to trout and other animals that require oxygen? How could the addition of sewage or animal wastes lower the dissolved oxygen to 0 mg/L?

Wastes and other organic matter in waterways are measured in terms of their **biochemical oxygen demand** (B.O.D.), the amount of oxygen that will be consumed by their biological decomposition. Now do you see why an algae bloom may eventually lead to a depletion of dissolved oxygen? Try explaining this to someone by describing the stages involved. Use the ideas of decomposers and B.O.D. in your explanation. Then talk through the pond scenarios that follow.

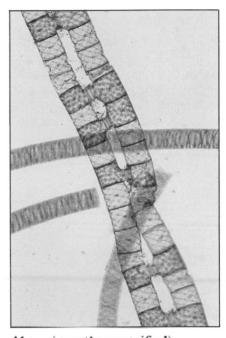

Algae (greatly magnified)

Pond Scenarios

Discuss the consequences of each of these pond scenarios in terms of the oxygen/carbon dioxide balance in the pond water. Try to use the idea of B.O.D. in your discussions.

1. The bottom becomes matted with organic matter and decomposers multiply.

2. An *algal bloom* occurs due to fertilizer seeping into the pond from nearby fields. Later the algae dies.

3. Animal manure is spread on a nearby field and water from the field seeps into the pond.

Comparing B.O.D. Levels

Most provinces have established standards for water quality. For example, Alberta Environment says the following about the B.O.D. of *surface waters* such as rivers and lakes.

"The B.O.D. must not exceed a limit which would create a dissolved oxygen content of less than 5 mg/L or 5 ppm."

What does this statement mean? Rephrase it in your own words. Measuring the B.O.D. of water requires apparatus that is quite expensive. However, you can compare values for B.O.D. using the following procedure.

You Will Need

- samples of water to be tested (These should be collected in 250 mL flasks with a tight stopper. The bottle should be filled to the top with water to prevent mixing with the air over the water.)
- eyedropper
- methylene blue solution — 1000 ppm (This can be prepared by dissolving 0.10 g of methylene blue in 100 mL of water.)

What To Do

1. Using the eyedropper, add about 1 mL of methylene blue solution to a flask completely filled with the water sample. The tip of the dropper should be in the water to prevent the methylene blue from absorbing oxygen from the air.

2. Stopper the bottle and place the bottle in a warm, dark place. The temperature should be as close to 20°C as possible.

3. Check the bottle every 12 to 24 h. The blue colour will remain as long as there is oxygen remaining in the water. When all the oxygen is used up, the blue colour will disappear. If the colour disappears in less than four days, then the B.O.D. is high.

A high B.O.D. means that there was insufficient dissolved oxygen to meet the demand for it by the decomposers acting on the suspended organic matter in the water.

A Pond System

The Crowchilds' pond continued to exist in a state of healthy equilibrium. The springs continued to supply fresh cold water, the winds lapped at the surface, and gases such as oxygen and carbon dioxide were exchanged between the atmosphere and the water. The Sun provided the energy for the <u>producers</u> of the pond. In turn, <u>herbivores</u> fed on these producers. The trout, being <u>carnivores</u>, fed on the insect life of the pond. Herbivores and carnivores are collectively known as consumers.

1. The pond is an example of an ecosystem. From this description, can you recall what an ecosystem is? What are some things that happen in an ecosystem?

2. Could the earth as a whole be considered as an ecosystem?

3. What do the underlined words mean? What other examples of producers, herbivores and carnivores can you suggest?

4. Within the ecosystem most organisms are a source of energy for another. A description of the flow of energy from one organism to another is called a food chain.

    (a) How do producers get their energy? herbivores? carnivores?

    (b) Look at the food chain for a pond ecosystem. What does the direction of the arrows indicate? What does the expression "at the top of the food chain" mean?

    (c) Draw a food chain with you in it.

An Ecosystem in a Bottle

Create a pond ecosystem in a large, transparent soft drink bottle. Add to the bottle: pond water (half-full), a few pond organisms, for example, insect larvae, material from the pond bottom, and some algae. Place the top on the bottle and place in a spot that is well-lit but won't get too warm. Over the next few weeks, note all changes that take place in the bottle. Try to explain the changes in terms of your recent studies on water quality. When is the dissolved oxygen increasing? decreasing? Examine drops of water under a microscope at various times. Can you detect the decomposers? Do their populations change over time?

You may notice that the water becomes cloudy or turbid at some point. Suspended matter that may consist of living and dead organisms, wastes, and silt will scatter and block incoming light. This characteristic of some water to scatter or block incoming light is referred to as **turbidity**. Turbidity can be expressed in milligrams per litre or parts per million of suspended matter in the water. At what stages did the turbidity of your bottle ecosystem increase? What do you think caused this change?

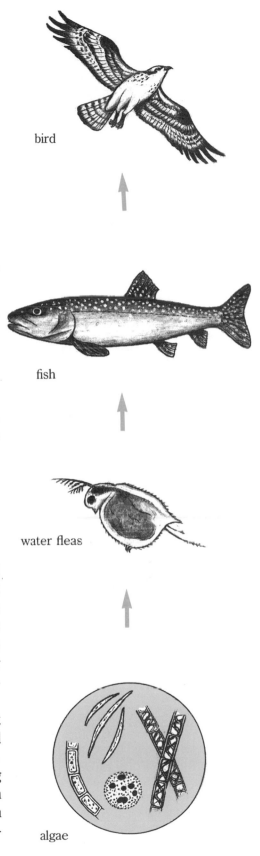

bird

fish

water fleas

algae

Canadian Technology — A Bioreactor

The following article is from the newsletter *Canadian Science.* As you read the article, identify the following stages in the development of this new technology:

1. understanding the problem — What is the problem that initiated the research?
2. developing a plan — What was the plan? What is the science involved in the plan?
3. carrying out the plan — Did the technology work?
4. evaluating the invention — How well did it work? What modifications could be made?

New "bioreactor" will purify agricultural waste water for reuse

A new agricultural waste management system, developed at the University of British Columbia, could help keep livestock farms' waste water from polluting nearby lakes and rivers.

Dr. Victor Lo and his colleagues in UBC's Bioresource Engineering Department have designed and built a 'bioreactor' — a large tank in which bacteria remove the organic material from agricultural waste water, leaving only carbon dioxide, dead bacteria, and decontaminated water that can be sprayed on fields or even used again to flush out barns.

Hogs' growth rate is reduced if ammonia in their urine becomes concentrated in their pens, so farmers flush hog barns with clean water a few times a day. This produces a lot of waste water which, if simply dumped outdoors, can severely pollute local water systems. To make matters worse, hog farmers usually have limited land, so they can't dilute the waste water by spreading it over a wide area.

The unit developed at UBC, a "sequencing batch reactor", treats batches of waste water in a sequence of four steps. First, the reactor is filled with waste water. Second, the water is aerated: a pump forces air through the water for a few hours, providing the oxygen the bacteria need to digest the organic materials in the liquid and multiply.

Third, the aerator is stopped and the bacteria settle to the bottom of the tank, where they form a sludge that amounts to about five per cent of the tank's volume; the rest is full of decontaminated water.

Finally, in the fourth step, the tank is emptied. The water can be safely disposed of or reused. Some of the bacteria are left to start on the next batch; the rest of the sludge can be used as fertilizer or made into a protein supplement for chicken feed, Lo says.

The purified water can be either recycled in the barn, or sprayed over fields, where it will be further purified by natural processes before it percolates into the ground or nearby waterways.

The whole process takes four to six hours, then a new batch of water is pumped into the tank. The researchers originally set up three tanks in a series, thinking that purifying the water would require considerable time and aeration. But only one tank, 4.5 m tall and 2 m in diameter, was needed to remove 95% of the organic materials.

The bacteria that clean the water do not have to be added: they are already present in the farm wastes. "What we are doing is simply providing the optimum conditions for them to convert the organic materials into carbon dioxide and water," says Lo.

The tanks will soon be available commercially. A system of three reactors (including pumps, hoses, and a programmable controller), costing about $20 000, can serve a farm producing about 4000 pigs a year. A one-tank system for a smaller farm would cost considerably less.

Development of the reactor was funded by the B.C. Ministry of Agriculture and Fisheries, the B.C. government's Agricultural Services Co-ordinating Committee, and the Agrifood Regional Development Subsidy Agreement — a collaboration between the federal and provincial governments.

Land and Soil

Land Use

In a country as large as Canada, having enough land for our needs may not appear to be a problem. Canada includes 922 million hectares of land. About 11% of this land is suitable for agriculture. Does this mean that the remaining land is of poor quality or is of little use? Trees can often grow where wheat will not and the forest industry is an important one in most parts of Canada. As well, the forest is a habitat for many of Canada's plants and animals. The Canadian North, although it is not as heavily populated as further south, is home to a wide variety of living things.

In some areas, however, there are stresses placed on land use. Most urban centres are located on what was once prime agricultural land. Transportation systems such as highways require land. Land is desired by the public as recreational areas and as parks to preserve natural habitat.

With a classmate, spend five minutes to "brainstorm" a list of land uses in your local area. What uses of land are suggested by the picture study at the beginning of the unit? Who can come up with the longest list in this time? Did you include the need for land by other living things? Sharing our environment will be examined later in the unit.

Was agriculture at the top of your list? Since about one job in ten depends on agriculture or agriculture-related industries, we all have a stake in it. In the following section, you will examine a number of soil quality characteristics associated with this important industry.

What Is Soil?

Soil is all around us. We walk on it, grow food in it, build our homes on it, and cover it with parking lots. We often treat soil as an unlimited resource. Is it?

Here are some statements about soil. From these statements and what you already know about soil suggest at least three soil quality characteristics.

- Soil scientists classify soil particles into sand, silt, and clay.
- Clay particles are smaller than 0.002 mm in diameter; silt particles range from 0.002 to 0.02 mm in diameter; sand ranges from 0.02 to 2.0 mm in diameter.
- Loam and silt loam are textural terms that refer to soils with a favourable proportion of sand, silt, and clay.
- Plants need air in the soil for best root development. Water movement in the soil increases air circulation.
- Too much clay in proportion to silt causes water to enter the soil very slowly. Too much sand lets water run through the soil too rapidly.
- Organic matter improves soil by increasing its water-holding capacity, reducing run off, improving aeration, and making soil crumbly and easier to work.

What is your definition of soil?

A Closer Look

The next time you are passing an excavation site, pause and examine the top metre of the hole. You may observe bands of colour called "horizons". These colours result from the action of water as it passes through the soil. Water carries with it dissolved minerals and organic materials, depositing some of these as it passes through the soil.

The top few centimetres may contain a lot of partially decomposed plant material. If it is present, this layer is called the **O** horizon.

Top soil, the **A** horizon, is the upper soil layer. It is darker in colour because of the organic or humus content of the soil. The humus content of soil is an important characteristic that you will investigate later.

Subsoil, the **B** horizon, is the middle soil layer. It has fewer organisms and plants don't grow as well in it.

The **C** horizon is the lowest layer. It is the weathered rock and partially weathered soil from which the soil layers above were formed.

A typical Prairie soil profile. Can you identify the O, A, and B horizons?

A soil profile is a slice of the earth that shows these layers of soil. Examine the diagram of the soil profiles and answer the following questions.

1. How is the grassland soil profile similar to that of the forest? How is it different?

2. In lands that have been cultivated, how many horizons would be visible? Why?

3. With a classmate, make a list of areas in your community where soil profiles can be found.

A comparison of the profiles of forest and grassland soils.

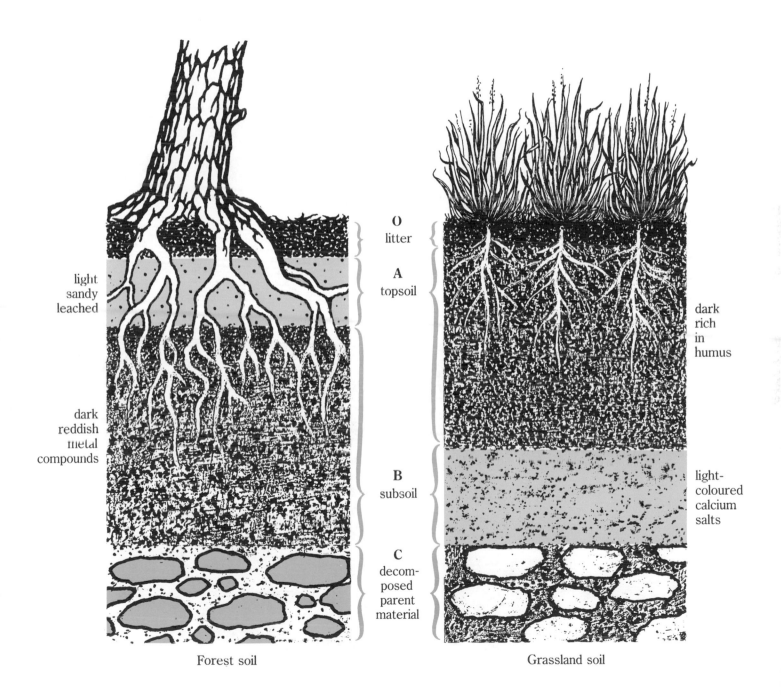

light sandy leached

dark reddish metal compounds

O litter

A topsoil

B subsoil

C decomposed parent material

dark rich in humus

light-coloured calcium salts

Forest soil

Grassland soil

Investigating a Soil Profile

In groups, or individually, go to a convenient location for viewing a soil profile.

1. Measure the depth of each horizon from the surface.

2. Draw a sketch of the soil layers.

3. Compare your observations of each horizon with those in the table.

   • How thick is each layer?
   • What colour is each layer?
   • Describe the structure of each layer.
   • Describe evidence of plant and animal life in each layer.

4. Bring a sample of the A horizon back to the classroom in a plastic bag to use in the next Exploration.

5. As a project, fill one container with soil from the A horizon and one with soil from the B horizon. Plant a bean seed in each one. Treat both containers the same way. Over the next few weeks, take daily measurements of the growth of both plants. Prepare a graph showing the daily measurements. What do you expect to observe? Why? Was your prediction right?

Horizon	Name	Colours	Structure	Processes Occurring
O	organic	black, dark brown	loose, crumbly, well broken up	decomposition of organic matter
A	topsoil	dark brown to yellow	generally loose, crumbly, well broken up	zone of leaching (minerals and organic materials are carried downward by water)
B	subsoil	brown, red, yellow, or grey	generally larger chunks, may be dense or crumbly, can be cement-like	zone of accumulation (minerals and organic material are deposited)
C	parent material (slightly weathered material)	variable depending on parent material	loose to compact	weathering, disintegration of parent material or rock

The Organic Content of Soils

Organic matter, or **humus**, is a vital component of soils. Humus holds the soil together and slows down erosion and compaction. It supplies vital nutrients to the soil that would otherwise have to be added in the form of chemical fertilizers. It helps to hold moisture in the soil. But organic matter around the world is being lost at an alarming rate. Scientists believe that it took Prairie soils about 10 000 years to form, yet in less than 100 years of farming, nearly half of the original organic content has been lost.

Percentages of organic matter lost from various Prairie soils

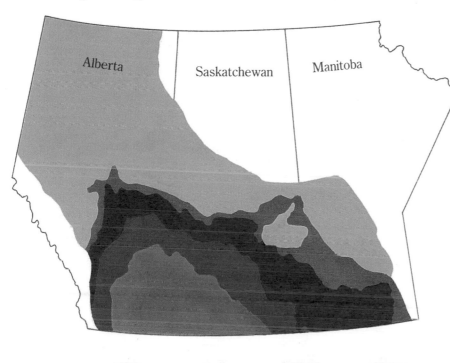

37%	43%	40%	44%	48%

A major cause for loss of organic matter is *summer fallowing*—the practice of tilling (turning over) the land and not planting for that year. This speeds up the decomposition of organic matter in the soil without adding new organic matter to replace what was there.

Determining the Organic Content of Soils

In this Exploration you will investigate the organic content of a variety of soils by heating a weighed sample to a high temperature in order to burn off the once-living matter. Before starting, examine the procedure carefully. From the description, prepare a data table which you will use to record the various measurements you will be making.

You Will Need

- a variety of soil samples taken from the top soil or *A horizon*. You can use garden soil, soil from cultivated fields, lawns, etc.
- balance
- Bunsen burner
- crucible and cover
- clay triangle
- ring
- support stand

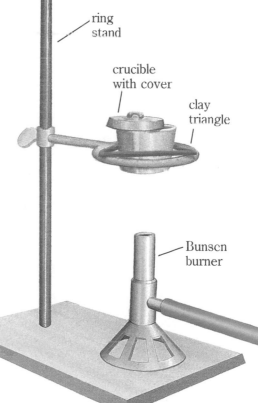

What To Do

1. Remove visible pieces of stems and roots from the soil.
2. Put the soil on a pie plate and heat it in an oven at 100°C until the soil is dry.
3. Find the mass of the crucible and cover.
4. Add soil so that the crucible is no more than half-full, and then find the mass of the crucible, cover, and soil.
5. Using the apparatus shown heat the soil at a high temperature for 10 min. When it is ready, there should be no smoke given off.
6. After they have cooled, find the mass of the crucible, cover, and burnt soil. Should the mass be more or less than what it was before?
7. Subtract to determine the mass of organic matter burnt off.
8. Determine the percentage of organic matter in your sample by using this formula.

per cent organic matter =

$$\frac{\text{mass of organic matter burnt off}}{\text{original mass of soil}} \times 100\%$$

Questions

1. If different groups analysed different soil samples, compare the per cent values of organic content. Suggest several reasons for any differences.
2. Why was the soil dried before doing this experiment?
3. Suggest how the following farming practices could conserve the soil organic content.
   (a) crop rotation — the periodic use of grasses or legumes as a crop instead of grains
   (b) continuous cropping — not allowing a field to lay fallow over a season
   (c) conservation tillage — reducing tillage to a minimum
   (d) spreading manure over crop land

4. Nitrogen, phosphorus, and potassium are among the essential plant nutrients. These are supplied by the humus in the soil and by the decomposition of plant residues, or by the addition of chemical fertilizers. Examine the graph.
   (a) What do the axes represent?
   (b) The dotted line represents the amount of nitrogen required to grow a barley crop of two tonnes per hectare (2 t/ha) on virgin Prairie soil. For a number of years this requirement was met by the decomposition of soil humus and crop residues. How many years will pass before fertilizers will be needed to supplement these sources of nitrogen?
   (c) What is happening over time to the proportion of nitrogen supplied by fertilizers? Why?

(based on virgin soils of the Prairies)

Graph. Y-axis: Amounts of nitrogen (kg/ha per year), ranging 0 to 80. X-axis: Years of grain production, 0 to 100. Labels: "approximate nitrogen requirement for a barley crop of 2 t/ha", "nitrogen needed from fertilizer", "nitrogen released by decomposition of crop residues", "nitrogen released by decomposition of soil humus".

Erosion and Compaction

Problems associated with soil quality tend to have interrelated causes and cures. How is soil erosion related to the organic content of soils? Could some of the practices that conserve organic content in soil also help to prevent soil erosion?

The Dust Bowl of the 1930s was an ecological as well as a social disaster. Erosion continues to be a major problem today. The rate at which soils are being formed in Canada is estimated to be between 0.25 and 1 t/ha per year. Annual erosion rates of 20 to 25 t/ha are not uncommon in land that is suffering from *gully erosion* (gullies are ditches made by heavy rains). Because soil nutrients are found in topsoil, erosion losses have a severe effect on soil fertility. This is illustrated in the graph to the right. Are there examples of this effect in your area?

1. minor loss of topsoil; yields can be maintained by increasing fertilizer

2. moderate topsoil loss, patchy areas, yields reduced despite increased fertilizer

3. major topsoil loss, serious gullying, rapidly declining yields

4. topsoil rapidly eroding, farm no longer economically viable, reclamation necessary

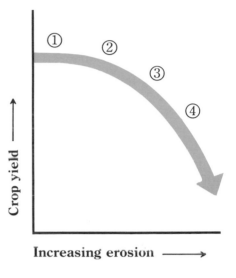

The effect of erosion on crop yields

Crop yield →

Increasing erosion ⟶

Today, farmers are practising a number of techniques that help to prevent undue erosion. Leaving crop cover on the fields lessens erosion caused by wind and water. Contour plowing can help to prevent soil loss through water erosion.

Soil compaction results from the use of heavy machinery — especially in wet conditions. Soil particles pack closer together due to the heavy load and the vibrations of the machine, resulting in poor conditions for root growth. Air and water circulation in the soil is decreased.

However, soil compaction is not only a problem in agricultural land. Playgrounds and park lands suffer from compaction as well. Why? In some woodland parks the forest floor is devoid of new growth because of compaction. Trees may not be receiving the water they require. One solution is to limit the public to designated paths or even to place fences around individual trees. Is compaction a problem around your school grounds? How could you compare the compaction of soil in different locations? You will explore these ideas in the next Exploration.

What practices may have decreased the extent of erosion shown here?

A Yard Survey

Part 1: Compaction

Where on the school property would you expect to find different degrees of soil compaction?

1. Devise a practical procedure that would allow you to compare soil compaction in different parts of the property.

2. Test your procedure while gathering data and observations.

3. Examine the area for evidence that shows whether compaction is a problem or not.

4. Place your observations and data on a map of the grounds showing the locations of your observations.

Part 2: Water Absorption

Compaction prevents water from being absorbed easily into the soil. This could increase erosion from rapid runoff of water. It also may mean that plants do not receive the water they require. How can you compare the rates at which water is absorbed into the soil? Here is what one class did.

> "Take a can with both ends removed. Twist it into the ground to a depth of one centimetre. Then add a volume of water and measure the time it takes for the water to disappear."

Is this a reliable plan? What variables must you control to compare different sites?

Use this method or one of your own to compare the rates at which water is absorbed by soil in different locations. Are the differences you observe due to compaction or could there be other reasons as well?

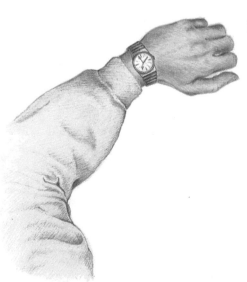

Other Soil Quality Characteristics

1. Earlier you studied the effects of pH on living things. This is another soil quality characteristic. Determine the pH of soils in your area. What crops grow best at different pH levels? What factors are affecting the pH of soils in your area?

2. In areas where irrigation is used to a large extent, soil salinity is a growing problem. The soil may become too salty to support crops. What causes this problem? What are some solutions?

Humans and Wildlife — Sharing an Environment

The global habitat is home to an amazing diversity of living things. This table provides an estimate of the numbers of kinds of organisms. Are you surprised? Why do you think there are so many species that have yet to be discovered?

Known and Estimated Diversity of Life on Earth

Forms of Life	Known Species	Estimated Total Species
insects and other arthropods	874 161	30 million insect species, extrapolated from surveys in forest canopy in Panama, most believed to be unique to tropical forests.
higher plants	248 400	Estimates of total plant species range from 275 000 to as many as 400 000; at least 10 to 15% of all plants are believed undiscovered.
invertebrates	116 873	True invertebrates may number in the millions.
lower plants, such as fungi and algae	73 900	not available
micro-organisms	36 600	not available
birds	9 040	98% have probably been discovered.
reptiles and amphibians	8 962	95% have probably been discovered.
mammals	4 000	4 000
total	1 390 992	10 million species is considered a conservative estimate; if total insect estimates are accurate, the total exceeds 30 million.

Canada, with its diversity of habitat, has given rise to a rich variety of wildlife. Canada has 172 species of land mammals and 380 species of birds. The Prairies have 17 species of mammals and 25 species of birds. Each species is usually restricted to, or is most abundant in, a particular habitat. Humans create a conflict as they claim more and more land for their use.

News Item

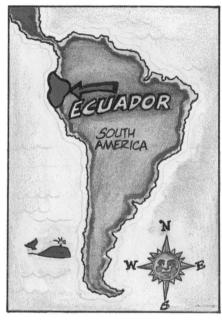

New Parrot Discovered

Ornithologist Robert Ridgely has added to the list of known species of birds by discovering a new species of parrot, the first to be discovered in the Western hemisphere since 1914. He made his discovery in the Andes Mountains of Ecuador.

This colourful bird (actually a parakeet belonging to a subgroup of the parrot family) has a limited range of no more than 26 000 ha of cloud forest. For this reason it is extremely endangered. The discoverer's next project is to persuade the government of Ecuador to preserve the area so as to protect the bird.

Large sections of land have been set aside as provincial and national parks. As well as providing land for recreational use, this preserves habitat that may be disappearing elsewhere. However, scientists are sometimes unsure of the size of habitat required for different species because not enough studies have been done.

These tables provide information on endangered mammals and birds in Canada. As you examine the tables, ask yourself:

- How many different examples of habitats can you find?
- How many different causes are listed for species being endangered?
- Are all causes human-related?

	Habitat	Threat to Species
Mammals		
eastern cougar	mixed and coniferous forests	hunting, loss of food source, human disturbance
Vancouver Island marmot	alpine and subalpine areas	loss of habitat
wood bison	upland Prairies, forests, lakes	hunting, disease (stable/recovering)
bowhead whale	southern edge of pack ice	commercially over-harvested
right whale	coastal waters of North America	commercially over-harvested
St. Lawrence beluga	St. Lawrence estuary	hunting, human disturbance, loss of habitat, pollution
sea otter	Pacific coast	commercially over-harvested (stable/recovering)
Birds		
Eskimo curlew	tundra and lichen woodland	human disturbance, hunting, habitat loss
greater prairie chicken	open, undisturbed grasslands	loss of habitat
Kirtland's warbler	dense jack pine stands	loss of habitat, parisitism by introduced species
peregrine falcon	taiga region, nests on cliffs	human disturbance, hunting, loss of habitat
piping plover	oceans, inland lakes and ponds	hunting, human disturbance
whooping crane	breeds in Wood Buffalo National Park	accidental shooting, loss of habitat (stable/ recovering)

The Rancher and the Bear — A Case Study

We share our habitat with many animals, birds, and plants; but when we share our habitat with grizzly bears, there is sure to be conflict. This is the situation in Poll Haven Community Pasture — a 26 km² section of rugged, densely forested land in the extreme southwestern corner of Alberta. The land is used for cattle grazing by local ranchers; it is also a habitat for grizzlies. The number of cattle killed seems to be increasing as the pasture is used for more cattle.

There are two sides to the conflict. Some ranchers were demanding the right to shoot grizzlies in order to decrease herd losses. Another, in a letter to the editor of the local paper, wrote:

> "We ranchers are paying a very small price in using the bears' home for our cattle ranges. Maybe we owe them a calf or two."

Suppose you were in a position to mediate this conflict. What position would you take? What information would you require? What studies would you do? After discussing in a small group, share your deliberations with others in your class.

Follow-Up

Choose an endangered or threatened species. Investigate its habitat and the changes that have occurred that have threatened its existence. What is being done today to ensure the survival of the species?

An Environment Quiz

This quiz is designed to be a review. You won't need a pencil, only your wits. Have fun!

1. Let's start with your opinion about the place of living things in the environment. If you think that: (a) the environment includes other living things but not humans, *go to 6*; (b) you are an important part of the environment, *go to 12*.

2. Canada has a lot of fresh water — but not that much. Canada has 7 000 000 km³, about 20% of the world's fresh water. Now *off to 8* for a question about the carbon cycle.

3. You are half right. Animals take in carbon through the food chain and breath out carbon dioxide during respiration. Plants take in atmospheric carbon dioxide through photosynthesis. *Return to 8* for a more complete answer.

4. Oh no! Remember that 1 ppm is the same as 1 mg/L. *Go back to 19* and try again.

5. Which statement best describes Canada's share of the world's fresh water? (a) Canada has 40% of the world's fresh water — *go to 2*; (b) Canada has 20% of the world's fresh water — *go to 9*.

6. Whoops! Bad start. *Go back to 1* and rethink your role in the environment.

7. You are right. Each pH value is a 10 fold increase or decrease in acidity. Now *off to 19* and a question about parts per million.

8. The following play a major role in the carbon cycle: (a) plants and animals — *go to 3*; (b) plants, animals, and industrial processes — *go to 11*.

9. Great! 20% of the world's fresh water is found in Canada. Now *try 10* and a question about acid rain.

10. Due to acid precipitation the pH of a lake changed from 7 to 5. Now the lake is: (a) twice as acidic as before — *go to 14*; (b) 100 times more acidic — *go to 7*.

11. You are back on track. Most industries use carbon fuels and give off large quantities of carbon dioxide into the air. *Now to 10* for a question on pH.

12. Good start! Human beings affect the environment more than any other living thing. *Off to 5* for a trivia question about one of Canada's greatest natural resources — water.

13. Yes, indeed! 1 g dissolved in 1 L of water has a concentration of 1000 ppm. Change track now and *go to 16*.

14. Oops! The pH scale is a strange one so *back to 10*.

15. Sorry. B.O.D. is the demand placed on dissolved oxygen by organisms in the water. Sewage will increase the rate at which decomposers work and this increase places a higher demand on the oxygen. Why not pretend you didn't try this answer and *go back to 18?*

16. In a pond ecosystem, organisms that use oxygen are: (a) consumers and decomposers only — *go to 21*; (b) consumers, producers, and decomposers — *go to 29*.

17. Sorry — 100 ppm requires 0.1 g to be dissolved in 1 L of water — *go back to 19*.

18. Let's try one about B.O.D. Sewage added to water will: (a) decrease the B.O.D. — *go to 15*; (b) increase the B.O.D. — *go to 20*.

19. If you dissolved 1 g of salt into 1 L of water, the concentration will be: (a) 1 ppm — *go to 4*; (b) 100 ppm — *go to 17*; (c) 1000 ppm — *go to 13*.

20. Absolutely. The demand on oxygen by decomposers has increased due to the added sewage. Down the home stretch *now with 30*.

21. This may be a bit of a trick question. *Go back to 16* and try again.

22. Oops! Missed again. *Back to 30* to try again.

23. *Off to 25* — you're almost home.

24. Tough break. This was a hard one. Loss of top soil is a severe problem, made worse by loss of organic matter in the soil. Come a long way haven't we? *Go to 27* for a wrap-up.

25. The problem of greatest concern to farmers is:
    (a) loss of organic matter in soil — *go to 28*.
    (b) loss of topsoil — *go to 24*.

26. Consumers such as you, fish, etc., do use up oxygen during respiration — but other organisms do as well. *Back to 16*.

27. Well, one way or another you're done. The shortest route took 17 steps. 1, 12, 5, 9, 10, 7, 19, 13, 16, 29, 18, 20, 30, 23, 25, 28, 27. How did you do?

28. Bingo. Loss of organic matter is considered to be the major problem resulting in the worsening of other problems including erosion. *Go to 27* for a wrap-up.

29. Way to go. You probably knew that consumers and decomposers use oxygen during respiration, but plants do as well. Plants undergo two processes, respiration and photosynthesis. *Now off to 18*.

30. This is another trivia question. Is your body made up of: (a) one-half water? *go to 22*; (b) two-thirds water? *go to 23*.

The Global Commons

One World

In the past, the term "commons" referred to communal fields or pastures that were open to all of the herdsmen from the area but were not owned by any of them. Recently, the term has been used to refer to natural resources that are freely accessible to anyone who wishes to use them.

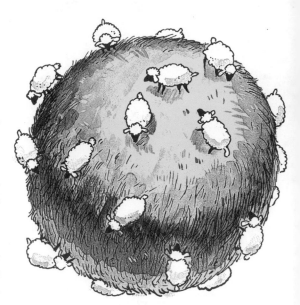

What are the *global commons*? Would you consider that the atmosphere and the oceans are two of our global commons? Why are they considered to be global commons? Back in history, the village commons were over-used and thus misused. This happened because of *over-grazing*. Can the same be said for the global commons? If something happens to the environment in one part of the world, does it have any impact on another part of the world? Can you give an example to support your answer? How do the following facts fit in your answer? Ocean currents carry oil spills and other pollutants to distant shores. Winds carry airborne pollutants across international boundaries. This is true of pollutants that cause acid rain as well as radioactive fall-out from nuclear disasters. Increasingly, scientists are recognizing that many problems of the global commons are not the concern of one nation alone but are *problems between nations* — that is, they are international in scope. This section focuses on one of the global commons — the atmosphere.

Brad's Project — The Greenhouse Effect

Here is a project that Brad submitted to the Symposium on the Environment. In doing the project, Brad:

- searched through newspapers and magazines for articles on his topic;
- wrote to Environment Canada for information;
- prepared a poster, in which he included his opinions and conclusions.

As you read about his project, think about these questions:

1. What is the *greenhouse effect?*
2. What are *greenhouse gases* and where do they come from?
3. How might cows and sheep contribute to a hotter atmosphere?
4. How might humans be contributing to an increase in the greenhouse effect?
5. Why are vegetation and the ocean often called *carbon dioxide sinks?*

6. What impact might the greenhouse effect have on the Earth and on you?

7. What causes acid rain and ozone depletion? Are they connected with the greenhouse effect?

8. Is the greenhouse effect reversible?

9. Is the greenhouse effect a problem? If so, what could we do about it?

After you have read a section of the report, look back to the questions and answer the appropriate ones. You may wish to discuss the answers with another person as you proceed. When you have read Brad's report, suggest two other questions that you would like answered.

Poster Session: The Earth as a Greenhouse

According to scientists, the Earth's average temperature has stayed within a fairly narrow range for millions of years. Despite several ice ages, the temperature range has been mild enough to allow for the development of many forms of living things. The Earth could have been as cold and desolate as our sister planet, Mars, or as hot as Venus. So why the difference?

The Earth has an atmosphere that contains carbon dioxide and other gases such as oxygen and nitrogen. But it has been the concentration of carbon dioxide that has maintained the temperature in a range suitable for life. Mars, with most of its carbon dioxide locked up in the solid state, is too cold; and Venus, with a much higher concentration of carbon dioxide, is too hot.

Both Venus and Earth have what is known as the *greenhouse effect*, but on Venus the effect results in a temperature too hot for life as we know it on Earth.

What is the greenhouse effect? You may have noticed how hot it tends to be in a greenhouse. The Sun's energy passes through the glass and is trapped inside. The heat is changed into a form which does not readily pass back through the glass. This means that more heat energy enters than leaves the greenhouse. Hence, the temperature in the greenhouse is higher than that outside.

The Earth and its atmosphere are like a giant greenhouse. Heat is *radiated* from the Sun to the Earth through the atmosphere (1). It is *absorbed* by the Earth and by things on the Earth. At night, part of the heat absorbed from the Sun is given off by the Earth (2).

Some of this heat is trapped by the atmosphere and can't return to outer space. Why? The carbon dioxide in the atmosphere traps the heat (3). Some people believe that, as the quantity of carbon dioxide increases because of human activity, more heat will be trapped and less will escape into outer space. This may cause the temperature of the Earth to increase (4).

The greenhouse effect

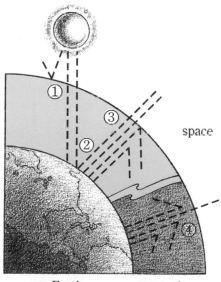

space

Earth   atmosphere

Livestock Add to the Greenhouse Effect

Are cows and sheep contributing to the greenhouse effect? The gases that cause this effect include methane as well as carbon dioxide. Cud-chewing animals, such as sheep and cattle, release methane from their digestive systems. With four times as many cattle as there were 100 years ago, some scientists think that livestock may be adding to the greenhouse warming.

Human Activity and the Greenhouse Effect

About 5 billion tonnes of carbon in the form of carbon dioxide are released into the atmosphere each year, mainly as the result of burning fossil fuels such as coal, gas, and oil.

In tropical areas such as the Amazon jungle, huge tracts of forest are burned to clear land for cultivation and development. Carbon stored in natural vegetation is released into the atmosphere as carbon dioxide — as much as 1 to 2 million tonnes per year. In Brazil alone, an area larger than Alberta has been depleted of its forest.

Not only does cutting and burning the forest release carbon dioxide, but vegetation that "uses up" carbon dioxide through photosynthesis is diminished. Since vegetation uses up carbon dioxide, vegetation is sometimes referred to as a *carbon dioxide sink*.

Another natural sink for carbon dioxide is the ocean. Oceans may be capable of dissolving half of the excess carbon dioxide that is released into the atmosphere each year.

Increases in carbon dioxide

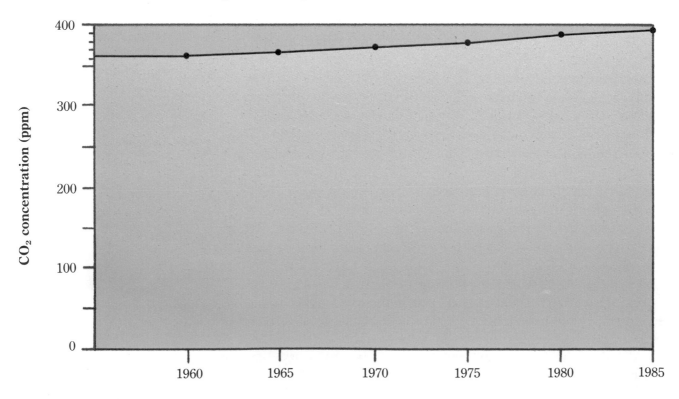

Possible Effects of Greenhouse Warming

Not all scientists agree that greenhouse warming is taking place. The Earth's temperature is affected by many other factors that we know very little about. If warming is taking place, it could have important effects. Some predictions suggest that an increase in global temperatures of 3.5°C would cause the following things to happen:

- Partial melting of the polar ice-caps would cause a rise in sea level. This would flood coastal areas of Canada and would have even more severe effects on countries such as Bangladesh that are already flood-prone.
- Canada's coasts would receive more precipitation and the interior regions, less. Prairie droughts could become more common.
- Much of Canada's downhill skiing would be eliminated and glaciers would recede more rapidly.
- Farmers would have to change the types of crops that they grow. Winter wheat could be grown in northern Alberta, which would have a longer, warmer growing season. Trees that could not adjust to the increased temperature would be replaced by species adapted to warmer climates.

Brad's Conclusions

I found the project really interesting and learned a lot about the greenhouse effect. Here is a summary of what I found out.

- Some scientists have suggested that gases such as carbon dioxide are causing the earth to heat up. However, other scientists say that this may not be so. More research is needed to find out who is right.
- Some people believe that the greenhouse effect is a bad thing; others believe that it would have beneficial effects.
- If there is a problem, everyone can help to relieve it. This could be done by conserving energy, making industries more energy efficient, and by planting trees, which absorb carbon dioxide.
- A lot of people are blaming people in tropical countries for cutting down too much of the rain forest. However, we have done much the same thing. At one time, much of eastern North America was covered with hardwood forests.
- Very little is known about why the temperature of the atmosphere fluctuates.

Summing Up

Brad certainly did a lot of work on his project and discovered a lot about an environmental controversy. Were you able to answer all of the questions at the beginning of this section?

Issues and Actions

There Are No Easy Answers

Examine the Web of Consequences on the opposite page. It was created by a class that was examining the use of pesticides on farms. Can you suggest other consequences that are not included in this web? Some people might suggest that the use of pesticides should be eliminated. Would you agree? Would farmers who depend on pesticides to maintain high crop yields agree? Would the consumer who wants high quality food at low cost agree? What about people who are concerned about pesticide residues on food? How could you determine how safe pesticide use is?

When it comes to environmental issues, there are often no easy answers. People with different interests will have different perspectives and opinions. How many issues have you examined in this unit that have no easy answers? What environmental issues are important in your community?

In groups, consider each of the following issues and possible actions. Several have been discussed in this unit. For each issue:

- Suggest who would agree and who would disagree with the proposed action. What reasons would they have for their opinions?

- Suggest other possible actions that other people might agree with.

- Suggest kinds of information that science may be able to provide to help people decide on possible actions.

ISSUE	POSSIBLE ACTION
1. The greater prairie chicken is endangered.	Why worry? They are not essential to human survival.
2. More water is needed for irrigation.	Build a dam on the river to create a reservoir.
3. Our climate may be warming up due to increases in "greenhouse gases".	Cut down fewer trees.

Your Turn

Share an issue and possible actions with your classmates. Your newspaper is a good source of information about local issues. Ask people in your family or neighbourhood what environmental issue concerns them most. Are their concerns local, regional, or global issues? What studies could be done to arrive at the "best" course of action? In the following Exploration you will survey public opinion on one of these issues.

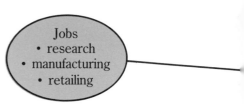

Jobs
• research
• manufacturing
• retailing

increased farm revenues

Examining Perspectives

1. Choose one issue that concerns people that live in your community. Come up with as many realistic actions that could be taken to deal with it as you can.

2. Design a questionnaire that will allow you to determine the perspectives and opinions of other people on the issue that you have chosen.

3. Give the questionnaire to your family and neighbours.

4. Analyse the results. Did everyone agree on one action to take? What was the most popular alternative? Do you know why?

Here is how one class set up their questionnaire.

> There have been a number of "letters to the editor" recently regarding the proposed development on the Westside Green. Our Grade 9 class would like your opinion on this issue. You do not have to sign your name. Thank you for participating in this survey.
>
> 1. The Westside Green is an undeveloped wooded area that was left to the town in a will. Which of the following statements best describes your opinions on the use of this land?
>   (a) The land should be left in its present undeveloped state. _____
>   (b) The land should be developed as a park. _____
>   (c) The land should be used for housing. _____
>   (d) There should be a mix of housing and park development. _____
>   (e) Other action: _____ _____
> 2. Briefly state why the land should be used as you suggest.
> 3. My occupation is: _____.

The Web of Consequences

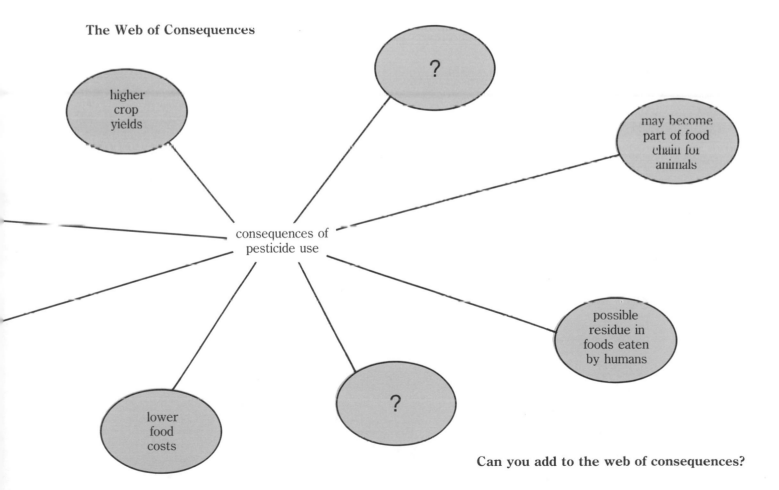

Can you add to the web of consequences?

Good News

Alden Nowlan, a Canadian poet, paints a bleak picture of the St. John River, which runs the complete length of New Brunswick. Happily, recent clean-up measures have improved the picture and the prospects for a rejuvenated salmon population. This is one solution that worked. There are many examples of good news regarding improved environmental quality.

Committed conservation efforts are saving a number of endangered species from extinction. For example, Wood Buffalo National Park, established in 1922, has provided sanctuary for the breeding ground of the world's entire population of whooping

The colour of a bayonet this river
that glitters blue and solid on the page
in tourist folders, yet some thirty towns
use it as a latrine, the sewage
seeping back to their wells,
    and farmers maddened
by debt or queer religions winter down
under the ice, the river bottom strewn
with heaps of decomposing bark torn
    loose
from pulpwood driven south, its acid
    juice
killing the salmon. August, when the
    stink
of the corrupted water floats like gas
along these streets, what most
    astonishes
is that the pictures haven't lied, the real
river is beautiful, as blue as steel.

St. John River
by Alden Nowlan

Whooping cranes

cranes. Their population in the park grew from 15 adults in 1941 to over 90 today. Similarly, 18 wood bison captured in 1963 and transported to the western shores of Great Slave Lake have grown to a herd of over 1000.

Share other good news examples by creating a *Good News* bulletin board. The bulletin board could contain newspaper articles and other items you heard about on the radio or television. For example, the following is another "good news" item. Do you agree?

Wood bison

Environmentally Friendly Products

What do the words "environmentally friendly product" mean to you? Many products now carry the "Ecologo", which indicates that such products are recyclable, biodegradable, free of ozone-depleting substances such as chlorofluorocarbons, or that they are made from recycled materials. In other words, the products are environmentally "friendly".

The three intertwined doves in the ecologo represent the three sectors of society that must work together to improve the quality of Canada's environment—consumers, industry, and government. The products range from re-refined motor oil and outdoor furniture made from recycled plastic to low-pollution paint.

The guidelines that products must meet were prepared by the Canadian Standards Association. One such guideline states that approved plastic products must contain at least 60% recycled plastic and that any plastic materials used to package these products must be recyclable.

Other product categories being considered include sanitary paper products made from recycled paper and products made from recycled rubber.

Choose a product that you are familiar with. What could be done to make it more environmentally friendly?

Look for this symbol.

Observing the Signs

Many years ago, miners took canaries down into the mines with them. If the birds died, the miners knew that the air was unsafe. Similarily, a decline in the population of a plant or animal species may provide a warning about the quality of our environment. Being observant of these signals provides time to take suitable action.

The following Exploration is a case study that started as a "bad news" item, but with suitable reaction, ended with positive results. It is an example of how becoming knowledgeable about a problem is the first step towards a solution. The "canaries" in this instance were the decline of such species as the peregrine falcon.

DDT—A Case Study

Part 1
Memories of a Farm Boy

DDT was a familiar material on dairy farms in the 1950s. It was used both inside houses and in barns to control flies. In farm kitchens, foodstuffs and cooking apparatus were covered with newspapers, and the room was sprayed so that the DDT hung as a mist in the air. In the barns, cattle would be swishing their tails in reaction to the many flies that would light on their bodies. Again, DDT would be sprayed to control the flies and those swishing tails. Some DDT would inevitably contaminate the milk kept in open buckets. Even though DDT was fatal to flies, little thought was given to the effect of this pesticide on humans.

1. Suggest two ways in which DDT could penetrate the human body.
2. Is there any evidence in this description that DDT is harmful to human health?

Part 2
DDT in the Food Chain

Dutch elm disease is caused by a fungus that plugs the water-conducting vessels of the elm, leading to the death of the tree. Since the fungus is spread by insects called *bark beetles,* it made sense to control the disease by controlling the beetle. At one time, DDT was used in this attempt. The following events took place.

- DDT dripped to the ground and the soil became contaminated. Soil may contain 5 to 10 ppm of DDT.
- Earthworms ingested the soil and its organic content. One earthworm may contain 30 to 160 ppm of DDT.
- Robins feeding on earthworms died from lethal doses of DDT.

1. Draw a food chain illustrating how DDT is accumulated by robins.
2. What appears to be happening with the concentration of DDT in the organism at each step in the food chain? If robins were the diet of another animal, how would its DDT content compare with that of the robins?

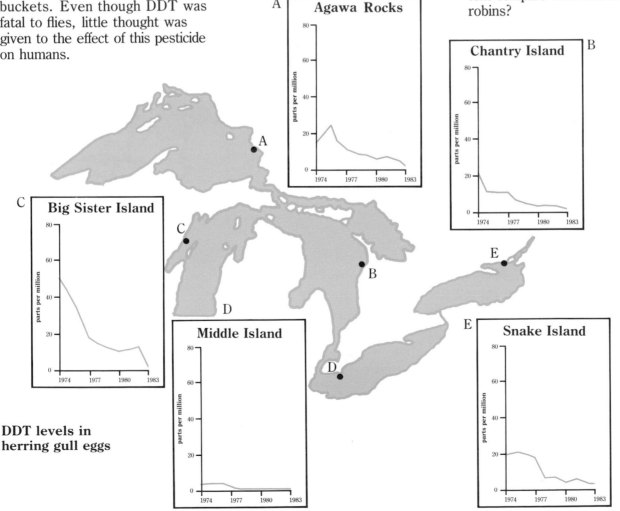

DDT levels in herring gull eggs

Part 3
DDT and Herring Gulls

Birds tend to accumulate DDT more rapidly than mammals. DDT has been implicated in the decline of several species of birds, including the bald eagle and the peregrine falcon. DDT appears to affect the ability of birds to produce the calcium needed to produce strong egg shells. Birds with large quantities of DDT in their fat produce shells that are substantially thinner and are thus easily broken, preventing their offspring from completing their development.

DDT has been found in the waters and bottom mud of the Great Lakes. It is concentrated by algae and plankton, which are the food sources for molluscs (such as clams) and fish. The herring gull, at the top of its food chain, may accumulate enough DDT to interfere with its reproduction.

Since 1969, the use of DDT has been restricted, and now it is not being produced at all in Canada. The diagrams on the opposite page show what has happened to the DDT residues found in herring gull eggs since then.

1. Draw a food chain that illustrates how the eggs of the herring gull become contaminated with DDT.

2. What general conclusions would you make regarding the amount of DDT found in the eggs of the herring gull between 1971 and 1983?

3. In the early 1970s, herring gull populations were on the decrease. What would you expect to be happening to the herring gull populations now?

4. How has this study been a good news story?

Post Script

"In terms of quantity, most parts of Canada are in no danger of running out of water or habitable space; of exhausting all our forests, fish or land resources, or of suffocating in industrial emissions. From other perspectives, however, whether it's resource harvesting, land use, or waste management, we do see much evidence of declining environmental quality."

Do you agree or disagree with this statement? Suggest examples from this unit and your symposium on the environment that supports this conclusion. What evidence have you found that this conclusion is too pessimistic?

Brain Teasers

1. "The environment keeps us alive. It provides the oxygen we breathe, the water we drink, the food we eat, and the resources we need. We are part of the environment; we are affected by it every moment of every day."

    Describe pages in the text and examples and activities you have done that support different parts of this quotation.

2. Construct *haikus* that show your appreciation of the following topics. Haikus are Japanese nature poems of 3 lines of 5, 7, and 5 syllables, respectively. You might put a little science as well as beauty into your poems. Here's one for a start.

    > To cherish our trees
    > And block our greenhouse problem
    > Is a cooling thought!

    (What science is there in this haiku?)

    (a) harm done in polluting the environment
    (b) good news in environmental practices
    (c) preservation of our natural environment
    (d) protecting endangered species
    (e) beneficial aspects of the environment
    (f) human efforts to improve environment quality
    (g) my own relationship with nature

3. Debbie made up a quiz for a class. She gave fictitious names to five solutions: *Algol*, *Sudine*, *Cortine*, *Zorbol*, and *Anax*. Using pH paper, the students got the following average pH values.

Algol	11
Sudine	3
Cordine	9
Zorbol	5
Anax	7

    (a) Which solutions are bases? acids? neither?

    (b) Actually, the solutions Debbie used happened to be *pure water*, *diluted ammonia water*, *undiluted ammonia water*, *acid rain*, and *apple juice*. Match the fictitious names with the actual solutions.

4. Some people argue that the cutting and burning of tropical rain forest is increasing the effects of greenhouse warming. As well, many species of plants and animals are disappearing. How would countries involved in this practice counter these arguments? How would we argue for the use of forests for lumber and paper in Canada?

5. When the habitat of a species changes, there is a danger that the species may not be able to adapt to the new conditions. With a classmate, discuss the trends that you see in the number of ducks in the Canadian Prairies. What could be causing any trends that you observe?

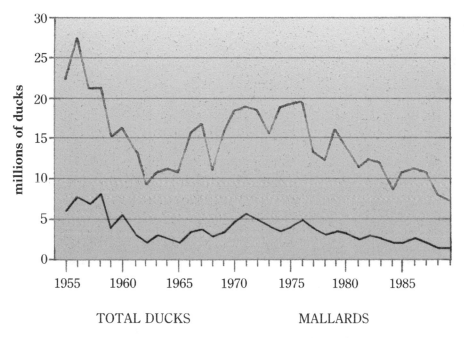

Number of ducks in the Canadian Prairies, 1955-89

TOTAL DUCKS   MALLARDS

6. (a) How many specific examples of the following do you know of in your community: air pollution, land pollution, water pollution?

   (b) How many specific examples of destructive environmental practices, apart from pollution, can you find in your community and its surroundings: forest destruction, animal destruction, urbanization, removal of green space?

   (c) How many specific examples can you find of positive environmental practices: replanting of trees; the establishing of green spaces and parks; recycling of wastes; air, land, and water pollution control?

7. A river near you has been tested and found to be unfit for swimming. Create a scenario of a discussion group consisting of a provincial official, a member of the town/city council, an interested citizen, a representative of an industry located on the river, and an environmentalist. The discussion is to consider whether action should be taken to improve the river situation.

8. In some rivers, the dissolved oxygen concentration may fall dangerously low — approaching 0 ppm — in the winter. What reasons can you suggest to account for this observation?

9. Most rivers have a variable dissolved oxygen concentration, which changes throughout the year. This is illustrated by the graph for the North Saskatchewan River. Describe what the graph is telling us. How do you explain the change which occurs?

Dissolved oxygen in the North Saskatchewan River

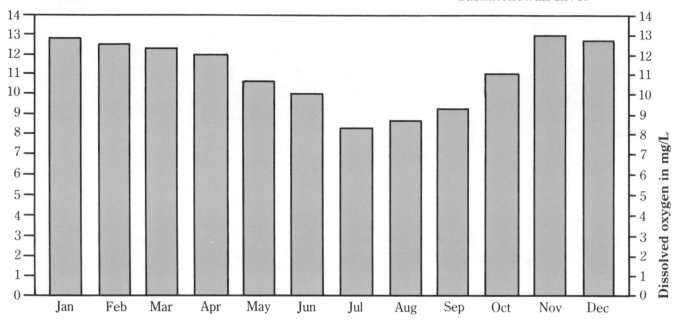

10. Earlier, in the unit Solutions, you investigated the solubility of many substances in water.
    (a) Which of the following graphs would most likely represent how many solids dissolve in water? how a gas dissolves in water?

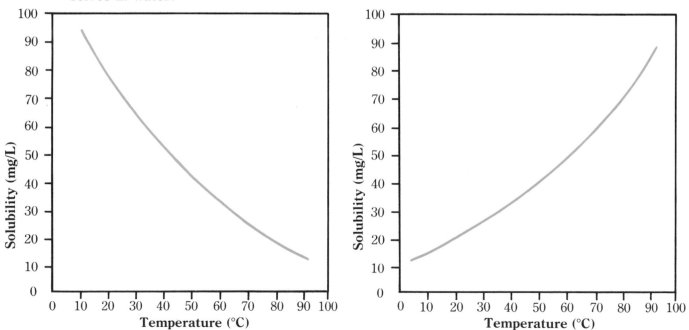

    (b) Table salt dissolves almost equally well in hot and cold water. What would its solubility-temperature graph look like?

11. On a sunny day, the leaves of a fully grown maple tree use about 4.2 kg of carbon dioxide and release about 3.0 kg of oxygen in the process of photosynthesis. Each day, in the process of respiration, you convert 0.82 kg of oxygen to carbon dioxide. You probably use another 4.4 kg of oxygen in the house to keep warm by burning fossil fuels.

    (a) For a winter day, calculate the amount of oxygen consumed by everyone in your community or city. How many maple trees are needed to supply this amount of oxygen?

    (b) Draw the carbon cycle and place the maple and yourself in it. Label the processes represented by the arrows you used.

12. A mini-experiment — do at home.
    Devise an experiment that would prove to someone who was several years younger than you that:
    (i) gases are dissolved in water;
    (ii) warm water is capable of dissolving less gas than cold water.
    Share your plan and results with others in your class.

13. This unit started with a number of questions to which you gave your opinions. Return to these questions and use them as a basis for a newspaper article entitled "You and the Environment".

14. You wish to design a quiz that would allow others to rate their environmental awareness. Here is the start of the quiz. What other items could you place on the quiz? Try to make a quiz of ten items.

    1. I try to be aware of the effects of my actions on the environment and to minimize them.
       (a) yes   (b) no
    2. When I have to go a distance less than a kilometre, I travel:
       (a) on foot or bicycle   (b) by car

Chemistry

Biochemistry

Kathleen Mailer is a biochemical researcher and university teacher with a Ph.D. in chemistry. Her research concerns the biochemistry of living tissues, mainly the heart. Kathleen says she loves research and greatly enjoys teaching. The most stimulating part of her job, she says, is the freedom to wonder whether an idea is true, then to try to find out.

Q: Why did you choose to do heart research?

Kathleen: The heart is the one tissue of the body that must never stop. Your muscles, your liver, and other organs can stop temporarily, but not your heart. The heart is like a super-efficient factory. Even during the sprint at the end of a marathon, only a part of its capacity is being used. It is said to be "over-engineered".

Nevertheless, the human heart can be afflicted with heart disease. Heart disease also occurs in rabbits, but very rarely in rats. It is curious that the same things that predispose human beings to heart attacks, such as absence of exercise or bad diets, also predispose rabbits to heart attacks — but not rats. It is important, therefore, to study the differences between rat hearts and rabbit hearts.

Q: Is your research carried out on animal hearts?

Kathleen: Yes, therefore it involves killing animals, usually rats.

Q: How do you feel about killing animals in order to do your research?

Kathleen: Killing an animal is never pleasant. Unfortunately, there is no substitute for it right now. So, you never waste an animal life. Every animal is important, so you share the animal with others, if possible. If you are using the heart, you give the liver, brains, or other organs to others who need them for their research. You must have respect for all life, and you have to be sure that the results justify what you are doing.

Chemistry Teaching and Research

Patricia Mullins has devoted years to teaching chemistry in high school and university. In addition, she did chemical research before becoming involved in university administration. The basic qualification for her field of work is a Ph.D. in chemistry. Patricia obtained her doctorate after a Bachelor of Arts in languages and a Master's degree in science. Her many and varied responsibilities as a researcher, teacher, and administrator make her life busy and rewarding.

Q: How did you get interested in science?

Patricia: Even as a child, I was curious and always wanted to know how things worked and why things were as they were. My interest in chemistry was sparked by a very enthusiastic high school teacher. I was fortunate to have enthusiastic chemistry teachers all through university. It helped when the studies became more difficult.

Q: What do you enjoy most about your work?

Patricia: I enjoy the opportunity of working with students, and I try to pass on some of the enthusiasm I have for chemistry and research. The thrill one gets when making a new compound that no one has made before, then finally determining the structure of the compound, makes all the effort very worthwhile.

Q: Are there any frustrations?

Patricia: Repeated failures to synthesize a new compound, the seeming lack of excitement of students over science, and the inability to please some people no matter how hard one tries, have been some of my frustrations.

Q: What subject areas are important for students who are interested in becoming chemists?

Patricia: First of all, I think they need to be able to read in order to understand any subject. They must also be able to write clearly, for all scientists have to write many reports and articles. They should have a knowledge of basic math and physics, as well as chemistry. Of course, these things are important for everyone. Scientific literacy is a must for today's world.

Q: Are there any particular abilities that are most important to a chemical researcher?

Patricia: An analytical problem-solving approach, logical thinking, attention to detail, the habit of continuous library research, and orderly recording of possibly useful information — these are all important abilities. One hour in the library recording what others have already discovered can save many hours in the lab.

Chemical Technology

Wade Gates is a chemical technologist. Technologists assist with research work and testing in industry, and with teaching in schools and universities. Some technologists obtain their basic qualifications by completing two or three years of specialized training after high school. Others are university science graduates. Wade Gates has a Bachelor of Science degree with a specialization in chemistry, and now works at a university.

Q: What does your job involve?

Wade: I am involved with research projects and laboratory teaching. I also do chemical testing for outside companies. There is a lot of variety, so it is quite interesting — more interesting than working in a company where you do the same test day in and day out.

Q: How did you become interested in chemistry?

Wade: I was always interested in chemistry. I also had a tremendous high school chemistry and physics teacher. He really got me interested in chemistry.

Q: Are there any experiences in your present job that you remember particularly?

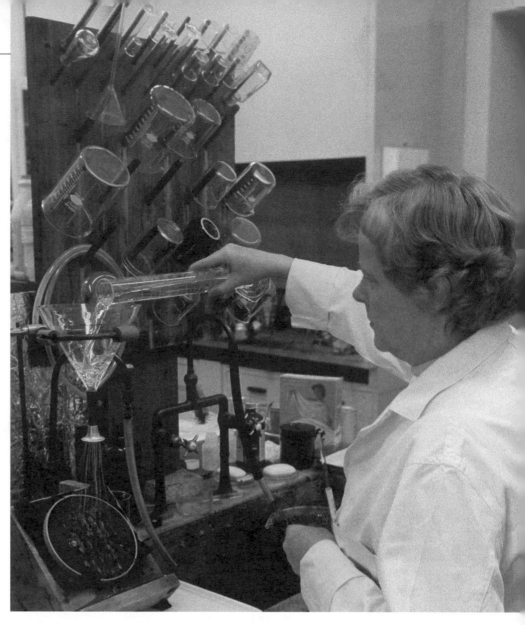

Wade: Yes. One of the big problems is that textbooks in chemistry often fail to associate particular chemicals with their practical applications in everyday life. We had a case where one of the students spilled some acetic acid (vinegar) on his face, which stings a little bit but won't do any harm. His partner panicked, and to help out he threw a handy beaker of water in the first student's face. Unfortunately, he let go of the beaker. The beaker broke and it took 14 stitches to close the cut on the first student's forehead.

The point I am trying to make is that chemistry texts should relate chemistry to everyday things. For example, sodium chloride is common table salt, calcium sulphate is gypsum, and glucose is sugar. Knowing these things, students will have less fear and more common sense about chemistry.

Q: Can chemistry be dangerous?

Wade: Students must use common sense and avoid panic. It is not necessary to be a genius to be a good student in chemistry and physics. But you must be safety-conscious. We do not let students wear contact lenses in the lab, for instance, and we require that safety glasses be worn for almost every experiment. Also, it is important to take off watches and rings, and to wear a lab coat or old clothes. It all comes down to basic common sense.

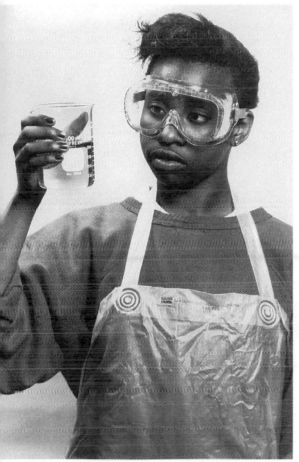

Proper safety equipment should be worn at all times in the lab.

Some Project Ideas

1. Practical chemistry is often a matter of following prescriptions or recipes. Baking is a good example. Many worthwhile experiments can be done in the kitchen. Start with a standard recipe. Vary the proportions of the ingredients, and compare the results. For example, what is the effect of varying the amount of salt, baking powder, yeast, or liquid ingredients when following a particular recipe for bread? What is the effect of varying the oven temperature?

2. A wide variety of useful chemical testing kits is readily available. You have already performed many chemical tests, including the use of indicators for starch, calcium, and acidity.

Identifying harmful chemical changes which take place around the home or school, and designing ways to counteract them, might be a worthwhile project. One example of such a harmful change is the oxidation or corrosion of surfaces.

The first task is to identify a problem. The second is to identify whether the cause of the problem is chemical, as opposed to physical. The next is to identify the chemical responsible. For this you will need to use a chemical testing kit. Finally, you should find a method of preventing or counteracting the problem.

Discussion with your science teacher and preliminary library research are usually the best approaches to a project such as this. Depending on your chosen problem, you might consult also chemists in schools, universities, industry, medicine, agriculture, and many other fields.

Remember: It is important to get advice about any safety precautions that might be required in doing chemical tests.

Fishing

Do you enjoy fishing? Cast your mind back to your most successful fishing experience. Was it in salt or fresh water? Were you angling for fish, or gathering shellfish from the shallows? What fishing gear did you use? What did you use for bait? At what depth were the fish feeding?

If you were successful, your fishing technique must have been suited to the feeding habits of the fish you caught. Find out more about the kind of fish you caught that day. Is it caught and sold commercially? What technology is used by the commercial fishermen who catch it? Where and how is the commercial catch processed? Is it iced for selling fresh, or is it frozen, canned, or dried and salted for shipping and storage?

The Technology of Fishing

Unless you have done commercial fishing, the technology you have used is not designed to catch the maximum number of fish. Government restrictions on the kind of fishing gear that is permitted are one way of limiting the number of fish caught by sports fishermen.

Find out about the technology of commercial fishing. If you live in or near a fishing community, find out directly from the fishermen about the equipment and methods they use to catch fish. Setting up a display which explains the feeding habits of a certain kind of fish and the technology used in catching that fish would be an interesting project.

Aquaculture

One of the greatest human discoveries was agriculture. The ability to grow our own food set us free from relying on fishing, hunting, and foraging — all unreliable food sources. Today, very little food is harvested from the wild. Indeed, only a small part of the world's present population could be supported by food which is available in Nature. Only fish is still harvested mainly from natural sources. However, even this is changing. **Aquaculture** — fish farming — is responsible for an increasing proportion of the fish consumed today.

Find out whether aquaculture is practised in your area. Is there a fish hatchery nearby which specializes in raising fish from eggs for release into the wild? Is any-

one in your area engaged in the culture of oysters or mussels? Is the culture of fish in cages, ponds, or tanks an important activity in your province? A visit to learn first-hand about fish farming in your area could be the basis of an interesting project.

Fish Conservation

Fish is an abundant and renewable resource. However, overfishing of a particular species of fish can drastically reduce its population. Conservation measures are necessary to ensure a continuing supply but, unfortunately, they often lead to disagreements.

Why do these disagreements arise? Who is involved? Is not conservation in everyone's interest?

Unlike most natural resources in Canada, fish are common property. The reason is that no one in Canada can own a waterway — or what it contains. Therefore, nobody owns a particular fish until it is caught. This encourages competition between fishermen to catch as many fish as is legally possible. Competition exists between sports and commercial fishermen, between one fishing enterprise and another, and between the fishermen of one country and those of another.

Unregulated, the competition for fish could lead to the depletion of stocks of some species. Because the oceans and their resources are the common property of all the people of the Earth, both international agreements and local regulations are essential if fish are to be conserved.

To be sure that your interests are taken into account by governments, you should find out how this issue concerns you, and take a stand. Start by doing some background research. Obtain information from the federal Department of Fisheries and Oceans and from your provincial fish and wildlife department, about the regulations, treaties, and agreements that are currently in force. Ask about current disputes, and government policy on these disputes. Ascertain the viewpoints of the fishermen's unions and of the companies which process fish. Contact scientists who do research on the fisheries. Find out about the abundance of different kinds of fish and about the effects of

changes in the population of one species of fish on other marine life. Obtain scientific information which has a bearing on current disputes.

To make others aware of the issues involved in fish conservation, organize a panel discussion. The panel should consist of students representing governments, fishermen, fish processing companies, and scientists. As an alternative (if you can arrange it) invite actual representatives of each of these groups to present their views.

Sources of Information

- Department of Fisheries and Oceans, Ottawa
- provincial departments of fisheries
- *Canadian Encyclopedia*

Index

Credits

Care has been taken to trace the ownership of copyright material used in this text. The publishers will welcome any information enabling them to correct any reference or credit in subsequent printings.

Photos

Credits from left to right are separated by semicolons, from top to bottom by dashes (unless otherwise indicated).

Key to abbreviations: GSC – Geological Survey of Canada. DRIE – Department of Regional Industrial Expansion, Ottawa. MTPRL – Metropolitan Toronto Public Reference Library. OMAF – Ontario Ministry of Agriculture and Food, Guelph. OMNR – Ontario Ministry of Natural Resources, Toronto. ROM – Royal Ontario Museum, Toronto.

Diversity of Living Things

6: Breck P. Kent/Animals, Animals—Michael Mitchell; Bill Ivy—Gordon S. Smith/Canapress; Michael Mitchell—Pat Morrow/DRIE.
7: Michael Mitchell; Steven Dalton/Canapress—Wayne Lankinen/Valan Photos; Canapress.
8: R.C. Simpson/Valan Photos; Bill Ivy—Peter Arnold Inc; Bill Ivy—Herman H. Giethoorn/Valan Photos—Ted Grand/DRIE. 9: Joyce Photographics/Valan Photos—(jellyfish) Bill Curtsinger/Photo Researchers; Milton Love/Peter Arnold Inc; Pierre St. Jacques/DRIE—R.C. Simpson/Valan Photos—Animals, Animals.
10: Bill Ivy—Ted Grant/DRIE—Ray Mendez/Animals, Animals—Bill Ivy. 11: Dave Milne/Prince George Citizen—Hans Pfletschinger/Canapress—James Soullier/Canapress; (tree) Bill Ivy—OMNR—Oxford Scientific Films/Canapress. 12: Anthony Bannister/Animals, Animals—Bill Ivy; Bill Ivy—Stouffer Production/Animals, Animals. 13: Mike Beedell/DRIES—J. Krasemann/Photo Researchers; Richard L. Carlton/Photo Researchers; Bill Ivy. 14: Canapress—Bill Ivy—OMNR; (cardinal) Bill Ivy—Canapress—Hans Pfletschinger/Canapress.
15: Bill Ivy; Rachel Lamoreux/Canapress—Karl Maslowski/Canapress. 20: S.J. Krasemann/Valan Photos; OMNR—OMNR. 21: Breck P. Kent/Animals, Animals—Peter Parks/Animals, Animals. 22-23: Canapress—The Bettmann Archive. 29: OMNR—Bill Ivy—Phillip A. Harrington/Peter Arnold Inc.; Bill Ivy—Bill Ivy—Martin Kuhnigk/Valan Photos; M.I. Walker/Photo Researchers—James Kent/Canapress.
30: Ben Cropp/Canapress—DRIE—Hans Pfletschinger/Canapress—OMNR—Oxford Scientific Films/Animals, Animals. 31: Jan Kapec/Canapress—Bill Ivy—Canapress; Hans Pfletschinger/Canapress—Bill Ivy—Dale Calder/ROM—Stan Osolanski/Canapress; OMNR—Ontario Science Centre—Bill Ivy—Bill Ivy—Bill Ivy. 32: Richard Kolar/Animals, Animals—Dale Calder/ROM; National Audubon Society/

Photo Researchers—Dale Calder/ROM; Bill Ivy—Bill Ivy—Dale Calder/ROM—S.J. Krasemann/Valan Photos. 33: (i) Fred Bavendam/Peter Arnold Inc.—(j) Paul L. Janosi/Valan Photos—(k) Doug Wechsler/Animals, Animals—(l) Pam Hickman/Valan Photos; (m) J.A. Wilkinson/Valan Photos—(n) Sea Studios/Peter Arnold Inc.; (o) Bill Ivy—(p) Bill Ivy—(q) Paul L. Janosi/Valan Photos—(r) Dale Calder/ROM; Zig Leszczynski/Animals, Animals—Zig Leszczynski/Animals, Animals—Stephen Dalton/Animals, Animals—E.R. Degginger/Animals, Animals. 36: OMNR—OMNR; Bill Ivy—OMNR; Bill Ivy—UNICEF—Bill Ivy. 37: (h) DRIE—(i) Breck P. Kent/Animals, Animals—Bill Ivy; (k) OMNR—(l) Bill Ivy—(m) OMNR; (n) DRIE—(o) Zig Leszczynski/Animals, Animals. 39: (a) Canapress—(b) Treat Davidson/Canapress—(c) Canapress; (d) Stephen Dalton/Canapress; (e) Canapress—(f) Hans Pfletschinger/Canapress. 40: G.I. Bernard/Animals, Animals—Zig Leszczynski/Animals, Animals—Bill Ivy—Bill Ivy; (k) Paul L. Janosi/Valan Photos; Wayne Lankinen/Valan Photos. 41: OMNR—Harold V. Green/Valan Photos—Kennon Cooke/Valan Photos—OMNR; Zig Leszczynski/Animals, Animals—Bill Ivy—Bill Ivy; Biophoto Associates/Photo Researchers—Zig Leszczynski/Animals, Animals—Stephan J. Krasemann/Valan Photos. 42: OMNR—Bill Ivy. 43: Bill Ivy. 44: The Bettmann Archive/Painting by Orata 46: Canapress; UNICEF. 47: UNICEF. 58: Canapress—The Bettmann Archive/Painting by Orata—Stan Osolanski/Canapress—Canapress. 59: Canapress. 62: Halifax Chronicle Herald—Vancouver Sun/Canapress—Allan Templeton; The Globe and Mail, Toronto; Jim Cochrane/Canapress—UNICEF; Eric de Mare/Canapress. 63: DRIE—DRIE—OMAF—R.C. Simpson/Valan Photos; Bill Ivy—OMAF—OMNR—OMNR; Bill Ivy—Bill Ivy—DRIE—Bill Ivy; OMNR—Val Whelan/Valan Photos—DRIE—Bill Ivy.

Chemical Changes

88: Art Wolfe/Image Bank. 90-93: Michael Mitchell*. 97-98: (all) Ann Ronan Picture Library. 100-101: Alcan Aluminum Limited. 102: Michael Mitchell*. 104: (top) Alvin Uptis/Image Bank; (bottom two) Michael Mitchell.
105: From the picture by Marcus Stone, R.A — David Thomson. 106: Bettmann Archive/engraving by Seiberitz—DRIE. 107:—MTPRL Picture Collection—Chris Schwarz/Canapress—SSC/Canadian Photo Centre. 118-119: Michael Mitchell*. 123: Michael Mitchell; David Thomson.

Heat Travel

139-141: Michael Mitchell*. 142: Michael Mitchell; Michael Mitchell—Canapress. 143-153: Michael Mitchell*. Thermometers courtesy Queen St. Camera Exchange Ltd. 157: Daedalus Enterprises Inc. 163-168: Michael Mitchell*. 171: Canapress 172: John Duricka/Canapress.

Fluids

190: John Kelly/The Image Bank—Frank Whitney/The Image Bank. 195: Larry Dale

Gordon/The Image Bank—Art Wolfe/The Image Bank. 196: Eric Meola/The Image Bank—Mike Wevrick. 197: Anne Rippy/The Image Bank; Derek Berwin/The Image Bank. 198: (oil rig) Canapress; (pin) Michael Mitchell. 199: Canapress. 201: MTPRL. 202: David W. Hamilton. 212: Stockphotos Inc./The Image Bank. 217: Boreal Laboratories Ltd. 218: NASA. 221: OMNR—U.S. Coast Guard/Canapress. 222: Canapress. 223: TV Ontario. 227: Anne Van Der Varen/The Image Bank. 230: Robert Estall. 231: Kay Chernush/The Image Bank. 232: Frank Whitney/The Image Bank. 244: Albert Normandin/The Image Bank. 246: Cesar Lucas/The Image Bank.

Electromagnetics

258: Canapress. 259: Bob Scott. 275: Michael Mitchell. 311: Wayne Decker/Fundamental Photographs. 314: Canadian Standards Association. 318: AP/Canapress.

Environmental Quality

353: Kennon Cooke/Canapress—Les Szurkowski/Canapress—J. Eascott/V. Momatiuk/Valan Photos; Ken Patterson/Valan Photos. 354: Wouterloot-Gregoire/Valan Photos; C. Wallis/Fotolex Associates—Steve Proehl/The Image Bank. 358: Jeff Foott/Valan Photos. 359: General Motors. 365: Bill Ivy. 367: John Cancalosi/Valan Photos. 369-370: Ken Mills/Department of Fisheries and Oceans. 376-377: Harold V. Green/Valan Photos. 381: T. Kitchin/Valan Photos; Canapress—Harold V. Green/Valan Photos. 382: OMAF. 387: Prairie Farm Rehabilitation Administration. 391: Paul Lally. 400: Arthur Burchell/Valan Photos—Jeff Foott/Valan Photos. 401: Environment Canada.

Science in Action

68: Connaught Labs/Canapress. 69: David Channer/Canapress; Canapress. 128-129: Ontario Ministry of Education. 182: Canadian Pacific/Canapress. 183: Canapress; R. Alfimov/Canapress. 184: Craig Hodge/Canapress. 185: The Toronto Star. 252: Canapress. 252: Ford Motor Company. 342-345: Canapress. 346: Fred Gallagher; Abitibi-Price. 346-347: Ontario Hydro. 347: Canapress. 408: Kathleen Miller; Pat Mullins. 409: Don Rutledge/Canapress. 410: Duncan Cameron/SSC Photocentre. 411: Birgitte Nielson; OMAF.

Science on Your Own

70: OMAF; John de Visser. 71: Canapress. 130: Glen Gerger/Canapress. 131: Keith Beaty/Canapress; Toronto Star; Chuck Stoody/Canapress. 186: Canapress. 187: Richard Furlong/The Toronto Star—Nova Scotia Tourism/Canapress. 253: Lockheed/Canapress; De Havilland Aircraft Company of Canada. 348: Canapress. 349: Telesat/Canapress—Dick Loek/Toronto Star. 412: Canapress. 412/413: Canapress. 413: North Bay Nugget/Canapress.

*Equipment supplied courtesy Sargent Welch Scientific. Special thanks to Elaine Freedman for help in assembling props.

Illustrations

Text Credits